КОНСТАНТЫ НЕСТОЙКОСТИ КОМПЛЕКСНЫХ СОЕДИНЕНИЙ

KONSTANTY NESTOIKOSTI KOMPLEKSNYKH SOEDINENII

INSTABILITY CONSTANTS OF COMPLEX COMPOUNDS

INSTABILITY CONSTANTS
OF
COMPLEX COMPOUNDS

K. B. *YATSIMIRSKII* IАt͡simirskiĭ

and

V. P. VASIL'EV

TRANSLATED FROM RUSSIAN

CONSULTANTS BUREAU, NEW YORK
1960

This work was originally published by the Academy
of Sciences, USSR, Press in, Moscow in 1959.

Responsible Editor: Academician I. I. Chernyaev

TABLE OF CONTENTS

CHAPTER IV

Tables of Instability Constants of Complex Compounds

vii

Tables of Complete Thermodynamic Characteristics of
Complex Formation Reactions in Solution

ix

PREFACE

Many investigators have recently paid considerable attention to the quantitative characteristics of complex compounds and complex formation in solution. Instability constants quantitatively characterize the equilibrium in solutions of complex compounds and, in this connection, are very widely used by chemists in different fields (analytical chemistry, electrochemistry, technology of nonferrous and rare metals, etc.) for appropriate calculations.

Despite the abundance of numerical material, until now no reasonably complete summaries of the instability constants of complex compounds have been published. The individual summaries that are available are far from complete and, in most cases, references to the literature sources are not given. Meanwhile, the present state of complex compound chemistry urgently requires the fullest possible systematization of material on instability constants and further extension of work in this field with the application of the latest physicochemical methods.

In this work we give the instability constants of 1381 complex compounds.

We considered it advantageous to preface the summary of instability constants with an introductory section of a general theoretical nature. In it we examine methods of calculating instability constants from experimental data, the effect of external conditions (temperature and ionic strength) on the stability of complexes, and the main factors determining the stability of complex compounds in aqueous solutions.

In compiling the summary we used mainly original and abstract literature through 1954 and in part work published in 1955-1956.

It should be noted that despite careful examination of the literature, it is possible that isolated papers were missed.

We would be grateful for any remarks concerning shortcomings found in this work and comments of various types as well as individual communications from readers regarding references that we have overlooked.

K. B. Yatsimirskii
V. P. Vasil'ev

THEORETICAL PART

Chapter I

SOME FUNCTIONS CHARACTERIZING STEPWISE COMPLEX FORMATION IN SOLUTION

The main thermodynamic characteristic of a complex particle* in solution is the equilibrium constant of the dissociation of the complex into its component central ion and addend or addends. In contemporary physicochemical work on the determination of such equilibrium constants in aqueous solutions of electrolytes, solutions of constant ionic strength are often used. This makes it possible to use the equilibrium concentrations of the substances participating in the reaction in the equation for the constant of the law of mass action instead of the activities.**

The dissociation of the complex particle MA_n in solution may be represented by the equation

$$MA_n \rightleftarrows M + nA \tag{I.1}$$

(the particle charges are omitted for simplicity).

The equilibrium constant of process (I.1)

$$K_n = \frac{[M] \cdot [A]^n}{[MA_n]} \tag{I.2}$$

is called the instability constant of the complex particle MA_n.

---

* In this work, together with the term "complex particle," we also use the synonymous terms "complex compound" and "complex". These three terms are used with approximately equal frequency in Russian and foreign literature on complex compounds. By complex compound, complex particle, or complex we understand a particle formed from two or more particles and capable of independent existence in solution (one of these particles is usually a metal ion).
** For more details on this, see p. 63.

The instability constant is the most objective character-istic of the stability of the complex particle in solution as regards dissociation since in the physical sense its deter-mination does not depend on the concentration conditions (pH of medium, reagent excess, etc.) or on the method of deter-mination. It is related to the change in free energy during complex formation by the well-known thermodynamic rela-tionship

$$\Delta Z = RT \ln K_n$$

In actual fact, the breakdown of the complex particle is more complex and, like the dissociation of polybasic acids, it proceeds stepwise:

$$MA_n \rightleftarrows MA_{n-1} + A, \tag{I.3}$$
$$MA_{n-1} \rightleftarrows MA_{n-2} + A \tag{I.4}$$

Depending on the addend concentration, the solution con-tains different amounts of products from the stepwise dis-sociation of the complex MA_n, $MA_{n-1}, MA_{n-2},....., MA$. The equi-libria between these particles are described by a series of equations of the type (I.3).

The corresponding equilibrium constants

$$k_n = \frac{[MA_{n-1}] \cdot [A]}{[MA_n]}, \tag{I.3a}$$

$$k_{n-1} = \frac{[MA_{n-2}] \cdot [A]}{[MA_{n-1}]} \tag{I.4a}$$

are usually called intermediate or successive instability con-stants, in contrast to the over-all or composite instability constant expressed by (I.2).

The successive constants are related to the over-all in-stability constant by the simple relation

$$K_n = k_1 \cdot k_2 \ldots k_{n-1} \cdot k_n. \tag{I.5}$$

The term "over-all instability constant" naturally refers not only to complexes with maximum coordination saturation

6

but also to the other particles existing in solution as a result of stepwise dissociation.

Thus, for example [1], the interaction of soluble nickel salts with ammonia in aqueous solution forms the ions $NiNH_3^{2+}$, $Ni(NH_3)_2^{2+}$, $Ni(NH_3)_3^{2+}$, $Ni(NH_3)_4^{2+}$, $Ni(NH_3)_5^{2+}$, and $Ni(NH_3)_6^{2+}$. Each of the particles formed is in equilibrium both with the rest of the products of stepwise dissociation and with ammonia and nickel ions.

For the simplest complex, $NiNH_3^{2+}$, the conceptions of over-all and successive instability constants coincide:

$$NiNH_3^{2+} \rightleftarrows Ni^{2+} + NH_3, \qquad (I.a)$$

$$K_1 = k_1 = \frac{[Ni^{2+}]\,[NH_3]}{[NiNH_3^{2+}]}. \qquad (I.6)$$

For the particle $Ni(NH_3)_2^{2+}$ the equilibrium of the stepwise dissociation is conveyed by the equation

$$Ni(NH_3)_2^{2+} \rightleftarrows NiNH_3^{2+} + NH_3, \qquad (I.b)$$

and the equilibrium of the over-all dissociation by

$$Ni(NH_3)_2^{2+} \rightleftarrows Ni^{2+} + 2NH_3. \qquad (I.c)$$

Then the successive instability constant of the complex $Ni(NH_3)_2^{2+}$ is

$$k_2 = \frac{[Ni(NH_3)^{2+}]\cdot[NH_3]}{[Ni(NH_3)_2^{2+}]}, \qquad (I.7)$$

and the over-all one is

$$K_2 = \frac{[Ni^{2+}]\cdot[NH_3]^2}{[Ni(NH_3)_2^{2+}]}. \qquad (I.8)$$

For the particle of maximum coordination, $Ni(NH_3)_6^{2+}$, the stepwise and over-all dissociations are expressed by (I.d) and (I.e), respectively:

$$Ni(NH_3)_6^{2+} \rightleftarrows Ni(NH_3)_5^{2+} + NH_3, \qquad (I.d)$$

$$Ni(NH_3)_6^{2+} \rightleftarrows Ni^{2+} + 6NH_3, \qquad (I.e)$$

7

while the successive and over-all instability constants are given by (I.9) and (I.10), respectively.

$$k_6 = \frac{[Ni(NH_3)_5^{2+}] \cdot [NH_3]}{[Ni(NH_3)_6^{2+}]},$$ (I.9)

$$K_6 = \frac{[Ni^{2+}] \cdot [NH_3]^6}{[Ni(NH_3)_6^{2+}]}.$$ (I.10)

Together with the term "instability constant," the term "stability constant" is sometimes used in the literature. This value is the reciprocal of the instability constant,

$$K_y = \beta = \frac{1}{K_n},$$ (I.11)

correspondingly, the successive stability constant is

$$k_y = \varkappa = \frac{1}{k_n}.$$ (I.12)

It is quite evident that

$$\beta_n = \varkappa_1 \varkappa_2 \ldots \varkappa_{n-1} \varkappa_n.$$ (I.5a)

The terms "complex dissociation constant" and Bjerrum's "complexity constant" [1] are used much less frequently.

Successive instability constants are of very great importance in understanding the most varied processes in chemical technology (for example, hydrometallurgical and electrochemical processes) and chemical analysis. In this connection, in an overwhelming majority of papers published in the last decade on ionic equilibria in complex formation, the stepwise nature of complex formation has been considered in some way or other and the successive instability constants have almost always been calculated.

To find these constants it is advantageous to use a series of functions which are readily calculated from experimental data and which, in turn, are quite simply related to the instability constants. Frequently, the mathematical expression of these relations is much simpler if the stability constants are used instead of the instability constants. Therefore, in future discussion we will use both stability constants (especially in the proof of mathematical relationships) and instability constants.

Some of the functions characterizing stepwise complex formation have recently become very widely used.

A series of interesting mathematical methods has been put forward for calculating instability constants by means of these functions, but their use has been limited to the potentiometric method, ion exchange, distribution between two solvents, and, in particular, polarography.

Meanwhile, at the present time there is only one possible approach to the study of equilibrium in stepwise complex formation, and a considerable extension of the range of application of existing methods of processing experimental data is possible.

At the present time the so-called "formation function," $\bar{n}$, proposed by Bjerrum [1] is most widely used:

$$\bar{n} = \frac{c_a - [A]}{c_M} , \qquad (I.13)$$

where c_a and c_M are the over-all concentrations of addend and metal-complex former ion in solution and [A] is the equilibrium concentration of addend.

The formation function, $\bar{n}$, is the ratio of the concentration of addend bound in the complex (or in the complexes) to the over-all concentration of the metal-complex former ion. In the physical sense, the formation function is a peculiar average coordination number and may vary from zero, when there is no complex formation in solution ($c_a = [A]$), to the limiting maximum value of the coordination number. In the absence of stepwise complex formation and with a sufficient excess of addend, $\bar{n}$ equals the coordination number.

The instability constants and $\bar{n}$ are related by the following expression:

$$\bar{n} = \frac{\beta_1 [A] + 2\beta_2 [A]^2 + \ldots + n\beta_n [A]^n,}{1 + \beta_1 [A] + \beta_2 [A]^2 + \ldots + \beta_n [A]^n} , \qquad (I.14)$$

9

or, in a shortened form:

$$\bar{n} = \frac{\sum_{i=1}^{i=n} i\beta_i [A]^i}{1 + \sum_{i=1}^{i=n} \beta_i [A]^i}. \tag{I.14a}$$

Leden [2], Fronaeus [3], and a series of other investigators used the function Φ, which is the ratio of the over-all concentration of metal, c_M, to the equilibrium concentration of free metal ions:

$$\Phi = \frac{c_M}{[M]}. \tag{I.15}$$

K. B. Yatsimirskii [4] proposed that this function should be called the "degree of complex formation" since it characterizes the extent to which complex formation occurs in the given system. The degree of complex formation may vary from 1 (in the absence of complex formation $c_M = [M]$) to any high value determined by the instability constants and the addend concentrations.

Since the over-all concentration of metal in solution (c_M) is the sum of the concentrations of complexes of the type MA_i, it follows that

$$\Phi = 1 + \beta_1 [A] + \beta_2 [A]^2 + \ldots + \beta_n [A]^n, \tag{I.16}$$

or in a shortened form,

$$\Phi = 1 + \sum_{i=1}^{i=n} \beta_i [A]^i. \tag{I.16a}$$

Sometimes it is advantageous to find the fraction of a given complex which is the ratio of the concentration of the given complex (MA_m) to the total concentration of metal in the solution (c_M)

$$\alpha_m = \frac{[MA_m]}{c_M}. \tag{I.17}$$

10

The value of α_m may vary from 0 (when the given complex is absent) to 1 (when other complexes are absent). Strictly speaking, α_m varies from a value close to zero to a value close to 1, since a close examination shows that in any solution with complex formation, the ion of the metal-complex former is in the form of at least two particles, namely, M_{aq} and MA_m.

The connection between α_m and stability constants is given by the following equation:

$$\alpha_m = \frac{\beta_m [A]^m}{1 + \beta_1 [A] + \beta_2 [A]^2 + \ldots + \beta_n [A]^n} , \qquad (I.18)$$

or, after simplification,

$$\alpha_m = \frac{\beta_m}{[A]^{-m} + \beta_1 [A]^{1-m} + \ldots + \beta_n [A]^{n-m}} , \qquad (I.18a)$$

and in a shortened form,

$$\alpha_m = \frac{\beta_m}{\sum\limits_{i=0}^{i=m} \beta_i [A]^{i-m}} . \qquad (I.18b)$$

With an increase in the concentration of the addend, α_m passes through a maximum. It can be shown [5] that at the maximum point

$$\alpha_m = \frac{\sqrt{\dfrac{\varkappa_m}{\varkappa_{m+1}}}}{2 + \sqrt{\dfrac{\varkappa_m}{\varkappa_{m+1}}}} , \qquad (I.19)$$

$$[A] = \frac{1}{\sqrt{\varkappa_m \varkappa_{m+1}}} . \qquad (I.20)$$

The formation function, the degree of complex formation, and the fraction of the given complex are interrelated by mathematical relationships. A partial examination of this question can be found in published work [6—8].

By differentiation of (I.16) we find

$$\frac{\partial \Phi}{\partial [A]} = \sum_{i=1}^{i=n} i\beta_i [A]^{i-1}. \qquad (I.21)$$

From (I.21) and (I.14a) it follows that

$$\bar{n} = \frac{\dfrac{\partial \Phi}{\partial [A]} [A]}{\Phi}. \qquad (I.22)$$

After the simplest rearrangement, we obtain

$$\bar{n} = \frac{\partial \lg \Phi}{\partial \lg [A]}. \qquad (I.23)$$

The value of $\bar{n}$ may be found by graphical differentiation of Φ. If we construct a graph of the logarithm of the degree of complex formation against the logarithm of the equilibrium concentration of addend, then the tangent of the slope at any point will numerically equal $\bar{n}$.

From (I.23) it follows that

$$\lg \Phi = \int \bar{n} \, d\lg [A] + B. \qquad (I.24)$$

If the formation function $(\bar{n})$ is known, then the degree of complex formation may be found by graphical integration of the curve of $\lg [A]$ against n.

From (I.16) and (I.18) it follows that

$$\alpha_m = \frac{\beta_m [A]^m}{\Phi}, \qquad (I.25)$$

or in a logarithmic form,

$$\lg \Phi = \lg \beta_m + m \lg [A] - \lg \alpha_m. \qquad (I.25a)$$

By differentiating this equation and using (I.23), we obtain

$$\bar{n} = m - \frac{\partial \lg \alpha_m}{\partial \lg [A]}. \qquad (I.26)$$

At the maximum accumulation of complex MA , the following condition applies:

12

$$\frac{\partial \lg \alpha_m}{\partial \lg [A]} = 0; \tag{I.27}$$

and hence at the point of maximum accumulation of complex MA_m

$$\bar{n} = m; \tag{I.26a}$$

and from (I.25a) and (I.24) it follows that

$$\lg \alpha_m = \int (m - \bar{n}) \, d \lg [A] + \lg \beta_n + B. \tag{I.28}$$

If, in the determination of instability (or stability) constants, we determine experimentally the equilibrium concentration of the central ion or addend or that of one of the complexes, then in the first case the degree of complex formation is readily calculated, in the second, the formation function, and in the third, the fraction of the given complex. By using the relations established between the stability constants and the functions listed, we may calculate the corresponding instability constants.

Very often it is necessary to determine the composition of the complexes formed in measuring instability constants. Various physicochemical analysis methods and data on equilibria are used for this purpose. The problem of determining the composition of complex compounds formed in aqueous solution has been examined in considerable detail in the literature. Many very valuable methods have been described, for example, in the monograph of A. K. Babko [9]. Consequently, we will not dwell on this problem here.

Quite refined methods have now been established for calculating stability (or instability) constants by use of the formation function and the degree of complex formation. An examination of these methods without definite numerical illustrations based on concrete examples is hardly worthwhile. Therefore we will present later on the calculation of the formation function or the degree of complex formation and subsequent determination of the instability (or stability) constants

13

as applied to actual practical cases (though, for quite obvious reasons, only for methods which are most common in practice).

LITERATURE CITED

1. J. Bjerrum. Metalammine formation in aqueous solutions. Copenhagen, 1941; cited in Chem. Abst., 6527 (1941).
2. I. Leden. Z. phys. Chem., A, 188, 160 (1941).
3. S. Fronaeus. Acta Chem. Scand., 4, 72 (1950).
4. K. B. Yatsimirskii. J. Inorg. Chem., 1, 412 (1956).
5. K. B. Yatsimirskii. J. Anal. Chem., 10, 94 (1955).*
6. J. C. Sullivan, J. C. Hindman. J. Am. Chem. Soc., 74, 6091 (1952).
7. H. Irving and H. S. Rossotti. J. Chem. Soc., 3397 (1953).
8. J. Z. Hearon and J. B. Gilbert. J. Am. Chem. Soc., 77, 2594 (1955).
9. A. K. Babko. Physicochemical Analysis of Complex Compounds in Solution. [In Russian] Kiev, 1955.

---

* The journals indicated in the citations marked with an asterisk are available in English translations published by Consultants Bureau Enterprises, Inc., 227 West 17th Street, New York 11, N.Y.

Chapter II

EXPERIMENTAL METHODS OF DETERMINING INSTABILITY CONSTANTS

At the present time a great number of very varied methods are used for determining instability constants. We cannot describe the details of the experimental procedures themselves. This problem is dealt with by several textbooks and a whole series of monographs (for example, on potentiometry, polarography, spectrophotometry, etc.); we will therefore examine mainly methods of calculating instability constants from experimental data.

The methods of determining instability constants of complex particles may be conveniently divided into two large groups.

Group I includes methods which allow direct determination of the equilibrium concentration of one or several types of particles participating in reaction (I.1), (I.3), or (I.4) (solubility methods, potentiometry, etc.).

Group II includes methods based on consideration of changes in physicochemical properties of the systems which occur as a result of complex formation (changes in optical density, electrical conductivity, etc.). These methods cannot be used for direct calculation of equilibrium concentrations of the components in stepwise complex formation from an experiment.

Group I Methods

The methods included in Group I may be grouped in the following way:

A. Methods based on a study of heterogeneous equilibria.
1. The solubility method involves determination of the solubility of a sparingly soluble salt in the presence of complex-forming substances or the solubility of electrically neutral addends in aqueous solutions in which complex formation occurs. The dissolving substance forms particles in solution and these participate in the complex formation.
2. The distribution method involves a study of the distribution of the central ion, addend, or complex particle between two immiscible solvents (normally water and some organic solvent, for example, CCl_4).
3. The ion exchange method involves a study of the distribution of the central ion or addend between the solution and an ion-exchange resin (cationite or anionite).

To determine instability constants by these methods, the appropriate heterogeneous equilibrium involving the central ion, addend, or complex is studied quantitatively and the equilibrium constant of the heterogeneous process is determined. The equilibrium concentrations of the components in any phase are readily calculated from the numerical value of this constant.

B. Electrometric methods. These involve a study of the equilibrium between a free metal and its ions in solution or between ions of the same element in different oxidation states in order to determine the equilibrium concentrations of these particles in solution. The following methods may be mentioned here:
1. The potentiometric method makes it possible to measure (having selected a suitable electrode) the equilibrium concentration of the central ion or the addend.
2. The polarographic method makes it possible to determine the instability constant by plotting a polaro-

graphic curve in the presence and in the absence of substances producing complex formation.

C. Other methods of Group I.
1. The kinetic method is based on the measurement of the rate of any reaction involving one of the components of the dissociation equilibrium of the complex particle in the presence and in the absence of complex-forming substances. As the reaction rate depends on the concentration of reacting substances, this method makes it possible to determine experimentally the equilibrium concentration of the central ion, addend, or complex.
2. The "freezing" method is used for studying the equilibrium constants of slow complex-formation reactions. The use of tracers is extremely useful for determining the concentrations of dissociation products of the complex (or of the complex ions). Essentially the method consists of the rapid and quantitative removal from the reaction sphere of one of the substances participating in the dissociation equilibrium of the complex particle.
3. Colorimetric indicator method. The equilibrium concentration of the reacting substances may also be determined by determining the optical density of the solution which contains a colored compound that is in equilibrium with one of the participants of equilibrium (I.1) or (I.3). Thus, for example, the equilibrium concentration of iron ions may be found by the optical density of solutions containing thiocyanate ions; the equilibrium concentration of hydrogen ions may be found by studying the behavior of colored indicators.
4. The biological method is based on a study of the effect of an equilibrium concentration of some ion on the

function of a definite organ of a living organism (for example, the heart of a frog). The equilibrium concentration of the ion studied may be determined by the action of this organ in systems with complex formation.

5. The radioactive tracer method consists of measuring the rate of isotope exchange of a cation between a simple aquoion and a complex ion in solution and extrapolating the data obtained to "instantaneous" exchange.

Let us examine these methods in greater detail.

A. METHODS BASED ON A STUDY OF HETEROGENEOUS EQUILIBRIA

1. SOLUBILITY METHOD. The fact that a sparingly soluble salt dissolves in excess precipitant was noted long ago and this fact was often used and is still used as a qualitative indication of complex formation in the system. In this connection we should note that if solution in excess precipitant does not occur, this does not indicate that complex formation is impossible. Very often the solubility product of a sparingly soluble salt is much less than the instability constant of the complex formed. In this case there is practically no solution though the existence of complexes may be demonstrated.

The solubility method was used for quantitative calculation of instability constants at the beginning of this century [1, 2, 3] and has since been used in the study of complex compounds.

In using the solubility method to study equilibria involving complex ions, we may use as the substances saturating the solution (base phase) solid salts containing ions of the metal-complex former and electroneutral addends (solid, liquid, or gaseous), complex salts, and also salts whose anions are addends.

In the case of a sparingly soluble salt of the type MX_p, in a saturated solution there is an equilibrium which is characterized by a definite solubility product:

$$MX_p \rightleftarrows M^{pz+} + pX^{z-}. \tag{II.1}$$

Addends A* present in the solution bind the central ion and form with it a series of complexes of the type MA, $(MA, MA_2,..., MA$, $MA_n)$.

It is assumed that the anion X of the salt MX_p does not form complexes with M; the formation of mixed complexes of the type MXA is also excluded.

The solubility of the salt MX_p, i.e., the over-all concentration of the metal in solution, will be the sum of the concentrations of the separate complex particles and of the free metal:

$$S = (c_M + c_{MA} + c_{MA_2} + \ldots), \tag{II.2}$$

where S is the solubility of the salt MX_p in moles/liter, c_M is the concentration of metal ions not bound in the complex, and c_{MA}, c_{MA_2}, etc., are the concentrations of the complexes MA_1, MA_2, etc. The equilibrium concentration of M ions is found from the solubility product of the salt MX_p:

$$[M] = \frac{SP}{[X]^p}. \tag{II.3}$$

This makes it possible to calculate the degree of complex formation from the relation

$$\Phi = \frac{c_M^0}{[M]} = \frac{S[X]^p}{SP}. \tag{II.4}$$

In the case when the addend is not an anion of a sparingly soluble salt, the concentration of anions X is directly related to solubility.

$$x = pS \tag{II.5}$$

* The charge is omitted for simplicity.

and hence

$$\Phi = \frac{p^p S^{p+1}}{SP} .$$ (II.4a)

If the degree of complex formation is known, then the successive stability constants may be calculated by Leden's method [4]. In this case the value of β_1 is found from the equation

$$\psi_1 = \frac{\Phi - 1}{[A]} = \beta_1 + \beta_2 [A] + \beta_3 [A]^2 + \ldots$$ (II.6)

Equation (II.6) is readily obtained from (I.16) by elementary rearrangements.

The function ψ_1 is reduced to β_1 when $[A]=0$. The constant β_1 is found practically by graphical extrapolation of the function $\psi_1 = f ([A])$ as the intercept on the ordinate. The function ψ_2 may then be found by means of the equation

$$\psi_2 = \frac{\psi_1 - \beta_1}{[A]}$$ (II.7)

or

$$\psi_2 = \frac{\Phi - 1 - \beta_1 [A]}{[A]^2} .$$ (II.7a)

The function ψ_2 is obtained from (II.6) by a method analogous to that for obtaining ψ_1 from (I.16). This function may be represented in the following manner:

$$\psi_2 = \beta_2 + \beta_3 [A] + \ldots$$ (II.8)

The value of ψ_2 is found by extrapolating β_2 to a zero addend concentration.

The other stability constants are found by analogous plots of the functions ψ_3, ψ_4, and, in general, ψ_n.

The values of the degree of complex formation may be successively differentiated and the stability constants found from the series of values of the derivative.

Thus, when the degree of complex formation is known, the calculation of the successive stability constants presents no difficulties.

The calculation of the degree of complex formation in its turn requires a knowledge of the solubility values, the solubility product, and the equilibrium concentration of the addend. It is not always possible to calculate the solubility product from solubility determinations alone. Besides determining the solubility, it is usually necessary to carry out appropriate potentiometric or conductometric determinations and these make it possible to calculate accurately the degree of dissociation of the sparingly soluble salt. In some particular cases when, for example, the instability constants are known for particles formed in the solutions when the sparingly soluble salt dissolves, the solubility product may be calculated from solubility determinations alone.

In the study of stability of complexes by the solubility method, the equilibrium concentration of the addend is hardly ever determined experimentally, though such determinations are very valuable and considerably facilitate the calculations, particularly in those cases when the solubility is a value of the same order as the addend concentration. One of the following procedures is usually used for determining the equilibrium concentration of the addend.

If the solubility of the sparingly soluble salt is much less than the corresponding addend concentration, one may assume with a reasonable degree of accuracy that the equilibrium concentration of addend equals the original concentration. If, however, the solubility of the salt and the addend concentration are commensurate and especially when the difference in these values is small, the method of successive approximations is used. This method has several actual variations, but they are basically the same. In determining the equilibrium concentration of the addend by this method, one first assumes the existence of only one complex and the equilibrium concentration of the addend is calculated approximately by an equation of the type

$$\bar{c}_a = c_a^0 - \alpha S, \qquad (\text{II.9})$$

21

where $\bar{c}_a$ is the equilibrium concentration of the addend, c_a^0 is the over-all (total) addend concentration, S is the solubility of the salt, and α is a coefficient related to the coordination numbers of the complexes formed and the stoichiometric coefficients of the sparingly soluble salt studied. The coefficient α increases with an increase in addend concentration, since in this case the fraction of highly coordinated complexes increases in the solution, i.e., the so-called mean coordination number increases. However, to a first approximation, α is assumed to be constant and given a numerical value which depends on the actual conditions and the equilibrium concentrations are calculated. It may be shown that if the substance in the base phase has a formula of type MA and, when dissolved in a solution of addend A, forms complexes MA_2, MA_3, etc., then $\alpha \geqslant 2$; if the formula of the sparingly soluble salt is of the type M_2A and when dissolved the salt forms complexes MA, MA_2, etc., in this case also $\alpha \geqslant 2$. If the salt anion does not participate in the complex-formation processes, then regardless of the type of salt $\alpha \geqslant 1$.

For example, let complexes MA_2, MA_3, MA_4, etc., form when the sparingly soluble salt MA is dissolved in solutions of addend A at a concentration of c_a. The concentration of complexes of the type MA is usually so low that there is no need to consider it. By definition, the equilibrium concentration of the addend $\bar{c}_a$ is the difference

$$\bar{c}_a = c_a^0 - (c_a)_{\text{bound}}, \qquad (\text{II.10})$$

where c_a^0 is the over-all (total) concentration of addend in solution and $(c_a)_{\text{bound}}$ is the concentration of addend bound in a complex. $(c)_{\text{bound}}$ is expressed as

$$(c_a)_{\text{bound}} = 2c_{MA_2} + 3c_{MA_3} + 4c_{MA_4} + \ldots \qquad (\text{II.11})$$

If one considers that the solubility S is given by

$$S = c_{MA_2} + c_{MA_3} + c_{MA_4}, \qquad (\text{II.12})$$

then (II.11) reduces to

$$(c_a)_{\text{bound}} = 2S + c_{\text{MA}_3} + 2c_{\text{MA}_4}, \qquad \text{(II.11a)}$$

and (II.10) appears as

$$\bar{c}_a = c_a^0 - 2S - c_{\text{MA}_3} - 2c_{\text{MA}_4}. \qquad \text{(II.10a)}$$

Neglecting c_{MA_3} and $2c_{\text{MA}_4}$ in the first approximation, by comparison with $2S$ we finally obtain

$$\bar{c}_a = c_a^0 - 2S. \qquad \text{(II.10b)}$$

This expression may be simplified if one considers that

$$c_a^0 = c_a + S, \qquad \text{(II.13)}$$

where c_a is the original concentration of the addend. Then

$$\bar{c}_a = c_a - S. \qquad \text{(II.10c)}$$

Using the values obtained for the equilibrium concentrations, the values of the instability constant of the complexes formed are roughly evaluated and new values are found for the equilibrium concentrations. The values of the instability constants are again evaluated and new equilibrium concentrations are calculated and this operation is repeated until convergent results are obtained.

As an example, we give the calculation of the equilibria arising when AgCNS is dissolved in potassium thiocyanate solutions. Cave and Hume [5] described experimental determinations of the solubility of AgCNS in water and in potassium thiocyanate solutions over a wide range of concentrations at a constant ionic strength equal to 2.2. The solubility product of AgCNS at this ionic strength equaled $6.75 \cdot 10^{-12}$.

The equilibrium concentration of thiocyanate, required for calculation of the degree of complex formation, was calculated to a first approximation from (II.10c).

Table 1 gives results of experimental determinations of the solubility of AgCNS in thiocyanate solutions; the values of

Table 1. Solubility of AgCNS in Thiocyanate Solutions

Starting concentration of thiocyanate, c_{CNS}, M/liter	Solubility of AgCNS (S), M/liter	Equilibrium concentration of thiocyanate, c_{CNS}, M/liter	Degree of complex formation	ψ_2	ψ_3	ψ_4
0,00548	1,62·10⁻⁶	0,00548	1,31·10³	4,37·10	1,59·10⁹	3,47·10¹⁰
0,01033	3,65·10⁻⁶	0,01033	5,61·10⁸	5,23·10⁷	1,68·10⁹	2,70·10¹⁰
0,04133	3,00·10⁻⁵	0,04130	1,83·10⁵	1,07·10⁸	1,74·10⁹	8,25·10⁹
0,04440	3,36·10⁻⁵	0,04437	2,20·10⁵	1,12·10⁸	1,74·10⁹	7,67·10⁹
0,06662	7,99·10⁻⁵	0,06654	7,89·10⁵	1,78·10⁸	2,15·10⁹	1,12·10¹⁰
0,08885	1,39·10⁻⁴	0,08871	1,81·10⁶	2,32·10⁸	2,22·10⁹	9,25·10⁹
0,1111	2,38·10⁻⁴	0,1109	4,89·10⁶	3,17·10⁸	2,54·10⁹	1,03·10¹⁰
0,1334	3,56·10⁻⁴	0,1330	7,00·10⁶	3,96·10⁸	2,71·10⁹	9,86·10⁹
0,1779	7,24·10⁻⁴	0,1772	1,91·10⁷	6,05·10⁸	3,21·10⁹	1,02·10¹⁰
0,2224	1,28·10⁻³	0,2211	4,20·10⁷	8,40·10⁸	3,64·10⁹	1,01·10¹⁰
0,2744	2,21·10⁻³	0,2722	8,90·10⁷	1,20·10⁹	4,26·10⁹	1,05·10¹⁰
0,2774	2,28·10⁻³	0,2751	9,31·10⁷	1,23·10⁹	4,33·10⁹	1,06·10¹⁰
0,3343	3,70·10⁻³	0,3306	1,81·10⁸	1,61·10⁹	4,75·10⁹	1,02·10¹⁰
0,4443	8,26·10⁻³	0,4360	5,34·10⁸	2,82·10⁹	6,37·10⁹	1,13·10¹⁰
0,5572	0,0146	0,5426	1,17·10⁹	4,00·10⁹	7,30·10⁹	1,09·10¹⁰
0,5536	0,0146	0,5390	1,17·10⁹	4,02·10⁹	7,40·10⁹	1,11·10¹⁰
0,7783	0,0376	0,7407	4,13·10⁹	7,54·10⁹	1,01·10¹⁰	1,17·10¹⁰
1,114	0,0981	1,016	1,47·10¹⁰	1,44·10¹⁰	1,42·10¹⁰	1,26·10¹⁰
1,688	0,2684	1,420	5,64·10¹⁰	2,80·10¹⁰	1,97·10¹⁰	1,29·10¹⁰
2,252	0,5061	1,746	1,31·10¹¹	4,30·10¹⁰	2,46·10¹⁰	1,33·10¹⁰

the equilibrium concentrations of thiocyanate are calculated to a first approximation by (II.10c); the degree of complex formation, calculated by (II.4), is also a first approximation, since the values of the equilibrium concentration of thiocyanate and the function ψ_n are similar.

Having the numerical values of the equilibrium concentrations of thiocyanate and the degree of complex formation, we are able to calculate the corresponding stability constants. However, before automatically applying the formulas presented above, it is profitable to examine the actual peculiarities of the system studied. Thus, for example, in this case it is evident that the concentration of the complex AgCNS, whose stability is characterized by the stability constant β_1, does not depend on the thiocyanate concentration and is very low. This can be seen from the following simple calculation. Cave and Hume [5] found that the solubility of AgCNS in water equals $1.1 \cdot 10^{-6}$ M/liter and the SP of this salt, calculated from potentiometric measurements, equals $1.13 \cdot 10^{-12}$ (in terms of activities at zero ionic strength).

The concentration of Ag^+, equal to $\sqrt{SP}$, is $1.06 \cdot 10^{-6}$ and, consequently, the concentration of undissociated molecules, determined as the difference $1.1 \cdot 10^{-6} - 1.06 \cdot 10^{-6}$, is at least an order less than the solubility at the lowest concentration of thiocyanate used in the work.

The individual terms of the right-hand part of (11.6) are proportional to the concentrations of the corresponding complex particles; therefore, the term $\beta_1 [CNS]$ may be neglected. The insignificantly low concentration of AgCNS in solution, even in comparison with 10^{-6}, makes it possible to evaluate β_1 from available data. Therefore, here ψ_2 is calculated directly as

$$\psi_2 = \frac{\Phi}{[CNS^-]^2} = \beta_2 + \beta_3 [CNS^-] + \cdots \qquad \text{(II.7b)}$$

The data in Table 1 show that $\Phi \gg 1$ (as in an overwhelming majority of cases of the solubility method); therefore

25

$\Phi - 1 \simeq \Phi$, as was assumed in (II.7b). The numerical values of ψ_2 are presented in Table 1. Figure 1 gives a graph of the

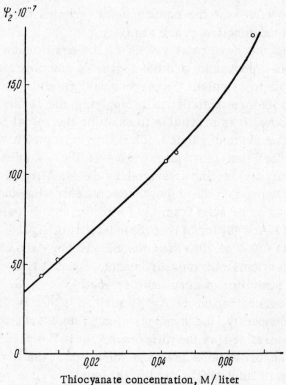

Fig. 1. Graphical determination of β_2.

relation of ψ_2 to the thiocyanate concentration; extrapolation to zero thiocyanate concentration gives $\beta_2 = 3.5 \cdot 10^7$.

The next function, ψ_3, is calculated from the formula:

$$\psi_3 = \frac{\psi_2 - \beta_2}{[CNS^-]} = \beta_3 + \beta_4 [CNS^-] + \ldots \quad (II.7c)$$

Graphical extrapolation in Fig. 2 to $[CNS^-] = 0$ leads to the value $\beta_3 = 1.4 \cdot 10^9$.

Analogous calculations of the function ψ_4 and extrapolation of the graph in Fig. 3 gives the value $\beta_4 = 1.0 \cdot 10^{10}$.

26

Having approximate values of the stability constants, we can calculate the equilibrium concentrations more accurately.

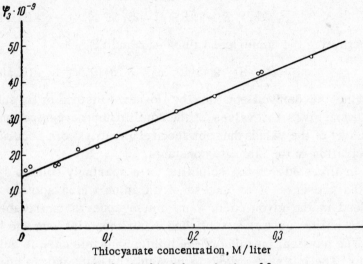

Fig. 2. Graphical determination of β_3.

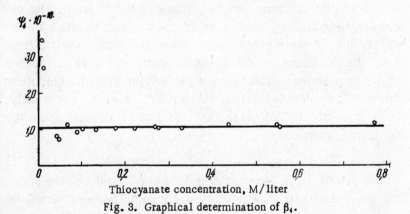

Fig. 3. Graphical determination of β_4.

Continuing the development on p. 22, we introduce into (II.10a) the concentrations of the complexes MA_3 and MA_4, expressed through the corresponding stability constants and the SP of silver thiocyanate, i.e.,

$$c_{MA_3} = \beta_3 \text{ SP } \bar{c}_a^2; \quad c_{MA_4} = \beta_4 \text{ SP } \bar{c}_a^3.$$

After substitution, allowing for (II.13), we obtain

$$\bar{c}_a = c_a - S - \beta_3 \text{ SP } \bar{c}_a^2 - 2\beta_4 \text{ SP } \bar{c}_a^3. \tag{II.10d}$$

Substituting the numerical values of β and SP,

$$\bar{c}_a = c_a - S - 9.45 \cdot 10^{-3} \bar{c}_a^2 - 6.75 \cdot 10^{-2} \bar{c}_a^3. \tag{II.10e}$$

Solving the derived equation by Horner's method or by substitution gives the values of the equilibrium concentrations. The use of the values thus obtained results in a more accurate calculation of the stability constants.

In the study of the solubility of a sparingly soluble salt in the presence of an excess of an anion which acts as an addend in the given case, a minimum appears on the solubility curve, as was established experimentally long ago [6, 7]. The physical meaning of the minimum in this case is quite clear. The initial decrease in the solubility of the salt in comparison with the solubility in pure water is caused by the action of the common ion according to the SP rule. The increase in solubility with a further increase in addend concentration, if there are grounds for neglecting the salt effect, i.e., the decrease in the activity coefficients, is connected with complex formation only. If the minimum on the solubility curve ("complex formation threshold") is fixed accurately, it is possible to calculate the instability constant from the following equation:

$$K_{\text{inst.}} = (^n/_m q - 1) c_a^q, \tag{II.14}$$

where m and n are the stoichiometric coefficients of the sparingly soluble salt $A_m B_n$, q is the coordination number of the complex formed at the minimum, and c_a is the addend concentration at the minimum.

Equation (II.14) is obtained by differentiating a solubility equation of the type (II.12) and setting the derivative $\frac{\partial S}{\partial c_a}$ equal to zero. A similar derivation of (II.14) and a series of examples of its application were presented in [8].

If we are studying the solubility of the salt MX'_p in solutions containing the ions M', forming a series of complexes of the type $M'X_l$ with X, it is most advantageous to calculate the formation function. In this case, the over-all concentration of the addend is calculated from the solubility of the salt, the equilibrium concentration of the addend from the solubility product of the salt MX_p, and the over-all concentration of the metal equals the original concentration of M' ($c^0_{M'}$)

$$\bar{n} = \frac{pS - \sqrt[p]{\frac{SP}{[M]}}}{c^0_{M'}}. \tag{II.15}$$

The metal M should not give complex compounds with the anion X and, consequently, the concentration of M is practically equal to the salt concentration. Hence

$$\bar{n} = \frac{pS - \sqrt[p]{\frac{SP}{S}}}{c^0_M}. \tag{II.15a}$$

When the solution is saturated with molecules of an electroneutral addend, its equilibrium concentration at constant temperature and constant ionic strength also remains constant (this concentration may be denoted by S_0). In solutions containing ions of the metal M, some of the addend molecules are bound in complexes of the type MA_i and the solubility of the addend increases, reaching the value S.

From the solubility of the addend in pure solvent (S_0) and in the presence of the complex former (S), the formation function can readily be calculated:

$$\bar{n} = \frac{S - S_0}{c_M}, \tag{II.16}$$

where c_M is the total concentration of ions of the metal-complex former M.

By studying the solubility of aromatic hydrocarbons in solutions of silver nitrate, Andrews and Keefer [9] established the existence of complexes of the type $AgAr^+$ (Ar is benzene, naphthalene, phenanthrene, toluene, etc.) and determined the instability constants of the corresponding complexes.

More complex variations of the application of the solubility method are also possible. Vosburgh and Derr [10] studied the solubility of silver iodate in ammonia solutions containing nickel. The equilibrium concentration of ammonia was calculated from the solubility of silver iodate and the instability constant of ammonia complexes of silver and hence the instability constants of nickel—ammonia complexes were obtained.

2. DISTRIBUTION METHOD. The study of the distribution of a substance between two immiscible solvents in the presence of complex formation and without it has long been used for determining instability constants [2].

In the study of complex formation by this method it is possible to measure the distribution of the salt, addend, or complexes formed; in practice the method is usually limited to a study of the distribution of a metal salt between aqueous and nonaqueous phases. As a rule, the distribution is studied at a constant pH value and with a sufficient excess of the reagent HB, forming an internal complex salt with the given metal:

$$M_{aq}^{z+} + z\,HB_{solv} \rightleftarrows MB_{z\,solv} + z\,H_{aq}^+. \qquad (II.17)$$

The subscripts aq and $solv$ denote particles in the aqueous solution and in the organic solvent, respectively. The equilibrium constant of this process is

$$K = \frac{[MB_z]_{solv}\,[H^+]_{aq}^z}{[M^{z+}]_{aq}\,[HB]_{solv}^z}. \qquad (II.18)$$

If we consider the condition of constant H^+ and HB concentrations, given above, then we obtain:

30

$$\frac{[\text{MB}_z]_{solv}}{[\text{M}^{z+}]_{aq}} = R_0, \tag{II.18a}$$

where R_0 is the conventional distribution coefficient in the absence of complex formation. The addend A may be introduced into the aqueous phase and then the ratio of the metal concentration in the organic solvent layer to that in the aqueous layer changes:

$$\frac{[\text{MB}_z]_{solv}}{c_{\text{M}_{aq}}} = R, \tag{II.18b}$$

where $c_{\text{M}_{aq}}$ is the over-all concentration of metal in the aqueous phase, and R is the conventional distribution coefficient in the presence of complex formation.

Then it follows from (I.15) that the degree of complex formation is given by the relation

$$\Phi = \frac{R_0}{R}. \tag{II.19}$$

Day and Stenghton [11] determined the instability constants of a whole series of thorium complexes by studying the equilibrium extraction of thorium in the presence of addends and without them. It was considered that in the absence of complex formation, the thorium was present in the aqueous phase as Th^{4+}. The nonaqueous phase used was a benzene solution of thenoyltrifluoroacetone (HT), which reacts with thorium to form the benzene-soluble complex ThT_4.

Thus, the equilibrium of the extraction may be represented by the scheme

$$\text{Th}^{4+} + 4\text{HT}_b \rightleftarrows (\text{ThT}_4)_b + 4\text{H}^+$$

and characterized by the equilibrium constant

$$K = \frac{[\text{ThT}_4]_b \cdot [\text{H}^+]^4}{[\text{Th}^{4+}] \cdot [\text{HT}]_b^4} ;$$

where the subscript b denoted the benzene phase.

On introduction of a substance HX (for example, HF), whose anion X^- (F^-) can form complexes with thorium, the following equilibria arise in the aqueous phase:

$$Th^{4+} + HF \rightleftarrows ThF^{3+} + H^+$$

$$Th^{4+} + 2HF \rightleftarrows ThF_2^{2+} + 2H^+$$

etc., and each of these is characterized by an equilibrium constant

$$k_1 = \frac{[ThF^{3+}] \cdot [H^+]}{[Th^{4+}] \cdot [HF]},$$

$$k_2 = \frac{[ThF_2^{2+}] \cdot [H^+]^2}{[Th^{4+}] \cdot [HF]^2}.$$

It can be shown that the distribution coefficient of thorium in this case can be determined by the expression

$$P = \frac{[Th^{4+}]}{[ThT_4]_b}\left(1 + k_1\frac{[HF]}{[H^+]} + k_2\frac{[HF]^2}{[H^+]^2} + \cdots\right),$$

and in the absence of complex formation:

$$P_0 = \frac{[Th^{4+}]}{[ThT_4]_b},$$

where the expression in brackets in the equation is the degree of complex formation Φ; consequently,

$$\Phi = \frac{P}{P_0}.$$

If the anion of a strong acid, for example, NO_3^-, is used as the addend, then the calculations are simplified since in this case the equilibrium concentration of addend does not depend on the solution pH.

3. ION EXCHANGE METHOD. If an ion-exchange resin, for example, some cationite containing the cation M_1^{z+}, is placed in a solution containing the ions M_2^{r+}, then there will be an exchange of ions between the resin and solution until an equilibrium is set up:

32

$$r\,M_1R_z + z\,M_{2\,aq}^{r+} \rightleftarrows z\,M_2R_r + r\,M_{1\,aq}^{z+}. \qquad (II.20)$$

In this case the equilibrium constant is expressed by the following equation:

$$K = \frac{[M_{1\,aq}^{z+}]^r\,[M_{2\,(R)}^{r+}]^z}{[M_{2\,aq}^{r+}]^z\,[M_{1\,(R)}^{z+}]^r}. \qquad (II.21)$$

Here the subscript aq denotes ions present in the aqueous solution and the subscript (R) denotes ions on the cationite.

If we now introduce into the solution the addend A which interacts with one of the ions and converts it into a complex which is not absorbed by the cationite, then the equilibrium (II.20) will be displaced. The equilibrium concentrations of all the reacting particles may be calculated by determining the analytical concentrations of the ions in solution (or on the cationite) and using the previously calculated equilibrium constant.

If an anionite is used as the ion-exchange resin and the ion exchange between anions in solution and anions in the ion-exchange resin is studied then the calculation is carried out by exactly the same method in this case. The corresponding equilibrium constant is calculated and then after introduction of the metal. the analytical concentrations are determined and the equilibrium concentrations calculated from the constant.

Depending on what the ion-exchange resin absorbs (metal ions or anions), the degree of complex formation or the formation function may be calculated.

A very frequent case in practice is the study of complex formation of doubly and triply charged central ions with a singly charged anion or a neutral addend. In this case the solution contains several particles with the same sign, for example, a positive charge, M^{z+}, MA^{z-1}, etc., which may be absorbed by a cationite.

A method of determining the composition of complex ions in solution and their stability constants in this case was proposed by Fronaeus [12—14].

33

If complexes formed by the doubly charged ion-complex former M^{2+} and the singly charged anion addend are studied, then according to Fronaeus, the ion exchange may be expressed by the equations

$$2RNa + M^{2+} \rightleftarrows MR_2 + 2Na^+, \qquad (II.22)$$

$$RNa + MA^+ \rightleftarrows MAR + Na^+; \qquad (II.23)$$

each of these is characterized by an equilibrium constant

$$K_1 = \frac{[MR_2][Na^+]^2}{[RNa]^2[M^{2+}]}, \qquad (II.22a)$$

$$K_2 = \frac{[MAR][Na^+]}{[RNa][MA^+]}. \qquad (II.23a)$$

In this case the expression for the distribution coefficient is complicated:

$$y = \frac{c_{MR}}{c_M} = \frac{[MR_2] + [MAR]}{c_M}. \qquad (II.24)$$

Calculation of the instability constant is also complicated.

A description of the calculation may be found in the work of Fronaeus cited or in the review article by V. V. Fomin [15]. They examined the possibilities and the most important limitations of this method.

B. ELECTROMETRIC METHODS OF DETERMINING INSTABILITY CONSTANTS

1. POTENTIOMETRIC METHOD. The potentiometric method is one of the oldest methods of determining instability constants. It is also used very successfully at the present time and several variations of the potentiometric method are known.

Metallic and amalgam electrodes, electrodes of the second order, oxidation—reduction systems, a glass electrode, etc., may be used for measuring instability constants by the potentiometric method.

The oldest variation of the potentiometric method consists in measuring the emf of the concentration cell:

$$M \,|\, M^{z+} \,|R^+ \, X^- \quad \begin{vmatrix} M^{z+} \\ MA_n \end{vmatrix} M.$$

One of the compartments of this cell contains a solution of a salt of the given metal and the other contains the same solution with addend added. The electromotive force (E) of the circuit equals

$$E = \frac{RT}{nF} \ln \frac{c_M}{[M]}, \qquad (II.25)$$

where c_M is the over-all concentration of the metal salt (identical in the two compartments), and $[M]$ is the equilibrium concentration of metal ions in the compartment with complex formation.

The term whose logarithm appears in (II.25) is the degree of complex formation Φ; consequently,

$$\ln \Phi = \frac{nF}{RT} E. \qquad (II.26)$$

The logarithm of the degree of complex formation and the emf of the concentration cell were found to be directly proportional values.

At the present time a much more common practice is potentiometric measurement of pH and, consequently, the equilibrium concentration of the addend (under conditions when the latter has acid—base properties). In this case the procedure consists in various forms of potentiometric titration. The substance titrated is, for example, a solution of a salt of the metal-complex former in an acid medium and a solution of addend (base) is added to it from a burette, thus changing the pH. The acid—base dissociation constant of the addend is determined previously under the same temperature and ionic strength conditions; the total (analytical) concentrations of metal and addend are known from the experimental conditions and the pH of the solution is determined experi-

35

mentally. Having the data mentioned makes it possible to calculate the formation function and the equilibrium concentration of addend. Such calculations are somewhat complicated with an increase in the basicity of the addend, but with known dissociation constants a quite rigorous solution is possible and the answers obtained are unequivocal.

Quite a large number of papers [17, 18, 25] have been devoted to methods of finding consecutive stability constants from a known formation function, and it is impossible to examine them here. We will limit ourselves to the more or less similar example of calculating the formation function and then the stability constants of propylenediamine complexes of nickel; the example is taken from Carlson, McReynolds, and Verhoek [16].

The interaction of a nickel ion with propylenediamine (pn) forms complexes of the type $Ni(pn)_n^{2+}$, where n may have the values 1, 2, or 3, depending on the propylenediamine concentration. The experiment was carried out in the following way: to 50.19 ml of a solution containing 0.5 M of potassium chloride, 0.1009 M of hydrochloric acid, and 0.04725 M of nickel chloride was added an exactly measured volume (4.822 M) of propylenediamine and the pH of the solution measured. The temperature was kept at 30°C.

The total concentration of propylenediamine, $|c_{pn}^0|$, was the sum

$$c_{pn}^0 = [pn] + [pn\,H^+] + [pn\,H_2^{2+}] + \bar{n}c_{Ni^{2+}}, \qquad (II.27)$$

where [pn], [pnH$^+$], and [pnH$_2^{2+}$] are the equilibrium concentrations of electroneutral propylenediamine and the products of the addition of one and two protons to it due to reaction with hydrochloric acid, respectively, $\bar{n}$ is Bjerrum's formation function, determined by (II.32), and $c_{Ni^{2+}}$ is the total concentration of nickel in solution.

Let us determine a as the ratio of the equilibrium concentration of propylenediamine molecules to the concentration of pn not bound in a complex, i.e.,

36

$$\alpha = \frac{[pn]}{[pn] + [pnH^+] + [pnH_2^{2+}]} =$$

$$= \frac{k_{pnH^+} \cdot k_{pnH_2^{2+}}}{k_{pnH^+} \cdot k_{pn\,H_2^{2+}} + k_{pnH_2^{2+}} \cdot [H^+] + [H^+]^2}, \qquad (II.28)$$

where

$$k_{pnH^+} = \frac{[H^+][pn]}{[pnH^+]} \quad \text{and} \quad k_{pnH_2^{2+}} = \frac{[H^+][pnH^+]}{[pnH_2^{2+}]}.$$

Let us find the average number of hydrogen ions $(\bar{n}_A)$ which must be on a propylenediamine molecule not bound in a complex:

$$\bar{n}_A = \frac{[pnH^+] + 2[pnH_2^{2+}]}{[pn] + [pnH^+] + [pnH_2^{2+}]} =$$

$$= \frac{k_{pnH_2^{2+}}[H^+] + 2[H^+]^2}{k_{pnH^+} \cdot k_{pnH_2^{2+}} + k_{pnH_2^{2+}}[H^+] + [H^+]^2}. \qquad (II.29)$$

By combining (II.27) and (II.29) we obtain for the formation function

$$\bar{n} = \frac{c_{pn}^0 - [pn] - [pn\,H^+] - [pn\,H_2^{2+}]}{c_{Ni^{2+}}} =$$

$$= \frac{c_{pn}^0 - \dfrac{c_{H^+} - [H^+]}{\bar{n}_A}}{c_{Ni^{2+}}}. \qquad (II.30)$$

An expression for calculating the equilibrium concentration of propylenediamine may be obtained by combining (II.28) and (II.29).

$$[pn] = \frac{\alpha([pn\,H^+] + 2[pnH_2^{2+}])}{\bar{n}_A} = \frac{\alpha}{\bar{n}_A}(c_{H^+} - [H^+]). \qquad (II.31)$$

Knowing the initial concentrations of propylenediamine, hydrochloric acid, and nickel salt and determining the pH of the solution experimentally, it is possible to calculate α and $\bar{n}_A$ from (II.28) and (II.29), and then the formation function and the equilibrium concentration of propylenediamine from

(II.30) and (II.31), respectively. The acid dissociation constants of propylenediamine must be measured previously at the same temperature and ionic strength.

The necessary experimental material and the results of calculations are presented in Table 2, as taken from [16].

Table 2. Formation Functions $\bar{n}$ for Complexes of Nickel with Propylenediamine (temperature 30°; ionic strength 0.5)

Initial concentrations, mole/liter			pH	$\alpha : 10^5$ from (II.28)	nA from (II.29)	n from (II.30)	$-\lg$ [pn]
HCl	NiCl$_2$	pn					
0,0997	0,04669	0,05677	5,00	0,0132	2,000	0,148	8,18
0,0995	0,04659	0,06679	5,25	0,0414	1,984	0,356	7,68
0,0994	0,04652	0,07472	5,38	0,0733	1,978	0,527	7,43
0,0990	0,04633	0,0937	5,61	0,213	1,965	0,937	6,97
0,0987	0,04615	0,1136	5,89	0,746	1,938	1,337	6,42
0,0982	0,04597	0,1305	6,16	2,46	1,888	1,708	5,89
0,0978	0,04577	0,1511	6,56	13,7	1,763	2,091	5,12
0,0974	0,04561	0,1671	6,89	47,5	1,597	2,326	4,54
0,0971	0,04544	0,1848	7,14	115	1,458	2,601	4,11
0,0967	0,04526	0,2031	7,40	259	1,312	2,859	3,72
0,0965	0,04518	0,2108	7,56	427	1,233	2,933	3,48

The formation function $\bar{n}$ is related to the stability constants of the complexes by the known equation

$$\bar{n} = \frac{x_1 \,[\mathrm{pn}] + 2x_1x_2\,[\mathrm{pn}]^2 + 3x_1x_2x_3\,[\mathrm{pn}]^3}{1 + x_1\,[\mathrm{pn}] + x_1x_2\,[\mathrm{pn}]^2 + x_1x_2x_3\,[\mathrm{pn}]^3}. \tag{II.32}$$

By solving this equation with respect to the separate stability constants, we obtain

$$x_1 = \frac{1}{[\mathrm{pn}]} \cdot \frac{\bar{n}}{(1 - \bar{n}) + (2 - \bar{n})\,[\mathrm{pn}]\,x_2 + (3 - \bar{n})\,[\mathrm{pn}]^2\,x_2x_3}, \tag{II.33}$$

$$x_2 = \frac{1}{[\mathrm{pn}]} \cdot \frac{(\bar{n} - 1) + \dfrac{\bar{n}}{[\mathrm{pn}]\,x_1}}{(2 - \bar{n}) + (3 - \bar{n})\,[\mathrm{pn}]\,x_3}, \tag{II.34}$$

38

$$\varkappa_3 = \frac{1}{[\text{pn}]} \cdot \frac{(\bar{n}-2) + \dfrac{\bar{n}-1}{[\text{pn}]\varkappa_2} + \dfrac{\bar{n}}{[\text{pn}]\varkappa_1\varkappa_2}}{(3-\bar{n})} \cdot \qquad \text{(II.35)}$$

These equations may be reduced to simple, approximate formulas if we consider that at a given concentration of addend, the solution contains only two particles, MA_{n-1} and MA_n. It is easy to see that if in this case $[MA_{n-1}] = [MA_n]$, then $\bar{n} = n - \frac{1}{2}$ and to a first approximation

$$\varkappa_n = \left(\frac{1}{[\text{pn}]}\right)_{\bar{n}=n-\frac{1}{2}} \qquad \text{(II.36)}$$

By using concentrations of addend at $\bar{n} = \frac{1}{2}$, $1\frac{1}{2}$, and $2\frac{1}{2}$ it is possible to calculate the stability constants $\varkappa_1$, $\varkappa_2$, and $\varkappa_3$. By substituting (II.36) in (II.33), (II.34), and (II.35), we obtain

$$\varkappa_1 = \frac{1}{[\text{pn}]_{\bar{n}=\frac{1}{2}}} \cdot \frac{1}{1 + 3\varkappa_2\,[\text{pn}]_{\bar{n}=\frac{1}{2}} + 5\varkappa_2\varkappa_3\,[\text{pn}]^2_{\bar{n}=\frac{1}{2}}}, \qquad \text{(II.33a)}$$

$$\varkappa_2 = \frac{1}{[\text{pn}]_{\bar{n}=\frac{3}{2}}} \cdot \frac{1 + \dfrac{3}{\varkappa_1\,[\text{pn}]_{\bar{n}=\frac{3}{2}}}}{1 + 3\varkappa_3\,[\text{pn}]_{\bar{n}=\frac{3}{2}}}, \qquad \text{(II.34a)}$$

$$\varkappa_3 = \frac{1}{[\text{pn}]_{\bar{n}=\frac{5}{2}}} \left(1 + \frac{3}{\varkappa_2\,[\text{pn}]_{\bar{n}=\frac{5}{2}}} + \frac{5}{\varkappa_1\varkappa_2\,[\text{pn}]_{\bar{n}=\frac{5}{2}}}\right). \qquad \text{(II.35a)}$$

If the stability constants of the complexes differ essentially in value, then even the approximate formula (II.36) gives good results.

The following procedure is usually used to find $\varkappa$ by the given method.

A series of values of [pn] which correspond to $\bar{n} = \frac{1}{2}$, $\frac{3}{2}$, and $\frac{5}{2}$, are chosen on the "formation curve" (Bjerrum's terminology), i.e., the graph of $\bar{n}$ against $(-\lg[\text{pn}])$ and $\varkappa$ found from (II.33a), (II.34a), and (II.35a).

Figure 4 shows the formation curve and Table 3 gives the results of calculations for determining the stability constants.

Table 3. Stability Constants of Propylenediamine
Complexes of Nickel

Calculated from the formation curve by (II.36)			Calculated from (II.33a), (II.34a), and (II.35a)		
lg x_1	lg x_2	lg x_3	lg x_1	lg x_2	lg x_3
7,48	6,23	4,27	7,41	6,30	4,29

The data in Table 3 show that in this case even (II.36) leads to quite accurate values.

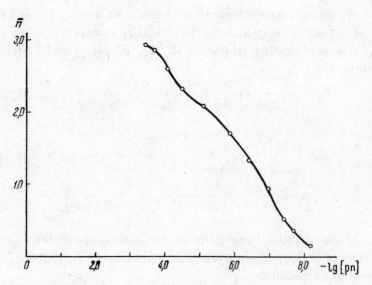

Fig. 4. Formation curve for the system Ni^{2+}—propylenediamine (pn).

The method considered is not the only one for finding stability constants from formation functions.

For example, by the method of Fronaeus [17], the formation function is integrated graphically in accordance with (I.24) and the degree of complex formation is calculated. The stability constants are then calculated by Leden's method [4].

We have already examined the application of Leden's method (p. 20). Various other methods are also known [18, 19].

K. Poulsen, Bjerrum, and J. Poulsen [20] recently proposed the following simple method for finding successive stability constants from the formation function. Their arguments may be reduced to the following.

Let us divide the formation function by the equilibrium concentration of the addend:

$$\frac{\bar{n}}{[A]} = \frac{\beta_1 + 2\beta_2 [A] + 3\beta_3 [A]^2 + \cdots}{1 + \beta_1 [A] + \beta_2 [A]^2 + \beta_3 [A]^3 + \cdots} \qquad (II.37)$$

and define

$$\frac{\bar{n}}{[A]} = f. \qquad (II.38)$$

It is quite evident that f tends to β_1 when the addend concentration tends to zero, i.e.,

$$\lim_{[A] \to 0} f \to \beta_1. \qquad (II.39)$$

Extrapolation of the function to $[A]=0$ in the system of coordinates $(f, [A])$ gives β_1.

By rearranging (II.37) and considering (II.38), we obtain

$$\frac{f - \beta_1}{[A]} = \frac{2\beta_2 + 3\beta_3 [A] - \beta_1^2 - \beta_1 \cdot \beta_2 [A] - \beta_1 \cdot \beta_3 [A]^2 + \cdots}{1 + \beta_1 [A] + \beta_2 [A]^2 + \beta_3 [A]^3 + \cdots}. \qquad (II.40)$$

It is evident that

$$\lim_{[A] \to 0} \frac{f - \beta_1}{[A]} = 2\beta_2 - \beta_1^2. \qquad (II.41)$$

Hence, it is possible to find $2\beta_2 - \beta_1^2$ and then β_2 by an analogous method.

All the successive constants are found by plotting functions analogous to (II.40) and extrapolating graphically. The method is somewhat reminiscent of Leden's method, which was presented previously.

Where various extrapolation methods are used for finding constants (for example, Leden's method), it is necessary to check the accuracy of the constants obtained. The principle of this type of checking consists in substituting the numerical values of the constants obtained in the basic equation relating the instability (or stability) constants, the equilibrium concentrations (of addend or metal), and the property measured experimentally in studying complex formation (solubility, potential, etc.).

If, for example, the extrapolation method is used for processing data obtained by the solubility method, then the experimentally found solubility is compared with the value calculated by means of the constants obtained. If the constants found are accurate, the discrepancies between the calculated and experimental values of the solubility are usually within the limits of possible experimental error and the deviations have a statistical character.

Sufficient attention is not always paid to this, though such checking of the constants is always necessary.

2. POLAROGRAPHIC METHOD. The polarographic and potentiometric methods have much in common, since they are both based on a study of the interaction of an electrode with ions in solution.

In the polarographic method the equilibrium concentration of metal (central ion) is determined by the shift in the half-wave potential when various concentrations of addends are introduced into the solution investigated. The method has become quite common, especially in recent years. The use of the polarographic method is limited to complexes containing cations which may be reduced at a mercury cathode. The complex compounds should be formed and decomposed instantaneously ("reversible complexes" in Heyrovsky's terminology).

Heyrovsky [21] first used polarographic curves for calculating instability constants. The equation for the displacement of the half-wave potential by complex formation was later refined and the following form (for 25°) is now used:

$$(E_{1/2})_{compl.} - (E_{1/2})_0 =$$

$$= \frac{0.059}{n} \lg K - \frac{0.059}{n} \lg \frac{f_M k_k}{f_k k_M} - \frac{0.059}{n} p \lg c_x f_x, \qquad (II.42)$$

where $(E_{1/2})_{compl.}$ and $(E_{1/2})_0$ are the values of the half-wave potentials in solutions of the complex (with the addition of addend) and simple salts, K is the instability constant, k_k and k_M are the proportionality coefficients between concentration and current strength for complex and simple ions, respectively, f_M, f_k, and f_x are the activity coefficients of the metal ions, complex ions, and addends x. respectively, and p is the coordination number of the complex formed.

Equation (II.42) is usually simplified by introducing a series of approximate assumptions, thus:

$$k_k = k_M \text{ and } f_M = f_k,$$

and we then obtain

$$(E_{1/2})_{compl.} - (E_{1/2})_0 = \frac{0.059}{n} \lg K - \frac{0.059}{n} p \lg c_x f_x. \qquad (11.42a)$$

Sometimes f_x is taken as unity and (II.42a) is simplified still further.

Equation (II.42a) has been used in this form by many investigators for the calculation of instability constants. This equation may be used to determine the coordination number (from the tangent of the plot of $\Delta E_{1/2}$ vs $\lg c_x$) of the complex formed and the instability constant of the latter. Equation (II.42) was derived on the assumption that only one complex with the coordination number p is formed in the solution. In actual fact several complexes with different coordination numbers exist in solution and as a result the plot of $\Delta E_{1/2}$ vs $\lg c_x$ is a curve, bulging toward the abscissa. The equilibrium constants of the intermediate stages of complex formation are very difficult and sometimes impossible to calculate by this equation. When the successive instability constants of the separate complex particles differ quite substantially from each other, it is sometimes possible to separate out straight-line sections on the graph of $\Delta E_{1/2}$ vs lg c. By applying (II.42a) to each section, it is possible to determine p and lg K.

K. B. Yatsimirskii [22] used a logarithmic graph to calculate successive constants. By assuming that two complexes existed for each concentration of addend, he obtained the equation

$$\Delta E_{1/2} = \frac{0,059}{n} \lg K - \frac{0,059}{n} (p-1) \lg c_x - \frac{0,059}{n} \lg \left(c_x + \frac{1}{k}\right). \quad \text{(II.43)}$$

Differentiation leads to

$$\frac{\partial \Delta E_{1/2}}{\partial \lg c_x} = -\frac{0,059}{n} \left(p - 1 + \frac{c_x}{c_x + k}\right). \quad \text{(II.44)}$$

At points where $c_x = k$, the tangent satisfies the condition

$$\frac{\partial \Delta E}{\partial \lg c_x} = -\frac{0,059}{n} (p - 1/2). \quad \text{(II.44a)}$$

By drawing a series of tangents satisfying (II.44a) at various values of p it is possible to find the coordination numbers of the complexes formed in solution and their instability constants.

Successive instability constants may also be calculated by Leden's method. The application of this method to the polar-ographic procedure for measuring constants has been described in the work of DeFord and Hume [23]. The authors showed that the shift in half-wave potential and the degree of complex formation were related in the following way:

$$\lg \Phi = 0,435 \frac{nF}{RT} \Delta E_{1/2} + \lg \frac{J_1}{J_2}, \quad \text{(II.45)}$$

where J_1 is the diffusion constant of the simple ion and J_2 is the apparent (mean) diffusion constant of the series of complex ions. The ratio of these constants is usually taken as 1 and therefore the second term in the right-hand part of (II.45)

44

disappears; $\Delta E_{1/2} = (E_{1/2})_0 - (E_{1/2})_{compl}$, i.e., the shift in half-wave potential with complex formation.

By substituting the constants in (II.45) we finally obtain (for 25°)

$$\lg \Phi = 17.0 n \Delta E_{1/2}. \tag{II.45a}$$

Hume, DeFord, and Cave [24] used the method developed for determining the stability constants of thiocyanate complexes of cadmium. All the experiments were at 30°. Under these conditions, (II.45) assumes the form

$$\lg \Phi = 34,5 \, \Delta E_{1/2}. \tag{II.45b}$$

The determination of successive stability constants when the degree of complex formation is known has already been considered.

C. OTHER METHODS OF THE FIRST GROUP

1. KINETIC METHOD. If one of the substances participating in the equilibrium of the dissociation of a complex particle

$$MA_n \rightleftarrows M + nA,$$

may react at a measurable rate with a third substance, then this reaction may be used for measuring the instability constant.

If the addend A reacts with substance B at a measurable rate, then the rate of the corresponding reaction, proceeding, for example, according to the bimolecular law

$$A + B \rightarrow D$$

is determined by the equation

$$-\frac{\partial c}{\partial t} = k c_A c_B.$$

By measuring the reaction rate at a known concentration of substance B and preliminarily determining the rate constant K, it is possible to calculate the equilibrium concentration of the substance c_A. Thus, for example, the equilibrium concentration of thiosulfate ions may be determined by the rate of reduction of ferric ions [26] and the equilibrium concentration of ferric ions by the rate of oxidation of iodide [27].

Of great importance here are the cases when the substance determined is a catalyst in a homogeneous catalytic reaction. Thus, for example, Bell and Prue [28] studied the rate of depolymerization of diacetone alcohol $CH_3COCH_2C(CH_3)_2OH \rightarrow \rightarrow 2CH_3COCH_3$. This is a catalytic reaction whose rate is proportional to the concentration of hydroxyl ions. By studying this reaction in the presence of different cations, the authors determined the instability constants of the hydroxo complexes $CaOH^+$ and $BaOH^+$.

When kinetic methods are used for determining instability constants either the degree of complex formation or the formation function can be calculated directly from the experimental data. If the equilibrium concentration of metal is determined from the experiment, it is best to calculate the degree of complex formation; if the equilibrium concentration of addend is known, then it is more convenient to calculate the formation function.

The use of the kinetic method is limited by the lack of study of the kinetics of appropriate reactions, though such reactions can be suggested for a large number of ions. The most studied reactions have been examined and the applications of the kinetic method systematized in the review [29].

2. "FREEZING" METHOD (CHEMICAL ANALYTICAL DETERMINATION OF EQUILIBRIUM CONCENTRATIONS). The "freezing" method is widely used in the study of equilibria in the gas phase. This method may also be used for studying instability constants of complexes which form and decompose slowly. The substance determined is rapidly and quantitatively isolated from the reaction sphere by precipitation or by binding in an almost undissociated compound. The concentration of the substance found in this way is the

equilibrium value since the systems chosen for investigation have equilibria which are established and disturbed slowly.

The instability constants of thiocyanate complexes of trivalent chromium, for example, were determined in this way [20].

Most complexes which are formed and decomposed slowly have an exceptionally high stability. Therefore the concentration of their decomposition products is very low and can only be detected by special methods. The use of tracers is especially convenient in this case.

Cook and Long [30] determined the instability constants of the iron ferroin complex by using tracers for this purpose for the first time. To determine the instability constants, they studied the equilibrium

$$Fe(Ph)_3^{2+} + 3H^+ \rightleftarrows Fe^2 + 3HPh^+.$$

A solution containing radioactive iron was prepared and left for two days; a solution of inactive $FeSO_4$ was then added to it and the complex cation subsequently precipitated with a solution containing CdI_4^{2-} ions. The Fe^{2+} ions which were not bound in the complex remained in solution. The radioactivity of the original solution and the solution after precipitation of the ferroin complex was measured.

The instability constant was readily calculated from these data and the known original concentrations of iron salt and ferroin.

In the further development and application of this method we should consider the results obtained by A. A. Grinberg and L. E. Nikol'skaya [31], who showed that even in the case of extremely stable complexes, the exchange of radioactive isotopes between ions in solution and ions in the complex particles proceeds quite rapidly. Meanwhile, reliable results can only be obtained when the exchange proceeds extremely slowly.

3. COLORIMETRIC INDICATOR METHOD. The equilibrium concentration of reacting substances may be determined

from the optical density of a solution which contains a colored compound in equilibrium with one of the dissociation products of the complex. Thus, for example, the equilibrium concentration of ferric ions may be found from the optical density of solutions containing thiocyanate ions [32]. The equilibrium concentration of hydrogen ions may be found by studying the behavior of colored indicators in the solution investigated. In the first case it is possible to calculate the degree of complex formation and in the second the experimentally determined pH of the solution can be used to calculate the equilibrium concentration of addend (if the addend has acid—base properties) and then the formation function.

The colorimetric indicator method has made possible the quantitative study of complexes which do not absorb light in the visible part of the spectrum. The principle behind this type of determination is the "decolorization" of a colored complex by the introduction of new addends or complex formers into the solution.

A. K. Babko and T. N. Rychkova [33] determined the instability constant of the salicylate complex of aluminum from the decolorization of the salicylate complex of iron on introduction of an aluminum salt into the solution:

$$FeSal^+ + Al^{3+} \rightleftarrows AlSal^+ + Fe^{3+};$$

$$K_p = \frac{[AlSal^+]\,[Fe^{3+}]}{[FeSal^+]\,[Al^{3+}]} = \frac{K_{FeSal^+}}{K_{AlSal^+}}.$$

The equilibrium constant of this process is determined experimentally and K_{FeSal^+} was known previously; K_{AlSal^+} is calculated from these data.

When any addend, for example, fluoride, is introduced into this solution, the corresponding complexes, in this case fluorides, of iron are formed; there will also be a decrease in optical density.

The data obtained are also used for calculation of instability constants.

48

4. BIOLOGICAL METHOD. To determine the instability constant of the citral complex of calcium, Hastings et al. [34] made use of the effect which calcium ions have on the contraction of the ventricle of an isolated frog's heart. Only calcium ions which were not bound in the complex showed a biological action, and therefore the method made it possible to determine the equilibrium concentration of calcium ions in solution. The unknowns connected with the activity of the heart were eliminated by comparing the effect produced by the solution examined and a standard; the concentration of the standard solution was chosen so that the amplitude of the contraction was the same in both cases.

This method is not of general interest due to its limited application, but it has been found to be irreplaceable for the investigation of certain systems. Its application is most effective where the normal methods of determining the concentration of free ions are not applicable; for example, in various types of biological systems where a considerable amount of buffer agents of natural origin is present.

5. RADIOACTIVE TRACER METHOD. In recent years radioactive tracers have been used widely in the most varied fields of chemistry, but this method is used very little for the determination of instability constants.

The work of Cook and Long [30] on the use of tracers in the "freezing" method was presented on p. 47.

Cook and Long [35] recently modified the tracer method for the determination of instability constants; the principle of this modification consists in measuring the rate of isotope exchange by the cation between aquoions and complex ions in solution.

By studying the exchange during different time intervals and extrapolating to zero time ("instantaneous exchange"), the equilibrium concentration of free metal ions is found. The method was applied to the study of ethylenediaminetetraacetate complexes of iron [36]. A necessary condition for this method to be applicable is that the exchange between aquoions and complex ions should proceed quite slowly.

Group II Methods

Many properties of solutions of complex compounds differ essentially from the sum of the properties of the starting reagent solutions. In the methods of the second group use is made of this deviation from additivity, which is connected with the amount of new complex particles formed in the system and their composition and properties.

The following methods belong to the second group:

1. The spectrophotometric method is based on a study of the optical density and absorption spectra of solutions.

2. Electroconductivity method. With the formation of new complex ions, the electroconductivity of a system is not an additive value. The deviation from additivity may be used for observing complex formation processes and calculating instability constants.

3. The cryoscopic and ebullioscopic methods are based on a study of the change in freezing or boiling point of solutions, which is connected with the change in the number of particles in solution during complex formation.

4. The calorimetric method makes it possible to evaluate the number of complex particles formed in solution from the value of the heat effect on mixing the starting solutions.

Let us examine the methods of Group II in more detail.

1. SPECTROPHOTOMETRIC METHOD. If one or more colored complexes are formed in a system, then the optical density of the solution changes with a change in the addend concentration. It is impossible to find the equilibrium con-

centrations of complexes directly by measurement of the optical density of the solution since it is necessary to know the molar extinction coefficients of each complex formed in the system.

If the complex is sufficiently stable and practically complete formation of the complex compound occurs at high addend concentrations, then the molar extinction coefficient may be found from these conditions or, in the extreme case, by extrapolation from several points obtained at high addend concentrations.

More complex cases of the light extinction coefficient have been examined in A. K. Babko's monograph [37].

Methods for calculating light extinction coefficients were developed by N. P. Komar' [38, 39] for cases when the color of the solution is produced not only by complex particles, but also by the natural color of the reacting particles. He examined cases when side processes (hydrolysis, acid—base interaction, etc.) occur in solution together with complex formation.

If only one colored compound is formed in solution, the calculation of equilibrium constants is comparatively simple.

Considerable difficulties arise when several complexes are formed in the system. The calculation of stability constants with stepwise complex formation from a study of physicochemical properties of solutions (including optical density) was examined by K. B. Yatsimirskii [40].

As a result of a series of determinations of the optical density of solutions containing complex compounds, it is possible to obtain a series of values of the average molar extinction coefficients from the formula

$$\bar{\varepsilon} = \frac{D}{C_M l},$$
(II.46)

where $\bar{\varepsilon}$ is the average molar extinction coefficient, D is the optical density of the solution, l is the thickness of the light absorbing layer, and c is the total concentration of metal ions.

The addends A present in the solution form with the metal ions M a series of complex particles MA_1, MA_2, ..., MA_n, whose stabilities are characterized by the corresponding stability constants β_1, β_2, ..., β_n.

According to the Bouger—Lambert—Beer law, the optical density of the solution may be expressed by the equation

$$\frac{D}{l} = \varepsilon_0 [M] + \varepsilon_1 [MA] + \varepsilon_2 [MA_2] + \ldots + \varepsilon_n [MA_n], \quad \text{(II.47)}$$

where ε_0, ε_2, ..., ε_n are the molar extinction coefficients of M, MA, MA_2, ..., MA_n, respectively.

Starting from the obvious relation

$$c_M = [M] + [MA] + [MA_2] + \ldots + [MA_n] \quad \text{(II.48)}$$

and (II.46) and (II.47), we obtain

$$\bar{\varepsilon} = \frac{\varepsilon_0 + \varepsilon_1\beta_1 [A] + \varepsilon_2\beta_2 [A]^2 + \ldots + \varepsilon_n\beta_n [A]^n}{1 + \beta_1 [A] + \beta_2 [A]^2 + \ldots + \beta_n [A]^n} . \quad \text{(II.49)}$$

If we subtract ε_0 from both sides of (II.49), we obtain

$$\overline{\Delta\varepsilon} = \frac{\Delta\varepsilon_1\beta_1 [A] + \Delta\varepsilon_2\beta_2 [A]^2 + \ldots + \Delta\varepsilon_n\beta_n [A]^n}{1 + \beta_1 [A] + \beta_2 [A]^2 + \ldots + \beta_n [A]^n}, \quad \text{(II.50)}$$

where $\overline{\Delta\varepsilon} = \bar{\varepsilon} - \varepsilon_0$; $\Delta\varepsilon_1 = \varepsilon_1 - \varepsilon_0$; $\Delta\varepsilon_2 = \varepsilon_2 - \varepsilon_0$; $\Delta\varepsilon_n = \varepsilon_n - \varepsilon_0$.

Equation (II.50) is correct not only for the molar extinction coefficients, but also for the optical densities if all measurements are made in cells with the same thickness of the light-absorbing layer.

As a result of a series of determinations it is possible to obtain a large number of values of $\overline{\Delta\varepsilon}$ and, consequently, a large number of equations of the type (II.50). The problem consists of searching for methods of finding coefficients for these equations ($\Delta\varepsilon$ and β).

The principle of the method of solving these equations put forward by K. B. Yatsimirskii consists in constructing a series of auxiliary functions and extrapolating them to a zero value of the variable.

Let us examine the simple auxiliary function

$$f_1 = \frac{\overline{\Delta\varepsilon}}{[A]}. \tag{II.51}$$

From (II.49) and (II.50) it follows that

$$f_1 = \frac{\Delta\varepsilon_1\beta_1 + \Delta\varepsilon_2\beta_2\,[A] + \Delta\varepsilon_3\beta_3\,[A]^2 + \ldots + \Delta\varepsilon_n\beta_n\,[A]^{n-1}}{1 + \beta_1\,[A] + \beta_2\,[A]^2 + \beta_3\,[A]^3 + \ldots + \beta_n\,[A]^n}. \tag{II.52}$$

Extrapolation of f_1 to zero addend concentration gives

$$\lim_{[A]\to 0} f_1 = a_1 = \Delta\varepsilon_1\beta_1. \tag{II.53}$$

This extrapolation can be achieved by a graphical method if the equilibrium concentration of addend is plotted along the abscissa and the value of f_1 [calculated by (II.51)] is plotted along the ordinate. The intercept on the ordinate is then numerically equal to $\Delta\varepsilon_1\beta_1$.

Differentiation of the function f_1 and extrapolation of the derivative to zero addend concentration gives

$$\lim_{A\to 0} \frac{df_1}{d[A]} = a_2 = \Delta\varepsilon_2\beta_2 - \Delta\varepsilon_1\beta_1^2. \tag{II.54}$$

The value of a_2 can also be found by construction of a new auxiliary function f_2:

$$f_2 = \frac{f_1 - a_1}{[A]}. \tag{II.55}$$

On extrapolation to zero addend concentration, this function assumes the following value:

$$\lim_{[A]\to 0} f_2 = a_2 = \Delta\varepsilon_2\beta_2 - \Delta\varepsilon_1\beta_1^2. \tag{II.56}$$

A third auxiliary function f_3 is constructed analogously:

$$f_3 = \frac{f_2 - a_2}{[A]}. \tag{II.57}$$

By extrapolation of f_3 to zero addend concentration, we obtain

$$\lim_{[A]\to 0} f_3 = a_3 = \Delta\varepsilon_3\beta_3 - \Delta\varepsilon_1\beta_1^3. \tag{II.58}$$

The same result may be obtained by differentiation of f_2 and extrapolation of the derivative to zero addend concentration.

Quite analogously it is possible to construct the auxiliary functions f_4, f_5, f_6, etc.; in the general form:

$$f_i = \frac{f_{i-1} - a_{i-1}}{[A]}. \tag{II.59}$$

Extrapolation of such a function to zero addend concentration gives

$$\lim_{[A]\to 0} f_i = a_i = \Delta\varepsilon_i\beta_i - \Delta\varepsilon_1\beta_1^i. \tag{II.60}$$

Since we are determining not only the values of the stability constants β_1, β_2, ..., β_n, but also the values of the molar extinction coefficient increments $(\Delta\varepsilon_1, \Delta\varepsilon_2, ..., \Delta\varepsilon_n)$, the total number of extrapolation equations is a factor of two less than the number of unknowns to be determined. In this connection it is advantageous to introduce a new variable y, related to the addend concentration by the very simple equation

$$y = \frac{1}{[A]}. \tag{II.61}$$

After dividing the numerator and denominator of the right-hand side of (II.50) by $[A]^n$ and considering (II.61), we obtain

$$\Delta\bar{\varepsilon} = \frac{\Delta\varepsilon_n\beta_n + \Delta\varepsilon_{n-1}\beta_{n-1}y + ... + \Delta\varepsilon_1\beta_1 y^{n-1}}{\beta_n + \beta_{n-1}y + ... + \beta_1 y^{n-1} + y^n}. \tag{II.62}$$

Extrapolation of the value of $\Delta\bar{\varepsilon}$ to zero value of y gives

$$\lim_{y\to 0} \Delta\bar{\varepsilon} = b_1 = \Delta\varepsilon_n. \tag{II.63}$$

Differentiation of $\Delta\bar{\varepsilon}$ with respect to y and extrapolation of the derivative to zero value of y leads to the following result:

$$\lim_{y\to 0} \frac{\partial\Delta\bar{\varepsilon}}{\partial y} = (\Delta\varepsilon_{n-1} - \Delta\varepsilon_n)\frac{\beta_{n-1}}{\beta_n}. \tag{II.64}$$

54

An analogous result may also be obtained by construction of the auxiliary function φ_1:

$$\varphi_1 = \frac{\overline{\Delta\varepsilon} - b_1}{y}. \qquad \text{(II.65)}$$

On extrapolation of this function to zero value of y, as can be seen from (II.62), we find

$$\lim_{y \to 0} \varphi_1 = b_2 = (\Delta\varepsilon_{n-1} - \Delta\varepsilon_n) \frac{\beta_{n-1}}{\beta_n}. \qquad \text{(II.66)}$$

Then by the same scheme, the functions $\varphi_1, \varphi_3, \ldots, \varphi_{n-1}$ are constructed and extrapolated to zero value of y.

By combination of the values obtained by extrapolation of the functions $\varphi_1, \varphi_2, \ldots, \varphi_{n-1}$, with the values obtained by extrapolation of the functions $f_1, f_2, f_3, \ldots, f_n$, it is possible to find all the coefficients of (II.50).

Thus, for example, when the solution contains only two complexes MA and MA$_2$, we obtain

$$a_1 = \Delta\varepsilon_1\beta_1,$$
$$a_2 = \Delta\varepsilon_2\beta_2 - \Delta\varepsilon_1\beta_1^2,$$
$$b_1 = \Delta\varepsilon_2,$$
$$b_2 = (\Delta\varepsilon_1 - \Delta\varepsilon_2)\frac{\beta_1}{\beta_2}$$

This system of equations is solved very simply; hence, together with the stability constants β_1 and β_2, we find the optical characteristics $\Delta\varepsilon_1$ and $\Delta\varepsilon_2$.

The values of the coefficients in (II.50) found by this method then require checking, which is done by comparing the calculated values of $\overline{\Delta\varepsilon}$ with the experimental values over the whole range of addend concentrations used.

In the case of extremely stable complexes, calculation of the equilibrium concentration of addend presents certain difficulties. If the complexes do not have a high stability, then the total addend concentration will not differ essentially from the equilibrium value.

The calculation method presented was used by K. B. Yatsimirskii and T. I. Fedorova [41] for calculation of the stability constants of acetate complexes of divalent chromium. A series of variants for the calculation of equilibria from spectrophotometric data is given in A. K. Babko's monograph [37].

2. ELECTROCONDUCTIVITY METHOD. Some of the first electroconductivity methods were used by I. I. Chernyaev and S. I. Khorunzhenkov [42] for studying platinum complexes.

This method was subsequently used by many investigators for studying the instability constants of various acidocomplexes.

The principle of the electroconductivity method consists in studying the electroconductivity of solutions of the pure salts M_nA and RX_m, mixing them, and studying the electroconductivity of the solution obtained. If the complex RA^{m-n} is formed in the solution by the scheme

$$R^{m+} + A^{n-} \rightleftarrows RA^{m-n},$$

then the electroconductivity of the mixture is less than the electroconductivity which would be observed in the solution if there were no complex formation by a certain value equal to

$$(\varkappa_0 - \varkappa) \, 10^3 = an\lambda_A + am\lambda_R - a\lambda_{RA}. \qquad \text{(II.67)}$$

In this equation $\varkappa_0$ and $\varkappa$ are the specific electroconductivities of the solution, $\varkappa_0$ in the absence of complex formation (calculated from data on the electroconductivity of the pure salts M_nA and RX_m) and $\varkappa$ found experimentally; λ_A, λ_R, and λ_{RA} are the equivalent electroconductivities of the ions A^{n-}, R^{m+} and RA^{m-n}, respectively; n and m are the charges of the ions A^{n-} and R^{m+}, and a is the concentration of the complex RA^{m-n} in gram-ions (or gram-moles) per liter. The ionic electroconductivities at different electrolyte concentrations may be evaluated from the equation

$$\lambda_A = \lambda^0_A - B^{1/2}$$

where λ_A^0 is the ionic electroconductivity at infinite dilution and B is a coefficient which may be found from experiments on the electroconductivity of the pure salts.

The ionic electroconductivity of the complex RA^{m-n} equals zero if m and n are equal and the complex particle does not bear an electric charge. It is usually taken that the ionic electroconductivity of this particle is simply related to the electroconductivity of the anion A^{n-} (in the case of anionic complexes) or the cation R^{m+} (where the complex has a positive charge):

$$\lambda_{RA} = \frac{n-m}{n} \lambda_A \qquad (II.69)$$

or

$$\lambda_{RA} = \frac{m-n}{m} \lambda_R . \qquad (II.70)$$

After substitution of the corresponding values in (II.67), a is found and the instability constant is calculated from the equation

$$K = \frac{(c_R^0 - a)(c_A^0 - a)}{a}, \qquad (II.71)$$

where c_R^0 and c_A^0 are the over-all (initial) concentrations of the ions R^{m+} and A^{n-}.

The electroconductivity method has not been used up to now for studying systems in which several complexes are formed.

3. CRYOSCOPIC AND CALORIMETRIC METHODS. These methods have not been used at all widely in the study of complexes. The principle of the first of these consists in calculating the change in number of particles in the system from the depression of freezing point [43].

Equilibria in solutions with complex formation may also be studied by measuring the heat of mixing with a change in addend concentration. In the general form, the principle of the method used here is that presented in the examination of the spectrophotometric method (p. 50). In certain of the

57

Summary of Methods of Determining Instability Constants

Method of determination	Number of constants determined by the given method*	Conditions of application	Notes
Solubility method	89	The existence of a sufficiently insoluble base phase whose solubility increases sharply with complex formation	It is possible to choose a simple salt, addend, or complex salt as the base phase
Distribution method	32	The existence of a solvent reversibly extracting a salt of the given metal from aqueous solution	The method is complicated by the simultaneous extraction of addends or complex compounds
Ion exchange method	33	Reversible exchange by ions between solution and ionite	
Potentiometric method	968	a) The existence of an electrode, reversible with respect to ions of the metal or addend b) With the pH method—the existence of clearly expressed acid—base properties of the addend	
Polarographic method	63	Reversible and instantaneous discharge of the complex ions on a mercury electrode	
Kinetic method	23	The existence of a reaction proceeding at a measurable rate in which ion-complex formers or addends participate (as a reagent or catalyst)	

58

Summary of Methods of Determining Instability Constants (Continued)

Method of determination	Number of constants determined by the given method*	Conditions of application	Notes
"Freezing" method	2	The formation and dissociation of the complexes proceeds very slowly	
Colorimetric indicator method	Included in spectro-photo-metric method	The existence of a reversible reaction with the formation of a colored compound, one of whose participants may form complexes with ions of the complex former or addend, respectively	
Biological method	1	The existence of a quantitative dependence of the functioning of a living organ on the concentration of an ion forming part of the complex studied	
Spectrophoto-metric method	98	A change in optical density with complex formation	
Electrocon-ductivity method	60	A change in electroconductivity with complex formation	Inapplicable with the formation of complexes with neutral addends
Other methods	12		

*Only constants presented in our tables are considered in this column. Other constants given in additional literature are not included in the summary.

simpler cases, for example, when only two types of particles exist in solution, the calculations are considerably simplified [44].

To conclude the chapter, we present a summary, which gives an idea of the distribution of different methods of determining instability constants (in the statistical sense of the word) and the main conditions of their application.

LITERATURE CITED

1. G. Bodländer, R. Fittig. Z. phys. Chem., 39, 597 (1902).
2. H. Morze. Z. phys. Chem., 41, 709 (1902).
3. H. Euler. Ber., 36, 2878 (1903).
4. I. Leden. Z. phys. Chem., A, 188, 160 (1941).
5. G. S. Cave, D. N. Hume. J. Am. Chem. Soc., 75, 2893 (1953).
6. W. D. Harkins. J. Am. Chem. Soc., 33, 1807 (1911).
7. M. Barre. Ann. Chem. Phys., 24, 145 (1911).
8. C. A. Raynolds, W. I. Argensinger. J. phys. Chem., 56, 417 (1952).
9. L. J. Andrews, R. M. Keefer. J. Am. Chem. Soc., 71, 3644 (1949).
10. P. E. Derr, W. C. Vosburgh. J. Am. Chem. Soc., 65, 2408 (1943).
11. R. A. Day, Jr., R. W. Stenghton. J. Am. Chem. Soc., 72, 5662 (1950).
12. S. Fronaeus. Acta Chem. Scand., 5, 859 (1951).
13. S. Fronaeus. Acta Chem. Scand., 6, 1200 (1952).
14. S. Fronaeus. Acta Chem. Scand., 7, 21 (1953).
15. V. V. Fomin. Prog. Chem., 24, 1010 (1955).
16. G. A. Carlson, J. P. McReynolds, and F. H. Verhoek. J. Am. Chem. Soc., 67, 1334 (1945).
17. S. Fronaeus. Acta Chem. Scand., 4, 72 (1950).
18. H. Irving and H. S. Rossotti. J. Chem. Soc., 3397 (1953).
19. J. T. Edsall, G. Felsenfeld, D. W. S. Goodman, and F. R. N. Gurd. J. Am. Chem. Soc., 76, 3054 (1954).

20. K. G. Poulsen, J. Bjerrum, and J. Poulsen. Acta Chem. Scand., 8, 921 (1954).

21. J. Heyrovsky. The Polarographic Method. [In Russian] United Sci. Tech. Press, 1937.

22. K. B. Yatsimirskii. Collection of Articles on General Chemistry. [In Russian] 1953, Vol. I, p. 193.

23. D. D. DeFord and D. N. Hume. J. Am. Chem. Soc., 73, 5321 (1951).

24. D. N. Hume, D. D. DeFord, and G. C. B. Cave. J. Am. Chem. Soc., 73, 5323 (1951).

25. J. Bjerrum. Metalammine formation in aqueous solutions. Copenhagen, 1941.

26. K. B. Yatsimirskii. J. Anal. Chem., 10, 339 (1955).*

27. K. W. Sykes, and H. J. Fudge. J. Chem. Soc., 124 (1952).

28. R. P. Bell, and J. E. Prue. J. Chem. Soc., 362 (1949).

29. K. B. Yatsimirskii. Industrial Lab., 21, 1410 (1955).

30. C. M. Cook, and F. A. Long. J. Am. Chem. Soc., 73, 4119 (1951).

31. A. A. Grinberg, and L. E. Nikol'skaya. J. Appl. Chem., 22, 542 (1949).

32. A. K. Babko, and K. E. Kleiner. J. Gen. Chem., 17, 1259 (1947).

33. A. K. Babko, and T. N. Rychkova. J. Gen. Chem., 18, 1617 (1948).

34. A. B. Hastings et al. J. Biol. Chem., 107, 351 (1934).

35. C. M. Cook, and F. A. Long. Cited in J. phys. Chem., 56, 25 (1952).

36. S. S. Jones, and F. A. Long. J. phys. Chem., 56, 25 (1952).

37. A. K. Babko. Physicochemical Analysis of Complex Compounds in Solution. Kiev, 1955.

38. N. P. Komar'. Sci. Rep. Kharkhov University, Vol. 37; Trans. Sci. Res. Inst. Chem., Vol. 8, Kharkhov, 1951.

39. N. P. Komar'. Sci. Rep. Kharkhov University, Vol. 54; Trans. Chem. Faculty and Sci. Res. Inst. Chem., Vol. 12, Kharkhov, 1954.
40. K. B. Yatsimirskii. J. Inorg. Chem., 1, 2306 (1956).
41. K. B. Yatsimirskii, and T. I. Fedorova. J. Inorg. Chem., 1, 2310 (1956).
42. I. I. Chernyaev, and S. I. Khorunzhenkov. Bull. Inst. Plat., No. 7, 98 (1929).
43. K. Sushil, Suddhanta. Chem. Abs., 45, 7317 (1949).
44. K. B. Yatsimirskii, and V. P. Vasil'ev. J. Phys. Chem., 30, 901 (1956).

* The journals indicated in the citations marked with an asterisk are available in English translations published by Consultants Bureau Enterprises, Inc., 227 West 17th Street, New York 11, N.Y.

Chapter III

COMPLETE THERMODYNAMIC CHARACTERISTICS OF COMPLEX FORMATION IN SOLUTION

In order to have the most accurate approach for an investigation of the nature of the forces acting within complex particles when they are formed in solution, it is necessary to know the energy changes accompanying the reactions studied. Instability constants are related directly only to changes in isobaric thermodynamic potential. However, one must know the changes in enthalpy during complex formation reactions (thermal effect) to calculate the changes in entropy during complex formation and the changes in stability of the complex particles with a temperature change to evaluate the bond energy.

A knowledge of the entropy changes during the reactions makes possible a new approach to the evaluation of certain factors which determine the stability of complex compounds. A thorough study of complex formation processes in solution requires knowledge of the complete thermodynamic characteristics of the reactions studied, i.e., at least the determination of the changes in enthalpy (ΔH), entropy (ΔS), and isobaric thermodynamic potential (ΔZ).

The selection of a standard state is of the utmost importance for an unequivocal determination of the changes in basic thermodynamic functions. The majority of authors choose a hypothetical molar solution with the properties of an infinitely dilute solution as the standard state. Besides the obvious advantages of such a choice for the standard state (elimination

63

of the effect of ionic strength and unequivocal nature), there are certain disadvantages due to the necessity for extrapolating, and not always reliably, the data obtained to zero ionic strength. Of late, therefore, a molar solution which is characterized by a given value of the ionic strength ($\mu =$ const)[*] has been chosen and this is also hypothetical to a certain degree. With such a choice of standard state, there is no need for extrapolation of the values obtained for the thermodynamic functions mentioned above. One must ensure that all the thermodynamic functions determined, calculated, and compared are related to the same standard state.

The thermodynamic functions may be used to characterize the over-all complex formation reaction

$$M + nA = MA_n, \qquad \text{(III.1)}$$

and the separate stages of this process

$$MA_{i-1} + A = MA_i. \qquad \text{(III.2)}$$

Since reaction (III.1) may be represented as the sum of reactions of the type (III.2), the thermodynamic functions of reaction (III.1) may also be represented as the sum of the corresponding functions characterizing reactions of the type (III.2). From this point of view, one may speak of over-all (total) and successive changes in enthalpy, entropy, and isobaric thermodynamic potential.

It is possible to calculate the over-all and successive changes in isobaric thermodynamic potential directly from data on equilibria:

$$\Delta Z_{\text{overall}} = - RT \ln \beta, \qquad \text{(III.3)}$$

$$\Delta Z_{\text{succ.}} = - RT \ln \varkappa. \qquad \text{(III.4)}$$

Or, taking into account the relations between the stability constant and the instability constant,

[*] The temperature is taken to be 25° in all cases.

$$\Delta Z_{\text{overall}} = RT \ln K, \qquad \text{(III.5)}$$

$$\Delta Z_{\text{succ.}} = RT \ln k. \qquad \text{(III.6)}$$

In all such calculations it is necessary to bear in mind the standard state chosen and all values of ΔZ are calculated for the value taken for the ionic strength.

The changes in enthalpy in reactions (III.1) and (III.2) are the thermal effects of the corresponding reactions. They may be found both by direct calorimetric measurements and also indirectly by means of the equations of an isobaric chemical reaction from data on equilibrium constants, measured at several temperatures.

The equation of an isobaric reaction

$$\frac{d \ln \beta}{dT} = \frac{\Delta H}{RT^2}, \qquad \text{(III.7)}$$

where T is the absolute temperature and R the universal gas constant, is most conveniently written in the following form:

$$\frac{d \lg \beta}{d \,(1/T)} = \frac{\Delta H}{4,57}. \qquad \text{(III.8)}$$

For the calculation of ΔH, a graph of $1/T$ against $\lg \beta$ is first constructed. If a comparatively narrow temperature

Table 4. Thermal Effect during the Formation of BaEdta^{2-} in Solution

Temperature, °C	$1/T$	pK	Temperature range, °C	$T_1 \cdot T_2$	ΔH from (III.10), kcal/mole
0	$3,66 \cdot 10^{-3}$	8,01	—	—	—
5	$3,59 \cdot 10^{-3}$	7,95	0—5	$7,60 \cdot 10^4$	— 4,2
10	$3,53 \cdot 10^{-3}$	7,89	5—10	$7,88 \cdot 10^1$	— 4,3
15	$3,47 \cdot 10^{-3}$	7,84	10—15	$8,16 \cdot 10^4$	— 3,8
20	$3,41 \cdot 10^{-3}$	7,78	15—20	$8,48 \cdot 10^4$	— 4,7
25	$3,36 \cdot 10^{-3}$	7,73	20—25	$8,74 \cdot 10^4$	— 4,0
30	$3,30 \cdot 10^{-3}$	7,68	25—30	$9,04 \cdot 10^4$	— 4,2

range is chosen for the investigation, then the value of ΔH remains approximately constant over it and the relation of lg β to $1/T$ is expressed by a straight line. The slope of this line on the graph is numerically equal to $-\frac{\Delta H}{4,57}$. If the graph obtained is not a straight line, then the value of the slope at the point corresponding to 25° (or any other temperature of interest to the investigator) is found.

It is also possible to integrate (III.8) approximately on the assumption that the value of ΔH remains constant over the temperature range from T_1 to T_2; we then obtain

$$\lg \frac{\beta''}{\beta'} = \frac{\Delta H \cdot (T_2 - T_1)}{4,57 \cdot T_1 \cdot T_2}, \qquad (III.9)$$

where β'' and β' are the values of the stability constants at the temperatures T_2 and T_1, respectively.

Written in a somewhat different form, this equation appears as

$$pK'' - pK' = \frac{\Delta H (T_2 - T_1)}{4,575 \cdot T_1 \cdot T_2}. \qquad (III.10)$$

With the aid of (III.9) or (III.10) it is possible to calculate the thermal effect of the reaction (ΔH) without constructing a graph.

If we choose temperature intervals ($T_2 - T_1 = 10°$) and the temperature interval 20–30° (average temperature 25°), then after substituting these values in (III.10) and converting ΔH to kcal/mole we obtain

$$\Delta H = 40,6 \ \Delta pK_{(20-30°)}. \qquad (III.10a)$$

Consequently, a thermal effect of 1 kcal/mole corresponds to a change in pK of 0.025 with a temperature change of 10°.

As an example let us examine the calculation of the thermal effect of the reaction

$$Ba^{2+} + Edta^{4-} = BaEdta^{2-}$$

(Edta^{4-} is the anion of ethylenediaminetetraacetic acid).

The data presented in Table 4 show that the values of the thermal effect calculated by (III.10) are not very accurate.

As stated above, the method of determining heat effects examined is an indirect one. Its use requires an extremely accurate determination of the equilibrium constants of reactions (III.1) and (III.2) since, as a rule, they change very little over a narrow temperature range. Determinations should be made for a series of accurately fixed temperature points (not less than three). As a rule, the values of ΔH obtained by this method are less accurate than the values obtained by direct calorimetric measurements.

To determine the heats of reactions of type (III.1) or (III.2) it is necessary to make a series of calorimetric measurements of the heats of mixing of salt solutions containing ions of M with a series of solutions containing addend A in different concentrations. It is also necessary to determine the heats of dilution of the initial solutions of the salt of the metal M and addend A and introduce appropriate corrections into the values obtained for the heats of mixing. The corrected values of the heats of mixing are average values of the heats of formation of the complexes and are related to the actual values of the heats of formation by the following equation:

$$\Delta \overline{H} = \alpha_1 \Delta H_1 + \alpha_2 \Delta H_2 + \alpha_3 \Delta H_3 + \ldots, \qquad \text{(III.11)}$$

where $\Delta \overline{H}$ is the corrected heat of mixing, referred to one gram-ion of metal; α_1, α_2, α_3... are the fractions of complexes of the type MA_1, MA_2, MA_3,..., respectively; ΔH_1, ΔH_2, ΔH_3... are the heats of reactions of type (III.2) for values of n equal to $1, 2, 3,\ldots$, respectively.

If we consider the relations derived previously, we obtain

$$\Delta \overline{H} = \frac{\beta_1 \Delta H_1 [A] + \beta_2 \Delta H_2 [A]^2 + \beta_3 \Delta H_3 [A]^3 + \cdots}{1 + \beta_1 [A] + \beta_2 [A]^2 + \beta_3 [A]^3 + \cdots}. \qquad \text{(III.12)}$$

The values of ΔH_1, ΔH_2, ΔH_3,... are calculated on the basis of a series of measurements of the heats of mixing (these measurements should be not less than the number of values of the heats of reaction being determined); the values of all the stability constants and equilibrium concentrations of addend must be known. In all cases it is necessary to check the values of ΔH_n obtained by resubstituting them in (III.12). This substitution has meaning only when the number of values found for the heats of mixing is greater than the number of heats of reactions of type (III.2) being determined.

Equation (III.12) may be used both as indicated above and for finding the stability constants of complexes from thermodynamic data.

The heats of reaction of complex formation found by two different methods should agree. Nonetheless, substantial discrepancies may actually be observed between these two series of figures. As an example, Table 5 gives values of the heats of formation of ethylenediaminetetraacetate complexes found by the two methods indicated. As the table shows, in some cases the values of ΔH obtained differ not only in value but also in sign.

Table 5. Comparison of Thermal Effects Determined Calorimetrically and Calculated from the Isobar Equation

Reaction equation	Thermal effect, kcal/mole	
	determined calorimetrically	found from the isobar equation
$Mg^{2+} + Edta^{4-} = MgEdta^{2-}$	3,1	—2,9
$Ca^{2+} + Edta^{4-} = CaEdta^{2-}$	—5,8	—2,5
$Sr^{2+} + Edta^{4-} = SrEdta^{2-}$	—4,2	—4,1
$Ba^{2+} + Edta^{4-} = BaEdta^{2-}$	—5,1	—4,1

The values of the change in isobaric thermodynamic potential are simply related to the stability constants, and therefore all the rules given above for the changes in the successive constants may be applied to changes in ΔZ also. As a rule, the value of ΔZ increases with stepwise complex formation.

An exception occurs only in the cases examined above for complexes of mercury, cadmium, indium, and, apparently, some others with tetrahedral coordination of addend anions.

In most cases the changes in the successive heats of addition of addends have a different character. In the formation of ammonia complexes, the successive heats of complex formation remain approximately constant. In most cases, during the formation of acidocomplexes the changes in enthalpy accompanying the addition of each new addend become more negative; the addition reaction becomes more exothermal despite the decrease in stability of the complex particles formed.

The different character of the changes in ΔZ and ΔH during stepwise complex formation is explained by the large role of the entropy factor.

The change in entropy during the reactions considered is calculated with the aid of the well-known equation

$$\Delta S = \frac{\Delta H - \Delta Z}{T}. \tag{III.13}$$

In using (III.13) it is necessary to be especially careful that the standard state is the same for the determination of ΔH as for the determination of ΔZ, since the magnitude of the ionic strength has a particularly strong effect on the entropy change.

Entropy changes during complex formation reactions may be considered as 1) changes (always negative) connected with the decrease in the number of particles during complex formation, and 2) changes (always positive) connected with dehydration of the reacting particles during complex formation. An addend occupying several coordination positions displaces several water molecules, and therefore the addition of such an addend involves a greater positive entropy change than that of an addend which occupies one coordination position and displaces one water molecule. Ions with a high electric charge are hydrated more strongly than ions with a lower charge; this phenomenon also leads to a greater positive entropy change during complex formation with highly charged ions.

Any sort of comparison of changes in thermodynamic functions is best made in series of monotypic reactions, i.e., reactions in which the central ion adds the same number of the same addends with the formation of particles with the same steric configuration.

In these cases the entropy change obeys the quite simple rule:

$$\Delta S = 0.1 L_M + B, \tag{III.14}$$

where L_M is the heat of hydration of the ion M, and B is constant for the whole series of monotypic reactions.

During stepwise complex formation, the addition of each new particle is accompanied by an ever decreasing entropy change. It is this phenomenon that produces a decrease in stability of complexes as their composition becomes more complex.

Chapter IV

FACTORS DETERMINING THE STABILITY OF COMPLEX COMPOUNDS IN SOLUTION

The stability of a complex particle (ion or molecule) in solution is determined by the nature of the central atom and the addends. The most important characteristics of the central atom, determining the stability of the complex compound, are the degree of oxidation (the charge of the central ion, in the case of ionic complexes), the dimensions, and the electronic structure. In the case of complexes with monatomic addends, the stability depends on the same characteristics of the addend (charge, radius, and electronic structure). The strength of the bond with addend molecules and polyatomic ions depends in addition on the nature of the atoms through which the bond with the central atom is effected and the characteristics of the structure of the addend molecule (ion).

The effect of the charge of the central ion on the stability of complexes may be demonstrated by comparing the change in stability in a series of complex compounds with the same number of the same addends but with a varying charge on the central ion.

Central ions with approximately the same radii and the same electronic structure are chosen for the comparison. As an example of such series of cations we present the following: 1. Na^+, Ca^{2+}, Y^{3+}, Th^{4+} ($r_k = 1.04 \pm 0.06$ A); 2. K^+, Sr^{2+}, La^{3+} ($r_k = 1.27 \pm 0.06$ A); 3. Ag^+, Hg^{2+}, Tl^{3+} ($r_k = 1.09 \pm 0.04$ A).

Table 6 gives the instability constant indices for these three ionic series. In all of the cases presented the value of pK increases with an increase in the charges of the central ions. The value of pK changes especially sharply with a change

Table 6. Instability Constant Indices in Series of Ions with Varying Charge

| Types of complex ion | pK | | | |
| | Charge of central ions | | | |
	+1	+2	+3	+4
K^+, Sr^{2+}, La^{3+}				
ROH^{z-1}	(−0,7)	1,0	3,3	—
$RS_2O_3^{z-2}$	0,1	2,0	—	—
$RP_3O_9^{z-3}$	1,2	3,4	5,7	—
$RFe(CN)_6^{z-3}$	1,2	2,8	3,7	—
Na^+, Ca^{2+}, Y^{3+}, Th^{4+}				
RIO_3^{z-1}	—	0,9	—	2,9
RNO_3^{z-1}	—	0,3	—	0,6
RSO_4^{z-2}	0,7	2,3	3,5	4,1
$RC_2O_4^{z-2}$	—	3,0	7,3	—
$REdta^{z-4}$*	—	11,1	18,0	—
Ag^+, Hg^{2+}, Tl^{3+}				
ROH^{z-1}	2,3	10,3	14,8	—
RNH_3^z	3,2	8,8	—	—
RCl^{z-1}	2,7	5,3	8,1	—
RBr^{z-1}	9	9,1	9,7	—

* $Edta^4$—ethylenediaminetetraacetate.

in charge in those cases when the addends are small or highly charged ions (oxalate, ethylenediaminetetraacetate, etc.). In the case of large and low-charged anions (iodide, bromide, nitrate, iodate, etc.) the change in stability is considerably weaker.

In the case of central ions with a completed eight-electron shell, the change in pK with a change in charge is so regular that in some cases it is possible to find unknown values of instability constants by interpolation.

It might be thought that the stability of complexes would increase continuously with an increase in charge and that the most stable complexes would be formed by the most highly charged ions. In actual fact, highly charged ions very readily form compounds with oxygen anions due to interaction with water molecules (VO_2^+, MoO_2^{2+}, UO_2^{2+}, BiO^+, etc.). Since O^{2-} anions also have a comparatively high charge and small dimensions, the stability of such particles increases very rapidly with an increase in the charge of the central ion, and they begin to surpass in stability all other possible complex compounds.

The stability of some complex compounds in the series Cu^+, Zn^{2+}, Ga^{3+}; Ag^+, Cd^{2+}, In^{3+} decreases despite the increase in charge. Such changes in stability can hardly be explained by just the change in radius and polarizing action of the central ions. As will be shown below, a similar type of exception from the rule examined is observed in the case of internal complex particle formation by π-bonds between addends and the central atom.

On the basis of theoretical considerations, we showed [1] that the stability of complex compounds may increase, decrease, or pass through a maximum with a change in radius of the central ion. This idea may be demonstrated especially graphically on the example of complex compounds of magnesium, calcium, strontium, and barium.

The examples presented in Table 7 show that there is some optimal ratio of the dimensions of the reacting particles in complex formation: small cations form the most stable complexes with small anions and large cations form stable complex compounds with large anions. In the case of small, singly charged anions (anion radius less than 1.6 A), α-amino acids, and oxalate, the stability decreases with an increase in the cation dimensions, i.e., from the top to the bottom in the corresponding group of the periodic table.

Table 7. Change in Stability in Series of Complex Compounds of Elements of the Second Group of the Periodic Table

Formula of complex compound	pK value for complexes of the type			
	MgX^{2-z}	CaX^{2-z}	SrX^{2-z}	BaX^{2-z}
MOH^+	2,58	1,30	0,82	0,64
MCH_3COO^+	0,82	0,77	0,44	0,31
$MCH_3CHNH_2COO^+$	1,96	1,24	—	0,77
MC_2O_4	3,43	3,0	2,54	2,33
$MP_3O_9^-$	3,31	3,47	3,35	3,25
$MP_4O_{12}^{2-}$	5,17	5,47	5,11	5,0
$MEdta^{2-}$	8,69	10,59	8,63	7,76
MNO_3^+	0,0	0,28	—	0,92
MIO_3^+	0,72	0,89	1,00	1,05
MS_2O_3	1,84	1,98	2,04	2,33

In the case of large anions (nitrate, iodate, thiosulfate, etc.) the stability of complex compounds increases with an increase in the cation dimensions and, finally, in the case of some triply and quadruply charged anions (tetrametaphosphate, ethylenediaminetetraacetate, tartrate, etc.) the stability passes through a maximum, usually with complex compounds of calcium. The rules given here are usually obeyed so strictly that in a series of cases it is possible to estimate unknown instability constants by interpolation and extrapolation [2].

The rules examined here indicate the existence of a connection between the stability of complex compounds and the position of the corresponding elements in the periodic table for the main groups, i.e., for elements forming ions with complete electron shells like the shells of inert gas atoms. A similar type of connection also exists in the case of other elements but a quantitative examination of the problem is complicated by the fact that the chemical bond in the corresponding complex compounds deviates considerably from the ionic type and approaches a pure covalent bond in a number of cases. The strength of the covalent bond depends on a series of factors, a complete examination of which is sometimes quite difficult.

For complex compounds with the same number of the same addends, formed from ions of identical charge and approximately identical volume, it is possible to derive the following semiempirical relation [2]:

$$pK = a + nb\rho, \tag{IV.1}$$

where a is constant for a given series of isochoric, equally charged ions, n is the number of addends, b is the polarizability of the addend, and ρ is a value characterizing the polarizing action of the cation.

The term $nb\rho$ in the equation characterizes not only the polarization in the narrow sense of the word (displacement of the centers of gravity of the positive and negative charges), but reflects the increase in the degree of covalence of the bond due to the displacement of electrons from one addend atom to the central ion. In the limiting case, such a displacement leads to the formation of a donor—acceptor σ-bond.

To a first approximation, the polarizing action of ions changes symbatically with the ionization potentials of electrically neutral atoms, which are numerically equal to the electron affinity of the ions examined, since the change in energy during the addition of an electron to the gaseous, doubly charged ion numerically equals the second ionization potential:

$$M^{2+}_{(gas)} + \overline{e} = M^{+}_{(gas)}.$$

However, the existence of a connection between polarizing action and ionization potential should be considered only as a first approximation.

The simultaneous solution of equations of type (IV.1) for two series of complex compounds of isochoric, equally charged ions makes it possible to eliminate the unknown value of the polarizing action of the cation by choosing as an arbitrary value the instability constant indices of some well studied series of complex compounds. We propose to take the polarizability of alaninate as equal to unity ($b = 1$), and then for complexes of the type $MCH_3CHNH_2COO^+$;

$$pK_1^0 = a' + \rho. \tag{IV.2}$$

By substituting the value of ρ from this in the equation examined above, we obtain

$$pK = a + nb\rho K_1^0, \tag{IV.3}$$

where $a = a'(1 - nb)$, and pK_1^0 are the instability constant indices of the corresponding alaninates which have the following values: $Mg^{2+} - 2.0$; $Mn^{2+} - 3.0$; $Fe^{2+} - 4.0$; $Co^{2+} - 4.8$; $Ni^{2+} - 6.0$; $Cu^{2+} - 8.5$; $Zn^{2+} - 5.2$. Any addend may be chosen as the standard. The choice of alaninate is motivated by the fact that the values of the instability constants of these complexes are most reliable.

Equation (IV.3) was checked on 27 series of complex compounds. However, it was found to be applicable only when the internal sphere is filled by not more than four coordination positions. Therefore it can not be applied to complex compounds with ammonia of the type $M(NH_3)_5^{2+}$ and $M(NH_3)_6^{2}$, to complex compounds with ethylenediamine of the type MEn_3^{2+}, to complexes with ethylenediaminetetraacetate, and to other similar compounds. In cases when (IV.3) is applicable, the average deviation in the values of pK is ± 0.15.

Equation (IV.3) may be used for checking available data and for the calculation of unknown instability constants by interpolation and extrapolation. Table 8 gives the constants of (IV.3) for 27 series of complex compounds, calculated from 128 instability constant values.

The relative polarizability of the addend is primarily determined by the nature of the atoms through which the bond with the central atom is effected: if the bond is effected through

Table 8. Constants of the Equation $pK = a + nb_p$ for Complexes with Doubly Charged, Isochoric Ions (Radius 0.8–0.9 Å)

Addends	Number of addends	a	Relative polarizability
SO_4^{2-}	1	2,35	0,00
$P_3O_9^{3-}$	1	3,4	0,00
$P_4O_{12}^{4-}$	1	5,2	0,00
$S_2O_3^{2-}$	1	1,8	0,06
$CH_3CO_2^-$	1	0,7	0,18
$(CH_3CO_2)_2^{2-}$	1	1,8	0,18
$CH_2(CO_2)_2^{2-}$	1	2,0	0,41
$C_2O_4^{2-}$	1	2,5	0,47
$C_6H_3\big\langle\substack{CHO\\O^-\\CHO}$, SO_3^- , $C_6H_4\big\langle\substack{O^-\\CHO}$	1	0,0	0,62
OH^-	1	1,5	0,67
$H_2NCH_2CONHCH_2COO^-$ (glycylglycine)	1	1,4	0,62
	1	−0,2	0,46
	2	−2,0	0,80
o-Hydroxyquinolate	1	5,0	0,96
$(OHC_2H_4)_2NCH_2CO_2^-$	1	0,4	0,96
$H_2NCH_2COO^-$	1	0,9	0,90
$\mathbf{H_2NCH_2COO^-}$	2	0,4	0,90
$CH_3CHNH_2COO^-$	2	−1,0	1,00
$HN\big\langle\substack{CH_2CO_2^-\\CH_2CO_2^-}$	1	0,5	1,12
$HN(C_2H_4CO_2)_2^{2-}$	1	−0,8	1,19
$HN(CH_2CO_2)_2^{2-}$	1	2,2	0,97
$HOC_2H_4N(CH_2CO_2)_2^{2-}$	1	1,1	1,44
NH_3	1	−4,0	0,61
NH_3	2	−2,2	0,59
$C_2H_4(NH_2)_2$	1	−4,7	1,44
$CH_3C_2H_3(NH_2)_2$	1	−1,7	1,44
Diethylenetriamine	1	−3,0	2,3

oxygen, then the value of b does not exceed 0.7; for addends connected with the central atom through nitrogen, the value of b is always considerably greater. The presence of double bonds in the addend ion always leads to an increase in the value of the relative polarizability.

The linear relation between the instability constant indices of complexes of isochoric, equally charged ions given here may be used for predicting the possibility of the existence of new complexes and estimating their stability. If complex compounds of a given type are found in solution for magnesium, copper, and one of the intermediate members of the series, and the existence of a linear relationship between the pK values is established in this case, then complex compounds of the given type should also exist for the other four ions and their instability constant indices may be evaluated by interpolation.

A physical interpretation of the rules established for the change in the stability of complex compounds formed by ions with d-electrons may be given from the point of view of the theory of crystal fields [3–5]. The apparent deviations may also be explained from this point of view.

The polarizing action of the central ion depends on the nuclear charge (atomic number), the radius, and the shielding action of the electrons forming part of the atom:

$$\rho = A\frac{Z-S}{r}, \qquad (IV.4)$$

where A is a proportionality coefficient, Z is the atomic number, S is the shielding constant, and r is the radius of the ion.

The polarizing action of a spherical ion is the same in all directions; it remains thus for all ions in vacuum.

The basic physical idea of the theory of crystal fields is that the electrons of the central ion avoid those regions where negatively charged addends (or the negative poles of addends of dipolar molecules) exert strong electrical fields.

If the addends are arranged at the vertices of an octahedron, then the degenerate d-level of the central ion splits into two new levels: the lower one a triplet and the upper one a doublet. The axes of the electron shells of the upper level are directed toward the vertices of the octahedron and those of the lower level are arranged between them. Electrons of the lower level are designated d_ϵ and those of the upper level d_γ.

An increase in the number of d_ϵ-electrons increases the shielding in directions perpendicular to the centers of the faces of the octahedron and does not essentially affect the interaction of the central atom with the addends. A decrease in the number of d_γ-electrons sharply decreases the shielding in directions toward the vertices of the octahedron and hence sharply increases the polarizing action of the central ion in the given directions. The higher the number of d_γ-electrons, the weaker the polarizing action of the central ion, the weaker the chemical bond with the addends, and the lower the probability of the formation of a σ-bond.

Table 9 gives the distribution of electrons in terms of energy levels. In the case of octahedral complexes of the MA_6 type, the stability in the series Ti^{2+}, V^{2+}, Cr^{2+}, Mn^{2+}, Fe^{2+}, Co^{2+}, Ni^{2+}, Cu^{2+}, Zn^{2+} should decrease at Cr^{2+} (appearance of the first d_γ-electron), Mn^{2+} (appearance of the second d_γ-electron), Cu^{2+} (appearance of the third d_γ-electron), and Zn^{2+} (appearance of fourth d_γ-electron). The order of the change in stability of these complexes should be the following:

$$Ti^{+2} < V^{2+} > Cr^{2+} > Mn^{2+} < Fe^{2+} < Co^{2+} < Ni^{2+} > Cu^{2+} > Zn^{2+}$$
$$Ti^{3+} < V^{3+} < Cr^{3+} > Mn^{3+} > Fe^{3+} < Co^{3+} < Ni^{3+} < Cu^{3+} > Ga^{3+}.$$

The increase in stability of complex compounds from Mn^{2+} to Ni^{2+} and from Fe^{3+} to Cu^{3+} is connected with the continuous increase in polarizing action due to the increase in the atomic number of the element. Experimental data confirm the existence of this order of change in the stability of complex compounds.

With a reduction in symmetry of the electric field, caused by addends, there is further splitting of the energy levels and the appearance of new sublevels. Thus, in the presence of an axial field in addition to the octahedral one, the upper d_γ-level splits into two sublevels: $d_{\gamma'}$ and $d_{\gamma''}$. The electron shell of one of these $(d_{\gamma'})$ is oriented along a line connecting opposite vertices of the octahedron and the other $(d_{\gamma''})$ in a plane perpendicular to this line, passing through the other four vertices of the octahedron. The distribution of electrons with respect to sublevels in the presence of an axial field is presented in the same table.

Table 9. Distribution of Electrons with Respect to Energy Levels in an Octahedral Field

Ions	Number of d_ε -electrons	Number of d_γ -electrons	Distribution of electrons under the action of an axial field	
			Number of $d_{\gamma'}$-electrons	Number of $d_{\gamma''}$-electrons
Ti^{3+}	1	—	—	—
$Ti^{2+}V^{3+}$	2	—	—	—
$V^{2+}Cr^{3+}$	3	—	—	—
$Cr^{2+}Mn^{3+}$	3	1	1	—
$Mn^{2+}Fe^{3+}$	3	2	1	1
$Fe^{2+}Co^{3+}$	4	2	1	1
$Co^{2+}Ni^{3+}$	5	2	1	1
$Ni^{2+}Cu^{3+}$	6	2	1	1
$Cu^{2+}—$	6	3	2	1
$Zn^{2+}Ga^{3+}$	6	4	2	2

If the addends occupy not more than four coordination positions, arranged in one plane, then the shielding is determined by d_γ''-electrons and consequently the following order of change in stability of complex compounds should be observed:

$$Ti^{2+} < V^{2+} < Cr^{2+} > Mn^{2+} < Fe^{2+} < Co^{2+} < Ni^{2+} < Cu^{2+} > Zn^{2+}$$
$$Ti^{3+} < V^{3+} < Cr^{3+} < Mn^{3+} > Fe^{3+} < Co^{3+} < Ni^{3+} < Cu^{3+} > Ga^{3+}$$

The fall in stability in the case of complexes of Mn^{2+} and Zn^{2+} is explained by the appearance of the first and second shielding $d_{\gamma''}$-electrons, respectively. This order of change in stability is observed in a large number of cases for complexes of manganese, iron, cobalt, nickel, copper, and zinc; in foreign literature this order is called the Irving-Williams sequence. K. B. Yatsimirskii and T. I. Fedorova [6] established the position of Cr^{2+} in this series; complexes with the Cr^{2+} ion are actually more stable than the corresponding complexes of manganese.

It was shown above that there can be another order of change in stability of complex compounds with the filling of all six coordination positions or the addition of a fifth addend.

Table 10. Distribution of Electrons with Respect to Energy Levels in a Tetrahedral Field

Ions	Number of d_γ-electrons	Number of d_ε-electrons
Mn^{2+}	2	3
Fe^{2+}	3	3
Co^{2+}	4	3
Ni^{2+}	4	4
Cu^{2+}	4	5
Zn^{2+}	4	6

We use a completely analogous method of examination for complex compounds with addends arranged at the vertices of a tetrahedron. In the case of a tetrahedral field, the d_γ-levels are found to be lower and the d_ε-levels higher.

The axes of the electron shells of the d_ε-level are directed toward the vertices of the tetrahedron; an increase in the number of d_ε-electrons leads to an increase in the shielding and a decrease in the bond of the central ion with the addends. Table 10 gives the distribution of the electrons of central ions in the presence of a tetrahedral field.

As can be seen from the table, tetrahedral complexes of Co^{2+} should have maximum stability in this case. Experimental data confirm this hypothesis and the complex ions $CoCl_4^{2-}$ and $Co(CNS)_4^{2-}$ are particularly stable.

All the considerations presented here refer to complexes with addends characterized by the presence of comparatively weak fields. With an increase in the field strength there may be a decrease in the number of shielding electrons due to a decrease in the number of free electrons in the lower energy levels.

As can be seen, the change in stability of complex compounds in series of ions in the middle of the fourth period of the periodic table has a quite complex form. Here there are stability minima and maxima. The position of the maxima may change, depending on the steric configuration of the complex ions and the number of coordination positions filled.

Investigations of recent years show that the formation of a donor π-bond, due to interaction of filled d-orbits of the central atom with vacant p- or d-orbits in the valence shell of the addend atoms, leads to an increase in the stability of the complex compound. The possibility of the formation of such bonds in complex compounds was first pointed out by Pauling [7]. Ya. K. Syrkin and M. E. Dyatkina [8, 9] subsequently developed this idea by showing the wide distribution of π-bonds in complex compounds and discovering new possibilities of formation of such bonds ($d_\pi - d_\pi$-bonds).

For the formation of donor π-bonds at least three conditions have to be met: 1) the presence of a considerable number (more than three) of free d-electrons at the central atom; 2) the existence of vacant p- or d-orbits in the outer shell of this atom, through which the bond of the addend with the central atom is effected; depending on whether vacant p- or d-orbits are present, a $d_\pi - p_\pi$ or $d_\pi - d_\pi$-bond is formed; 3) the formation of a sufficiently strong σ-bond between the central atom and one of the addend atoms.

For the formation of a sufficiently strong σ-bond (three conditions), the central ion should have a high electron affinity. The electron affinity of the central ion M^{n+} is numerically equal to the nth ionization potential of the atom M, i.e., I_n.

Another necessary condition for the formation of a donor σ-bond is a high lability of the electrons of the addend atoms, which is connected with the polarizability of the addends or their ionization potentials (the ionization potential of an addend anion is numerically equal to the electron affinity of the electrically neutral atom).

The strength of the π-bonds depends on the lability of the free d-electrons of the central atom. In the first approximation, the lability of the d-electrons may be characterized by the value of the ionization potential of the ion $M^{n+}(I_{n+1})$. The smaller I_{n+1}, the stronger must be the corresponding π-bond.

Since the effective positive charge of the central atom increases during the formation of a donor π-bond due to the partial transfer of d-electrons from the central atom to the addends, the strength of donor π-bonds decreases with an increase in the charge of the central atom. With an increase in charge in a series of isostructural ions, the ionization potential I_{n+1} increases sharply and this should also lead to a decrease in the strength of the corresponding π-bond.

Thus, the strength of a π-bond should be greater, the greater the electron affinity of the cation, the lower its ionization potential and charge, and the lower the ionization potential of the addend.

In the light of what has been presented, the following ions and atoms are capable of forming donor π-bonds: Cu^+, Cr^{2+}, Mn^{2+}, Fe^{2+}, Co^{2+}, Ni^{2+}, Cu^{2+}, Zn^{2+}, the same elements in the $3+$ oxidation state (with the exception of chromium), and Ga^{3+} and also elements of the corresponding groups of the fifth and sixth periods. Ions with outer electron shells of the inert gas type (Li^+, Na^+, K^+, Rb^+, Cs^+, Be^{2+}, Mg^{2+}, Ca^{2+}, Sr^{2+}, Ba^{2+}, Ra^{2+}, Al^{3+}, Sc^{3+}, lanthanides, Ti^{4+}, Zr^{4+}, Hf^{4+}, Th^{4+}) and also In^+, Sn^{2+}, Sb^{3+}, Tl^+, Pb^{2+} and Bi^{3+} cannot form strong π-bonds.

Donor π-bonds are formed by chlorides, bromides, and iodides (but not fluorides); all addends whose bond with the central atom is effected through atoms of sulfur, selenium, phosphorus, and arsenic and also addends in which there are multiple bonds (cyanide, benzene, carbon monoxide, ethylene, etc.).

A consideration of the possibility of the formation of donor π-bonds makes it possible to explain a series of apparent anomalies in the change in stability of complex compounds.

For example, we can now understand the fall in stability of cyanide, iodide, bromide, thiourea, thiosulfate, and some other complex compounds in the series Cu^+, Zn^{2+}, Ga^{3+} and Ag^+, Cd^{2+}, In^{3+}. This is connected with the fact that the strength of the π-bonds decreases with increase in charge of the central ion. The stability of complex compounds with addends which are incapable of forming π-bonds (for example, with aliphatic amines) increases in these series. Addends with a particular tendency to form strong π-bonds (cyanide, iodide, and thiourea) stabilize lower oxidation states, while addends which do not form such bonds stabilize higher oxidation states as a rule.

The stability of halide complexes of metals which do not tend to form strong π-bonds decreases from fluoride to iodide complexes. Meanwhile, elements which have a particular tendency to form donor π-bonds (mercury, platinum, copper, silver, palladium, cadmium, and others) show the reverse order for the change in stability. This is connected with the fact that fluorides do not form π-bonds at all and the tendency for their formation increases in the order chloride—bromide—iodide.

The sharp fall in complex-forming capacity with a change from ions with 18 electrons in the outer shell to ions with $18+2$ electrons (Au^+—Tl^+, Hg^{2+}—Pb^{2+}, Tl^{3+}—Bi^{3+}) is explained by the impossibility of the formation of π-bonds in the latter cases (Tl^+, Pb^{2+}, Bi^{3+}). For the same reason, these ions do not form stable cyanide complexes. Thiocyanate complexes formed by these ions are less stable than the chlorides, bromides, and iodides, while the thiocyanate complexes of ions with d-electrons in the outer shell approach the bromide complexes in stability. The stability of thiocyanate complexes is apparently increased due to the formation of donor π-bonds.

As the strength of π-bonds increases with an increase in the number of d-electrons, the stability of compounds of the type MCl^+ increases continuously in the series Mn^{2+}, Fe^{2+}, Co^{2+}, Ni^{2+}, Zn^{2+}.

The existence of complex compounds of ions with a considerable number of d-electrons in the outer shell (Cu^+, Ag^+, Hg^{2+}, etc.) with aromatic hydrocarbons and a series of other molecules with multiple bonds is connected with the possibility of the formation of donor π-bonds.

The nature of the addend, like the nature of the central atom, affects the stability of the complex compound. On the basis of the ideas presented it is possible to give the following, most important characteristics of addends, determining the stability of the corresponding complex compounds.

1. The electrostatic characteristics: charge, radius (for ions), or dipole moment (for molecules and ions). The higher the electrostatic characteristics (maximal charge and dipole moment and minimal radius), the stronger are the corresponding ionic complexes. As was shown above, for the formation of a stable complex there must be a certain relation between the electrostatic characteristics of the central ion and the addend.

2. The tendency of the addend to form covalent σ-bonds. This tendency determines the lability of the outer electrons and therefore depends on the ionization potential of the addend ion (electron affinity of the atom), the polarizability of the addend, and, in connection with this, the nature of the atom through which the bond of the addend with the central atom is effected, increasing in the direction O, N, S, Se, etc. As in the

85

previous case, for complex formation there must exist a certain relation between the central atom and the addend: the central atom should also tend to form donor σ-bonds.

3. The possibility of the formation of donor π-bonds by the addend. This possibility appears when there are vacant p-orbits (addends with a multiple bond — cyanides, aromatic compounds, etc.) or vacant d-orbits in the valence shell of the addend atom (chlorine, bromine, iodine, sulfur, selenium, phosphorus, arsenic, etc.).

4. The number of coordination positions occupied by one addend particle. The more coordination positions occupied by a given addend, the stronger is the complex formed, since there is then more complete dehydration of the central ion and, in its turn, this is connected with a considerable positive entropy change.

The problem of the relation between successive instability constants is extremely important. According to A. K. Babko [10], successive instability constant indices (pk_n) are determined by the value of the first instability constant index (pk_1) and a factor α_{n-1} depending on the value of the charges of M and A in the complex particle MA_n:

$$pk_n = \alpha_{n-1} \cdot pk_1. \qquad (IV.5)$$

This equation is inapplicable to complex compounds with neutral addends; in this case, many use Bjerrum's equation [11]:

$$pk_n = pk_1 - \lg \frac{N(n+1)}{N-n}, \qquad (IV.6)$$

where N is the limiting number of addends that can be added to the central ion.

Recently van Panthaleon van Eck [12] proposed an empirical equation for successive instability constant indices:

$$pk_n = pk_1 - 2\lambda(n-1), \qquad \text{(IV.7)}$$

where λ is a constant value.

Analysis of experimental data shows that they are described most satisfactorily by this empirical equation. In particular, good agreement with experiment is observed in the case of fluoride and some bromide complexes and also many complex compounds with ammonia, imidazole, and hydrazine. Apparently, van Panthaleon's equation is very effective when the addends are arranged at the vertices of an octahedron.

The change in value of successive constants with a change in the number of addends added undoubtedly must be determined by structural characteristics of the given complex compound and therefore there cannot be a single, universal equation which does not allow for these stereochemical characteristics.

Thus, for example, in the formation of a complex ion with addend anions arranged at the vertices of a tetrahedron, the mutual repulsion of the anions in the particle MA_2 will be greater than the analogous repulsion in an octahedral complex ion with the three particles of MA_2 arranged in a straight line. This leads to the fact that in the case of tetrahedral coordination the second instability constants have too high values and the values of pk_2 deviate from the series. This phenomenon is observed in the case of acidocomplexes of indium and cadmium.

A particular type of substitution in the case of complex compounds of mercury [13] leads to a particular form of change in the successive instability constants of these compounds.

To evaluate the relations between successive instability constants it is therefore necessary to know not only the formula of the complex compound, but also its stereochemical characteristics.

LITERATURE CITED

1. A. A. Grinberg and K. B. Yatsimirskii. Bull. Acad. Sci. USSR, Div. Chem. Sci., No. 2, 211 (1952).*
2. K. B. Yatsimirskii. J. Gen. Chem., 24, 1498 (1954).*
3. L. Orgel. J. Chem. Soc., 4756 (1952).
4. J. Bjerrum and C. K. Iorgensen. Rec. trav. chim., 75, 658 (1956).
5. K. B. Yatsimirskii. J. Inorg. Chem., 1, 2451 (1956).
6. K. B. Yatsimirskii and T. I. Fedorova. J. Inorg. Chem., 1, 2310 (1956).
7. L. Pauling. The Nature of the Chemical Bond. [Russian translation] Moscow, 1947.
8. Ya. K. Syrkin and M. E. Dyatkina. J. Gen. Chem., 16, 345 (1946).
9. Ya. K. Syrkin. Bull. Acad. Sci. USSR, Div. Chem. Sci., No. 1, 69 (1948).
10. A. K. Babko. Physicochemical Analysis of Complex Compounds in Solution. Kiev, 1955.
11. J. Bjerrum. Metalammine formation in aqueous solutions. Copenhagen, 1941.
12. C. L. van Panthaleon van Eck. Rec. trav. chim., 72, 529 (1953).
13. C. L. van Panthaleon van Eck, H. B. M. Walters, and W. J. Jaspers. Rec. trav. chim., 75, 796 (1956).

* The journals indicated in the citations marked with an asterisk are available in English translations published by Consultants Bureau Enterprises, Inc., 227 West 17th Street, New York 11, N.Y.

TABLES OF INSTABILITY CONSTANTS
OF COMPLEX COMPOUNDS

EXPLANATION OF TABLES

In the tables we present data on the instability constants of 1381 complex particles, mainly with similar addends. These data are reproduced from literature sources published largely through 1954 and partially from 1955 to 1956.

The instability constants of polynuclear complexes and complexes with different (mixed) addends are given only partially here.

1. Arrangement of Material

The instability constants are systematized in groups of complex compounds with the same addends (for example, complexes with ammonia, bromide complexes, and chloride complexes). Such groups of complexes incorporate the two following divisions:

1) Complexes with inorganic addends;
2) Complexes with organic addends.

In the first division (complexes with inorganic addends) the groups of complexes are arranged predominantly in alphabetical order of the names of the addends (Russian alphabet).

In the second division (complexes with organic addends), due to the specific peculiarities of the nomenclature of organic compounds and also for a series of other reasons, the following subdivisions are introduced:

1) Complexes with amines;
2) Complexes with anions of organic acids;
3) Complexes with amino acids;
4) Complexes with diketones and aldehydes;
5) Complexes with other organic addends.

In each of these subdivisions, the groups of complexes are arranged predominantly in alphabetical order of the names of the addends (Russian alphabet). A separate list of all the addends is given and for convenience in using the tables, the order of the addends in the list is the same as in the tables.

In all the tables, within groups of complexes with the same addends, the complexes are arranged in alphabetical order with respect to the chemical symbols of the central ions (Ag, Al, Au, etc.).

2. Contents and Abbreviations Used

After the title, i.e., the name of the group of complex compounds (for example, acetate complexes, complexes with ethylenediaminetetraacetate), we give the chemical formula of the addend: for example,

$$CH_3COO - , \quad
\begin{array}{c}
H_2C-N \Big\langle \begin{array}{c} CH_2COO- \\ CH_2COO- \end{array} \\
| \\
H_2C-N \Big\langle \begin{array}{c} CH_2COO- \\ CH_2COO- \end{array}
\end{array}$$

In the case of large addend formulas, the conventional symbol for the addend is given next to the chemical formula (for example,

$$
\begin{array}{c}
H_2C-N \Big\langle \begin{array}{c} CH_2COO- \\ CH_2COO- \end{array} \\
| \\
H_2C-N \Big\langle \begin{array}{c} CH_2COO- \\ CH_2COO- \end{array}
\end{array}
\quad Edta^{4-}),
$$

and this is then used throughout the given group of complexes.

The first column of the tables ("Complex ion") gives the formula of the complex compound [for example, $Cu(CH_3COO)_2$ or $NiEdta^{2-}$].

The second column ("Temperature") gives the temperature in degrees Centigrade at which the instability constants were determined. In some cases "room" (room temperature) is given in this column, as a more accurate temperature was not given in the original work. In cases where the temperature was not given at all, room temperature is presumably implied.

The third column ("Ionic strength") gives the values of the ionic strength, equal to half the total product of the concentrations of the ions over the square of their charges. Omission of figures from the tables means that the value of the ionic strength was not given in the original work. Apparently, in these cases the value of the instability constant refers to solutions with a finite ionic strength (i.e., without extrapolation to zero value).

The fourth column ("Method") gives the method of determining the instability constant. The following abbreviations are used here:

1. Analysis—Analytical determination of concentrations
2. Biolog.—Biological method
3. Indic. meas. pH—Indicator measurement of pH (pH-color.)
4. Ion exch.—Ion exchange
5. Kinetic—Kinetic method
6. Cryoscop.—Cryoscopic method
7. Polarog.—Polarographic method
8. Potent.—Potentiometric method (pH-potent.)
9. Distrib.—Distribution between immiscible liquids
10. Sol.—Solubility method (s-bility)
11. Calc.—Calculation method
12. Spectr.—Spectrophotometric method
13. Thermody.—Thermodynamic method
14. Electrocon.—Electroconductivity method (elcon.)

The fifth column (k) gives the value of the successive instability constants k, which are the constants of the equilibrium reaction

$$MA_i \rightleftarrows MA_{i-1} + A,$$

i.e.,

$$k = \frac{[MA_{i-1}][A]}{[MA_i]}.$$

The sixth column (pk) gives the successive instability constant index pk, which is the negative logarithm of the constant

$$pk = -\lg k.$$

The seventh column (K) gives the value of the over-all instability constant, which is the constant of the equilibrium reaction

$$MA_i \rightleftarrows M + iA,$$

$$K = \frac{[M][A]^i}{[MA_i]}.$$

In the cases where $i = 1$, the values of the successive and over-all instability constants coincide.

The eighth column (pK) gives the over-all instability constant index pK, which is the negative logarithm of the instability constant

$$pK = -\lg K.$$

When a series of values of the instability constant are given in the literature for the same complex, determined by different authors, we chose the value which is most reliable in our opinion, though the values of instability constants determined by different authors agree well with each other in a number of cases.

The values of k or pk and K or pK presented in the tables have the same number of significant figures as in the originals. As no estimate of the accuracy of the determination was given in a series of papers, the number of significant figures does not always indicate the actual accuracy of the determination.

When values of instability constants at two ionic strengths are given in the tables, the less reliable figure is in brackets.

The literature references are given in the ninth and tenth columns ("Literature").* The ninth column ("Main literature") gives the literature source reporting the determination of the instability constant value presented in the table. The tenth column ("Additional literature") presents sources which give numerical values of instability constants, determined largely at other temperatures or ionic strengths in the solution, and also figures which, for a number of reasons, are not presented in our tables.

3. List of Addends

I. INORGANIC ADDENDS

1. Ammonia
2. Bromide
3. Bromate
4. Hydrazine
5. Hydroxyl
6. Hydroperoxide
7. Iodate
8. Iodide
9. Perchlorate
10. Nitrate
11. Selenocyanate
12. Pyrophosphate
13. Thiocyanate
14. Sulfate
15. Sulfite
16. Tetrametaphosphate
17. Thiourea
18. Thiosulfate
19. Trimetaphosphate
20. Phosphate
21. Fluoride
22. Chlorate
23. Chloride
24. Cyanide

* The journals indicated in the citations marked with an asterisk are available in English translations published by Consultants Bureau, Inc., 227 West 17th Street, New York 11, N.Y.

II. ORGANIC ADDENDS

1. AMINES
   1. Dipyridyl
   2. Diethylenetriamine
   3. Imidazole
   4. Pyridine
   5. Propylenediamine
   6. 1,2,3-Triaminopropane
   7. Methylamine
   8. Triaminotriethylamine
   9. Trimethylenediamine
   10. Triethylenetetramine
   11. Phenanthroline
   12. Ethylenediamine

2. ANIONS OF ORGANIC ACIDS
   1. Acetate
   2. Malate
   3. Glycolate
   4. Glycerate
   5. Gluconate
   6. Kojic acid
   7. Lactate
   8. Malonate
   9. Butyric acid
   10. Nitroacetate
   11. Oxalate
   12. Oxaloacetate
   13. Salicylate
   14. Succinate
   15. Tartrate
   16. Propionate
   17. Phthalate
   18. Citrate

96

3. AMINO ACIDS
   1. Alanine
   2. Aminobarbituric, N,N-diacetic acid
   3. Asparagine
   4. N-Hydroxyethylethylenediaminotriacetic acid
   5. Aspartic acid
   6. β-Hydroxyethyliminodiacetic acid
   7. Glycylglycine
   8. Glycine
   9. N,N-Dihydroxyethylglycine
   10. 1,2-Diaminocyclohexanetetraacetic acid
   11. Iminopropionic acid
   12. Iminodiacetic acid
   13. Iminopropionoacetic acid
   14. Nitrilodiacetopropionic acid
   15. Nitrilodipropionoacetic acid
   16. Nitrilotripropionic acid
   17. Nitrilotriacetic acid
   18. 2-Sulfonoanilinediacetic acid
   19. Trimethyldiaminetetraacetic acid
   20. Ethylenediaminetetraacetic acid

4. DIKETONES AND ALDEHYDES
   1. Acetylacetone
   2. β-Methyltropolone
   3. Sulfosalicylaldehyde
   4. Thenoyltrifluoroacetone
   5. Tropolone
   6. Salicylaldehyde
   7. α-Isopropyltropolone
   8. β-Isopropyltropolone
   9. α-Methyltropolone

5. OTHER ORGANIC ADDENDS
   1. Aminophenol
   2. 8-Hydroxy-2,4-dimethylquinazoline

3. 8-Hydroxy-4-methyl-2-phenylquinazoline
4. 8-Hydroxy-5-methylquinoline
5. 8-Hydroxy-2-methylquinoline
6. 8-Hydroxy-6-methylquinoline
7. 8-Hydroxy-7-methylquinoline
8. 8-Hydroxy-4-methylcinnoline
9. 8-Hydroxyquinazoline
10. 5-Hydroxyquinoxaline
11. 8-Hydroxycinnoline
12. 8-Hydroxyquinoline
13. Eriochrome blue-black B
14. Eriochrome blue-black R
15. Eriochrome black A
16. Eriochrome black T

1. COMPLEXES WITH INORGANIC ADDENDS

Complexes with ammonia

Complex ion	Temperature, °C	Ionic strength	Method	k	pk	K	pK	Literature main	Literature additional
$AgNH_3^+$	30	0,5—5,0	pH-potent.	$6,30\cdot10^{-4}$	3,20	$6,30\cdot10^{-4}$	3,20	[1]	[5]
$Ag(NH_3)_2^+$	30	0,5—5,0	"	$1,48\cdot10^{-4}$	3,83	$9,31\cdot10^{-8}$	7,03	[1]	[3,6]
$CdNH_3^{2+}$	30	0,5—5,0	"	$2,24\cdot10^{-3}$	2,65	$2,24\cdot10^{-3}$	2,65	[1]	[7,8]
$Cd(NH_3)_2^{2+}$	30	0,5—5,0	"	$7,94\cdot10^{-3}$	2,10	$1,78\cdot10^{-5}$	4,75	[1]	[7,8]
$Cd(NH_3)_3^{2+}$	30	0,5—5,0	"	$3,63\cdot10^{-2}$	1,44	$6,46\cdot10^{-7}$	6,19	[1]	[7,8,9]
$Cd(NH_3)_4^{2+}$	30	0,5—5,0	"	$1,17\cdot10^{-1}$	0,93	$7,56\cdot10^{-8}$	7,12	[1]	[8,10]
$Cd(NH_3)_5^{2+}$	30	0,5—5,0	"	2,1	−0,32	$1,6\cdot10^{-7}$	6,80	[1]	—
$Cd(NH_3)_6^{2+}$	30	0,5—5,0	"	46,0	−1,66	$7,3\cdot10^{-6}$	5,14	[1]	—
$CoNH_3^{2+}$	30	0,5—5,0	"	$7,75\cdot10^{-3}$	2,11	$7,75\cdot10^{-3}$	2,11	[1]	—
$Co(NH_3)_2^{2+}$	30	0,5—5,0	"	$2,34\cdot10^{-2}$	1,63	$1,81\cdot10^{-4}$	3,74	[1]	—
$Co(NH_3)_3^{2+}$	30	0,5—5,0	"	$8,90\cdot10^{-2}$	1,05	$1,62\cdot10^{-5}$	4,79	[1]	—
$Co(NH_3)_4^{2+}$	30	0,5—5,0	"	$1,73\cdot10^{-1}$	0,76	$2,80\cdot10^{-6}$	5,55	[1]	—
$Co(NH_3)_5^{2+}$	30	0,5—5,0	"	$6,6\cdot10^{-1}$	0,18	$1,85\cdot10^{-6}$	5,73	[1]	—
$Co(NH_3)_6^{2+}$	30	0,5—5,0	"	4,2	−0,6-	$7,75\cdot10^{-6}$	5,11	[1]	—
$Co(NH_3)_6^{3+}$	30	1,0—2,0	"	—	—	$3,1\cdot10^{-33}$	32,51	[1]	—
$CuNH_3^{2+}$	30	0,5—5,0	"	$7,10\cdot10^{-5}$	4,15	$7,10\cdot10^{-5}$	4,15	[1]	—
$Cu(NH_3)_2^{2+}$	30	0,5—5,0	"	$3,16\cdot10^{-4}$	3,50	$2,24\cdot10^{-8}$	7,65	[1]	[11]

Complex ion	Temperature, °C	Ionic strength	Method	k	pk	K	pK	Literature main	Literature additional
$Cu(NH_3)_3^{2+}$	30	0,5—5,0	pH-potent.	$1,29 \cdot 10^{-3}$	2,89	$2,89 \cdot 10^{-11}$	10,54	[1]	—
$Cu(NH_3)_4^{2+}$	30	0,5—5,0	"	$7,40 \cdot 10^{-3}$	2,13	$2,14 \cdot 10^{-13}$	12,67	[1]	[11,12]
$Cu(NH_3)_5^{2+}$	30	—	"	3,0	−0,5	—	—	[2]	—
$CuNH_3^+$	—	—	—	$6,6 \cdot 10^{-7}$	6,18	$6,6 \cdot 10^{-7}$	6,18	[3]	—
$Cu(NH_3)_2^+$	—	—	—	$2,04 \cdot 10^{-5}$	4,69	$1,35 \cdot 10^{-11}$	10,87	[3]	[12]
$FeNH_3^{2+}$	20—30	0,5—5,0	Calc.	$4,0 \cdot 10^{-2}$	1,4	$4,0 \cdot 10^{-2}$	1,4	[4]	—
$Fe(NH_3)_2^{2+}$	20—30	0,5—5,0		$1,6 \cdot 10^{-1}$	0,8	$6,4 \cdot 10^{-3}$	2,2	[4]	—
$HgNH_3^{2+}$	22	2,0	pH-potent.	$1,6 \cdot 10^{-9}$	8,8	$1,6 \cdot 10^{-9}$	8,8	[1]	—
$Hg(NH_3)_2^{2+}$	22	2,0	"	$2,0 \cdot 10^{-9}$	8,7	$3,2 \cdot 10^{-18}$	17,5	[1]	—
$Hg(NH_3)_3^{2+}$	22	2,0	"	$1,0 \cdot 10^{-1}$	1,00	$3,2 \cdot 10^{-19}$	18,5	[1]	—
$Hg(NH_3)_4^{2+}$	22	2,0	"	$1,66 \cdot 10^{-1}$	0,78	$5,3 \cdot 10^{-20}$	19,28	[1]	—
$MgNH_3^{2+}$	22	2,0	"	$5,9 \cdot 10^{-1}$	0,23	$5,9 \cdot 10^{-1}$	0,23	[1]	—
$Mg(NH_3)_2^{2+}$	22	2,0	"	1,41	−0,15	$8,3 \cdot 10^{-1}$	0,08	[1]	—
$Mg(NH_3)_3^{2+}$	22	2,0	"	2,63	−0,42	2,8	−0,34	[1]	—
$Mg(NH_3)_4^{2+}$	22	2,0	"	5,0	−0,7	10,9	−1,04	[1]	—
$Mg(NH_3)_5^{2+}$	22	2,0	"	8,9	−0,95	97,0	−1,99	[1]	—
$Mg(NH_3)_6^{2+}$	22	2,0	"	20,0	−1,3	1930,0	−3,29	[1]	—
$MnNH_3^{2+}$	20—30	0,5—5,0	Calc.	$1,6 \cdot 10^{-1}$	0,8	$1,6 \cdot 10^{-1}$	0,8	[4]	—

Complex ion	Temperature, °C	Ionic strength	Method	k	pk	K	pK	Literature main	Literature additional
Mn(NH$_3$)$_2^{2+}$	20—30	0,5—5,0	Calc.	$3,2 \cdot 10^{-1}$	0,5	$5,0 \cdot 10^{-2}$	1,3	[4]	—
NiNH$_3^{2+}$	30	0,5—5,0	pH-potent.	$1,62 \cdot 10^{-3}$	2,79	$1,62 \cdot 10^{-3}$	2,79	[1]	—
Ni(NH$_3$)$_2^{2+}$	30	0,5—5,0	"	$5,75 \cdot 10^{-3}$	2,24	$9,31 \cdot 10^{-6}$	5,03	[1]	—
Ni(NH$_3$)$_3^{2+}$	30	0,5—5,0	"	$1,86 \cdot 10^{-2}$	1,73	$1,73 \cdot 10^{-7}$	6,76	[1]	—
Ni(NH$_3$)$_4^{2+}$	30	0,5—5,0	"	$6,45 \cdot 10^{-2}$	1,19	$1,12 \cdot 10^{-8}$	7,95	[1]	—
Ni(NH$_3$)$_5^{2+}$	30	0,5—5,0	"	$1,78 \cdot 10^{-1}$	0,75	$2,00 \cdot 10^{-9}$	8,70	[1]	—
Ni(NH$_3$)$_6^{2+}$	30	0,5—5,0	"	$9,34 \cdot 10^{-1}$	0,03	$1,86 \cdot 10^{-9}$	8,73	[1]	—
TlNH$_3^+$	16	—	Spectr.	8,3	−0,92	8,3	−0,92	[3]	—
ZnNH$_3^{2+}$	30	0,5—5,0	pH-potent.	$4,26 \cdot 10^{-3}$	2,37	$4,26 \cdot 10^{-3}$	2,37	[1]	—
Zn(NH$_3$)$_2^{2+}$	30	0,5—5,0	"	$3,63 \cdot 10^{-3}$	2,44	$1,54 \cdot 10^{-5}$	4,81	[1]	[11]
Zn(NH$_3$)$_3^{2+}$	30	0,5—5,0	"	$3,16 \cdot 10^{-3}$	2,50	$4,87 \cdot 10^{-8}$	7,31	[1]	—
Zn(NH$_3$)$_4^{2+}$	30	0,5—5,0	"	$7,10 \cdot 10^{-3}$	2,15	$3,46 \cdot 10^{-10}$	9,46	[1]	[11]

LITERATURE CITED

1. J. Bjerrum. Metalammine formation in aqueous solutions. Copenhagen, 1941; cit. in Chem. Abs., 6527 (1941).
2. J. Bjerrum. Chem. Rev., 46, 381 (1950).
3. P. Job. Ann. chim. [10] 9, 113; cit. in Z. Bl., I, 2572 (1928).
4. K. B. Yatsimirskii. J. Gen. Chem., 24, 1498 (1954).*
5. W. C. Vosburgh, McClure. J. Am. Chem. Soc., 65, 1060 (1943).
6. G. Bodländer, R. Fittig. Z. phys. Chem., 39, 597 (1902)
7. P. F. Derr, W. C. Vosburgh. J. Am. Chem. Soc., 65, 2408 (1943).
8. C. G. Spike, R. W. Parry. J. Am. Chem. Soc., 75, 2726 (1953).
9. I. A. Korshunov, L. V. Lipatova. J. Gen. Chem., 21, 615 (1951).*
10. A. G. Stromberg, I. E. Bykov. J. Gen. Chem., 19, 245 (1949).*
11. C. G. Spike, R. W. Parry. J. Am. Chem. Soc., 75, 3770 (1953).
12. M. v. Stackelberg, H. v. Freyhold. Z. Elektrochem., 46, 120 (1940).

Bromide complexes

Complex ion	Temperature, °C	Ionic strength	Method	k	pk	K	pK	Literature main	Literature additional
Ag_2Br^+	Room	—	Sol.	—	—	$2 \cdot 10^{-10}$	9,70	[1]	—
$AgBr$	25	0,2	"	$7,1 \cdot 10^{-5}$	4,15	$7,1 \cdot 10^{-5}$	4,15	[2]	[23]
$AgBr_2^-$	25	0,2	"	$1,1 \cdot 10^{-3}$	2,96	$7,8 \cdot 10^{-8}$	7,11	[2]	[24]
$AgBr_3^{2-}$	25	0,2	"	$1,610 \cdot 10^{-2}$	1,79	$1,3 \cdot 10^{-9}$	8,90	[2]	[23,24,25,26]
$AgBr_4^{3-}$	25	0,2	"	0,50	0,30	$6,3 \cdot 10^{-10}$	9,20	[2]	[27]
$AuBr_2^-$	60	3	Potent.	—	—	$4 \cdot 10^{-13}$	12,4	[3]	—
$BiBr^{2+}$	18	—	"	$5 \cdot 10^{-5}$	4,30	$5 \cdot 10^{-5}$	4,30	[4]	—
$BiBr_2^+$	25	1,0—2,0	Sol.	$5,6 \cdot 10^{-2}$	1,25	$2,8 \cdot 10^{-6}$	5,55	[5]	[4]
$BiBr_3$	25	1,0—2,0	"	0,48	0,32	$1,3 \cdot 10^{-6}$	5,89	[5]	[4]
$BiBr_4^-$	20	1,5—1,6	Potent.	—	—	$1,5 \cdot 10^{-8}$	7,82	[5]	[4]
$BiBr_6^{3-}$	20	1,5—1,6	"	—	—	$2 \cdot 10^{-10}$	9,70	[6]	—
$CdBr^+$	25	3,0	"	$1,78 \cdot 10^{-2}$	1,75	$1,78 \cdot 10^{-2}$	1,75	[7]	[28,29]
$CdBr_2$	25	3,0	"	0,26	0,59	$4,5 \cdot 10^{-3}$	2,34	[7]	[28,29]
$CdBr_3^-$	25	3,0	"	0,105	0,98	$4,75 \cdot 10^{-4}$	3,32	[7]	[28,29,30]
$CdBr_4^{2-}$	25	3,0	"	0,26	0,38	$2 \cdot 10^{-4}$	3,70	[7]	[28,29,20,15]
$CeBr^{2+}$	Room	0,0	Ion. exch.	0,42	0,38	0,42	0,38	[8]	—
$CuBr_2$	18—20	0,02—0,5	Potent.	—	—	$1,3 \cdot 10^{-6}$	5,89	[9]	—
$CuBr^+$	22	1,0	Spectr.	0,5	0,30	0,5	0,30	[10]	[31,32]
$FeBr^{2+}$	26,7	1,0	"	2,0	—0,30	2,0	—0,30	[11]	—
$HgBr^+$	25	0,5	Potent.	$0,89 \cdot 10^{-9}$	9,05	$0,89 \cdot 10^{-9}$	9,05	[12]	[33]
$HgBr_2$	25	0,5	"	$5,4 \cdot 10^{-9}$	8,28	$4,8 \cdot 10^{-18}$	17,32	[12]	[33,34]
$HgBr_3^-$	25	0,5	"	$3,8 \cdot 10^{-2}$	1,42	$1,82 \cdot 10^{-20}$	19,74	[12]	—

Complex ion	Temperature, °C	Ionic strength	Method	k	pk	K	pK	Literature main	Literature additional
HgBr$_4^{2-}$	25	0,5	"	$5,5 \cdot 10^{-2}$	1,26	$1,0 \cdot 10^{-21}$	21,00	[12]	[34]
InBr^{2+}	25	1,0	Ion. exch.	$6,3 \cdot 10^{-2}$	1,20	$6,3 \cdot 10^{-2}$	1,20	[13]	[35]
InBr$_2^+$	25	1,0	"	0,26	0,58	$1,7 \cdot 10^{-2}$	1,78	[13]	[35]
InBr$_3$	25	1,0	"	0,20	0,70	$3,3 \cdot 10^{-3}$	2,48	[13]	[35]
PbBr$^+$	25	0	Electrocon.	$3,3 \cdot 10^{-2}$	1,15	$3,3 \cdot 10^{-2}$	1,15	[14]	[36]
PbBr$_2$	25	0,0	Polarog.	—	—	$1,2 \cdot 10^{-2}$	1,92	[15]	—
PbBr$_4^{2-}$	25	0,0	"	—	—	$1,0 \cdot 10^{-3}$	3,0	[15]	—
PdBr$_4^{2-}$	Room	—	Potent.	—	—	$8,0 \cdot 10^{-14}$	13,1	[16]	—
PtBr$_4^{2-}$	*	—	"	—	—	$3,0 \cdot 10^{-21}$	20,5	[16[	—
SnBr$^+$	25	3,0	"	$1,9 \cdot 10^{-1}$	0,73	$1,9 \cdot 10^{-1}$	0,73	[17]	[37]
SnBr$_2$	25	3,0	"	0,40	0,40	$7,2 \cdot 10^{-2}$	1,14	[17]	—
SnBr$_3^-$	25	3,0	"	0,62	0,21	$4,5 \cdot 10^{-2}$	1,35	[17]	—
TlBr^{2+}	25	0,1—0,2	"	$2 \cdot 10^{-10}$	9,7	$2 \cdot 10^{-10}$	9,7	[18]	—
		1,2	"		8,9		8,9	[19]	—
TlBr$_2^+$	25	0,1—0,2	"	$1,3 \cdot 10^{-7}$	6,9	$2,5 \cdot 10^{-17}$	16,6	[18]	—
		1,2	"		7,5		16,4	[19]	—
TlBr$_3$		0,1—0,2	"		4,6	$1,6 \cdot 10^{-22}$	21,2	[18]	—
		1,2	"	$2,5 \cdot 10^{-5}$	5,7		22,1	[19]	—
TlBr$_4^-$		0,1—0,2	"	$2 \cdot 10^{-3}$	2,7	$1,3 \cdot 10^{-24}$	23,9	[18]	—
		1,2	"		4,0		26,1	[19]	—
TlBr$_5^{2-}$		1,2	"		3,1		29,2	[19]	—
TlBr$_6^{3-}$		1,2	"		2,4		31,6	[19]	—
UBr^{3+}	20	—	"	0,67	0,18	0,67	0,18	[20]	—
UO$_2$Br$^+$	20	—	"	2,00	-0,30	2,00	-0,30	[21]	—
ZnBr$^+$	25	0,3	"	4,00	-0,60	4,0	-0,60	[22]	—

LITERATURE CITED

1. K.B. Yatsimirskii. Proc. Acad. Sci. USSR, 77, 819 (1951).
2. E. Berne, J. Leden. Z. Naturforsch., 8a, 719 (1953)
3. G. Grube. T. Morita. Z. Electrochem., 38, 117 (1932).
4. A.K. Babko. Sci. Rep. KDU, 4, 81 (1939).
5. K.B. Yatsimirskii. Collection of Articles on General Chemistry, Acad. Sci. USSR Press. 1953, Vol. I, p. 97.
6. A.K. Babko, A.M. Golub. Collection of Articles on General Chemistry, Acad. Sci. USSR Press, 1953, Vol. I, p. 64.
7. J. Leden. Z. phys. Chem., 188, 160 (1941).
8. S. W. Mayer, S. D. Schwartz. J. Am. Chem. Soc., 73, 222 (1951).
9. G. Bodländer, O. Storbeck. Z. anorg. Chem., 31, 458 (1902).
10. P. S. Farrington. J. Am. Chem. Soc., 74, 966 (1952).
11. E. Rabinowitch, W. Stockmayer. J. Am. Chem. Soc., 64, 335 (1942).
12. O. Bethge, J. Jonevall-Westöö, L. G. Sillen. Chem. Abs., 43, 4545 (1949).
13. J. A. Schuffe, H. M. Eiland. J. Am. Chem. Soc., 76, 960 (1954).
14. G. H. Nancollas. J. Chem. Soc., 1955, 1458.
15. A.M. Vasil'ev, V.I. Proukhina. J. Anal. Chem., 6, 218 (1951).
16. W.M. Latimer. Oxidation States of Elements and their Potentials in Aqueous Solutions. Foreign Lit. Press, Moscow, 1954. [Russian trans.]
17. C. E. Vanderzee. J. Am. Chem. Soc., 74, 4806 (1952).
18. R. Benoit. Bull. Soc. chim. France, 518 (1949). Chem. Abs., 43, 8939 (1949).
19. D. Peschanski, S. Valladas-Dubois. Compt. rend., 241, 1046 (1955).
20. S. Ahrland, R. Larsson. Acta Chem. Scand., 8, 137 (1954).
21. S. Ahrland. Acta Chem. Scand., 5, 1271 (1951).
22. L. G. Sillen, B. Liljeqvist. Chem. Abs., 40, 4588 (1946).
23. V. B. Vouk, J. Kratohvil, B. Težak. Arhiv Kem., 23, 200 (1951).
24. K.S. Lyaikov, V.N. Piskunova. J. Phys. Chem., 28, 127 (1954).
25. W. Erber. Z. anorg. Chem., 248, 32 (1941).
26. H. Chateau, J. Pouradier. Chem. Abs., 40, 8563 (1952).
27. G. Bodländer, W. Eberlein. Z. anorg. Chem., 39, 197 (1904).
28. H. L. Riley, V. Gallafent. J. Chem. Soc., 1932, 514.
29. L. Eriksson. Acta Chem. Scand., 7, 1146 (1953).
30. I.A. Korshunov, N.I. Malyutina, O.M. Balabanova. J. Gen. Chem., 21, 620 (1951).*
31. R. Näsänen. Chem. Abs., 44, 10415 (1950).
32. H. L. Riley, H. C. Smith. J. Chem. Soc., 1934, 1448.
33. H. Morze. Z. phys. Chem., 41, 709 (1902).
34. M. S. Sherill. Z. phys. Chem., 43, 705 (1903); 47, 103 (1904).
35. N. Sunden. Svenck Kem. Tidsk., 66, 20 (1954); Chem. Abs., 48, 9252 (1954).
36. H. Fromherz. Z. phys. Chem., 153, 376 (1931).
37. F. R. Duke, R. C. Pinkerton. J. Am. Chem. Soc., 73, 3045 (1951).

Bromate complexes

Complex ion	Temperature, °C	Ionic strength	Method	k	pk	K	pK
$ThBrO_3^{3+}$	25	0,5	Distrib.	0,155	0,81	0,155	0,81
$Th(BrO_3)_2^{2+}$	25	0,5	.	0,79	0,10	0,123	0,91

LITERATURE CITED

R. A. Day, R. W. Stoughton. J. Am. Chem. Soc., **72**, 5662 (1950).

Complexes with hydrazine

Complex ion	Temperature °C	Ionic strength	Method	k	pk	K	pK
$NiN_2H_4^{2+}$	20	0,5	pH-potent.	$1,75 \cdot 10^{-3}$	2,76	$1,75 \cdot 10^{-3}$	2,76
$Ni(N_2H_4)_2^{2+}$	20	0,5	"	$3,6 \cdot 10^{-3}$	2,44	$6,3 \cdot 10^{-6}$	5,20
$Ni(N_2H_4)_3^{2+}$	20	0,5	"	$7,1 \cdot 10^{-3}$	2,15	$4,5 \cdot 10^{-8}$	7,35
$Ni(N_2H_4)_4^{2+}$	20	0,5	"	$1,4 \cdot 10^{-2}$	1,85	$6,3 \cdot 10^{-10}$	9,20
$Ni(N_2H_4)_5^{2+}$	20	0,5	"	$2,8 \cdot 10^{-2}$	1,55	$1,9 \cdot 10^{-11}$	10,72
$Ni(N_2H_4)_6^{2+}$	20	0,5	"	$5,75 \cdot 10^{-2}$	1,24	$1,1 \cdot 10^{-12}$	11,96
$ZnN_2H_4^{2+}$	20	0,5	"	$4,0 \cdot 10^{-3}$	2,4	$4,0 \cdot 10^{-3}$	2,4
$Zn(N_2H_4)_2^{2+}$	20	0,5	"	$1,6 \cdot 10^{-2}$	1,8	$6,3 \cdot 10^{-5}$	4,2
$Zn(N_2H_4)_3^{2+}$	20	0,5	"	$5,0 \cdot 10^{-2}$	1,3	$3,26 \cdot 10^{-6}$	5,5
$Zn(N_2H_4)_4^{2+}$	20	0,5	"	$1,6 \cdot 10^{-1}$	0,8	$5,0 \cdot 10^{-7}$	6,3

LITERATURE CITED

G. Schwarzenbach, A. Zobrist. Helv. chim. Acta, **35**, 1291 (1952).

Hydroxo complexes

Complex ion	Temperature, °C	Ionic strength	Method	k	pk	K	pK	Literature main	Literature additional
AgOH	25	—	Potent.	$5,0\cdot10^{-3}$	2,30	$5,0\cdot10^{-3}$	2,30	[1]	—
AlOH²⁺	25	0	Potent., electrocon.	$1,38\cdot10^{-9}$	8,86	$1,38\cdot10^{-9}$	8,86	[2]	[8]
BaOH⁺	25	0	Kinetic	0,23	0,64	0,23	0,64	[3]	[20]
BeOH⁺	25	1,0	Potent.	$3,3\cdot10^{-8}$	7,50	$3,3\cdot10^{-8}$	7,50	[4]	—
Be₂OH³⁺	25	1,0	"	—	—	$3,3\cdot10^{-11}$	10,50	[4]	—
CaOH⁺	25	0	Kinetic	$5,0\cdot10^{-2}$	1,30	$5,0\cdot10^{-2}$	1,30	[3]	[20,28]
CdOH⁺	30	0,1	Potent.	$5,0\cdot10^{-3}$	2,30	$5,0\cdot10^{-3}$	2,30	[5]	—
CeOH²⁺	25	Variable	Spectr.	$2,0\cdot10^{-15}$	14,70	$2,0\cdot10^{-15}$	14,70	[6]	—
CoOH⁺	25	0,005	Potent., calc.	$4\cdot10^{-5}$	4,4	$4\cdot10^{-5}$	4,4	[7]	[5,33]
CrOH³⁺	25	0,005	Electrocon., potent.	$1,02\cdot10^{-10}$	9,99	$1,02\cdot10^{-10}$	9,99	[8]	[34]
CuOH⁺	25	0	Potent.	$3,4\cdot10^{-7}$	6,47	$3,4\cdot10^{-7}$	6,47	[9]	[5,35]
Cu(OH)₄²⁻	Room	Variable	Sol.	—	—	$7,6\cdot10^{-17}$	16,12	[10]	—
FeOH⁺	25	0	Potent., calc.	$1,3\cdot10^{-4}$	3,9	$1,3\cdot10^{-4}$	3,9	[7]	[36,37]
FeOH²⁺	25	0	Potent., calc.	$1,55\cdot10^{-12}$	11,81	$1,55\cdot10^{-12}$	11,81	[11]	[38]
"	25	0,1	Potent.	$7,9\cdot10^{-12}$	11,10	$7,9\cdot10^{-12}$	11,10	[12]	[39,40]
"	25	3,0	Potent.	$1,12\cdot10^{-11}$	10,95	$1,12\cdot10^{-11}$	10,95	[13]	[5]
Fe(OH)₂⁺	25	0,1	Potent.	$1,82\cdot10^{-11}$	10,74	$2,04\cdot10^{-22}$	21,69	[13]	[40]
Fe₂(OH)₂⁴⁺	25	0,0	Spectr.	—	—	$8,0\cdot10^{-26}$	25,10	[14]	[13,41]
"	25	3,0	"	—	—	$8,0\cdot10^{-26}$	25,10	[14]	—
GaOH²⁺	25	Variable	"	$2,5\cdot10^{-11}$	10,60	$2,5\cdot10^{-11}$	10,60	[15]	[42]
HgOH⁺	25	0,5	Potent.	$5,0\cdot10^{-11}$	10,30	$5,0\cdot10^{-11}$	10,30	[16]	—
Hg(OH)₂	25	0,5	"	$4,0\cdot10^{-12}$	11,40	$2,0\cdot10^{-22}$	21,70	[16]	[43]
InOH²⁺	23	0,006	Potent.	$5,0\cdot10^{-11}$	10,30	$5,0\cdot10^{-11}$	10,30	[17]	—
In(OH)₄⁻	Room	—	Polarog.	—	—	$2,5\cdot10^{-30}$	29,6	[18]	—

Complex ion	Temperature, °C	Ionic strength	Method	k	pk	K	pK	Literature main	Literature additional
$LaOH^{2+}$	25	0	Spectr.	$5,0 \cdot 10^{-4}$	3,30	$5,0 \cdot 10^{-4}$	3,30	[19]	—
$LiOH$	25	0	Potent.	0,66	0,18	0,66	0,18	[20]	[44]
$MgOH^+$	25	0	"	$2,5 \cdot 10^{-3}$	2,58	$2,5 \cdot 10^{-3}$	2,58	[21]	[5]
$MnOH^+$	30	0	"	$5,0 \cdot 10^{-4}$	3,30	$5,0 \cdot 10^{-4}$	3,30	[5]	—
$NaOH$	25	0	"	3	−0,48	3	−0,48	[20]	—
$NiOH^+$	30	0,1	"	$2,5 \cdot 10^{-5}$	4,60	$2,5 \cdot 10^{-5}$	4,60	[5]	**[33]**
$PbOH^+$	18	0	"	$6,0 \cdot 10^{-7}$	6,22	$6,0 \cdot 10^{-7}$	6,22	[22]	—
Pb_2OH^{3+}	25	1,0	"	$3,2 \cdot 10^{-13}$	12,49	$3,2 \cdot 10^{-13}$	12,49	[24]	[30]
$PuOH^{3+}$	25	1,0	"	$7,6 \cdot 10^{-10}$	9,12	$7,6 \cdot 10^{-10}$	9,12	[25]	—
$ScOH^{2+}$	25	3,0	"	$5,0 \cdot 10^{-13}$	12,30	$5,0 \cdot 10^{-13}$	**12,30**	[26]	[45,46]
$SrOH^+$	25	0	"	0,15	0,82	0,15	0,82	[20]	[47]
$SnOH^+$	25	1,0	Potent.	$2,0 \cdot 10^{-10}$	9,70	$2,0 \cdot 10^{-10}$	9,70	[27]	—
$ThOH^{3+}$	25	0	Sol.	0,15	0,82	**0,15**	0,82	[28]	[3]
$TlOH$	25	3,0	Potent.	$7,9 \cdot 10^{-15}$	14,10	$7,9 \cdot 10^{-15}$	14,10	[29]	[48,49]
$TlOH^{2+}$	25	3,0	"	$6,8 \cdot 10^{-15}$	14,17	$5,4 \cdot 10^{-29}$	28,27	[29]	—
$Tl(OH)_2^+$	25	0	"	$4,8 \cdot 10^{-14}$	13,32	$4,8 \cdot 10^{-14}$	**13,32**	[30]	[50]
UOH^{3+}	25	0,5	"	$3,2 \cdot 10^{-13}$	12,50	$3,2 \cdot 10^{-13}$	12,50	[30]	—
VOH^{2+}	25	Variable	"	$8,3 \cdot 10^{-12}$	11,08	$8,3 \cdot 10^{-12}$	11,08	[31]	[51]
$V(OH)_2^+$	25	"	"	$3,2 \cdot 10^{-11}$	10,50	$2,6 \cdot 10^{-22}$	21,58	[31]	—
$ZnOH^+$	25	0	"	$4,0 \cdot 10^{-5}$	4,40	$4,0 \cdot 10^{-5}$	4,40	[9]	[5]
$Zn(OH)_3^-$	Room	—	Polarog.	—	—	$4,3 \cdot 10^{-15}$	14,37	[18]	—
$Zn(OH)_4^{2-}$	25	Variable	Sol.	—	—	$3,6 \cdot 10^{-16}$	15,44	[32]	[52,53]

LITERATURE CITED

1. J. Bjerrum. Chem. Rev., **46**, 381 (1950).
2. T. Ito, N. Yui. Chem. Abs., **48**, 5613 (1954).
3. R. P. Bell, J. E. Prue. J. Chem. Soc., 1949, 362.
4. G. Mattock. J. Am. Chem. Soc., **76**, 4835 (1954).
5. S. Chaberek and others. Am. Chem. Soc., **74**, 5057 (1952)
6. T. J. Hardwick, E. Robertson. Chem. Abs., **46**, 3372 (1952).
7. K.B. Yatsimirskii. J. Gen. Chem., **24, 1498 (1954).**
8. N. Bjerrum. Z. phys. Chem., **59**, 336 (1907).
9. B. B. Owen, R. W. Gurry. J. Am. Chem. Soc., **60**, 3074 (1938).
10. W. Feitknecht. Helv. chim. Acta, **27**, 771 (1944).
11. T. H. Siddal, W. C. Vosburgh. J. Am. Chem. Soc., **73**, 4270 (1951).
12. T. V. Arden. J. Chem. Soc., 350 (1951).
13. B. Hedström. Arkiv. Kemi., **6**, 1 (1953); Chem. Abs., **47**, 11939 (1953).
14. R. Milburn, W. C. Vosburgh. J. Am. Chem. Soc., **77**, 1352 (1955).
15. T. Moeller, G. L. King. J. phys. colloid. Chem., **54**, 999 (1950).
16. S. Hietanen, L. G. Sillen. Chem. Abs., **47**, 2577 (1953).
17. E. M. Hattox, T. De Vries. J. Am. Chem. Soc., **58**, 2126 (1936).
18. J. Heyrovsky. Polarographic Method. [In Russian] ONTI (1937).
19. C. W. Davies. J. Chem. Soc., 1951, 1256; I. M. Kolthoff, R. Elmquist. J. Am. Chem. Soc., **53**, 1217 (1931).
20. F. G. R. Gimblet, C. B. Monk. Trans. Farad. Soc., **50**, 965 (1954).
21. D. J. Stock, C. W. Davies. Trans. Farad. Soc., **44**, 856 (1948).
22. K. J. Pedersen. Chem. Abs., **40**, 4588 (1946).
23. A. B. Garrett, S. Vellenga, C. M. Fontana. J. Am. Chem. Soc., **61**, 367 (1939).
24. S. W. Rabideau, J. F. Lamons. J. Am. Chem. Soc., **73**, 2895 (1951).
25. M. Kirpatrick, L. Pokras. J. Electrochem. Soc., **100**, 85 (1953); Chem. Abs., **47**, 11963 (1953).
26. C. E. Vanderzee, D. E. Rhodes. J. Am. Chem. Soc., **74**, 3552 (1952).
27. K. A. Kraus, R. W. Holmberg. J. phys. Chem., **58**, 325 (1954).
28. R. P. Bell, J. H. B. George. Trans. Farad. Soc., **49**, 619 (1953).
29. G. Biedermann. Arkiv. Kemi, **5**, 441 (1953); Chem. Abs., **47**, 11938 (1953).
30. K. A. Kraus, F. Nelson. J. Am. Chem. Soc., **72**, 3901 (1950).
31. L. Meites. J. Am. Chem. Soc., **75**, 6059 (1953); G. Jones, W. A. Ray. J. Am. Chem. Soc., **66**, 1571 (1944).
32. H. G. Dietrich, J. Johnson. J. Am. Chem. Soc., **49**, 1419 (1927).
33. K. Gayer, L. Woontner. J. Am. Chem. Soc., **74**, 1436 (1952).
34. A. B. Lamb, G. R. Fonda. J. Am. Chem. Soc., **43**, 1155 (1921).
35. H. Guiter. Compt. rend., **228**, 569 (1949).
36. D. L. Leussing, J M. Kolthoff. J. Am. Chem. Soc., **75**, 2476 (1953).
37. B. Hedström. Arkiv. Kemi., 5, 457 (1953); Chem. Abs., **47**, 11938 (1953).
38. W. C. Bray, A. V. Hershey. J. Am. Chem. Soc., **56**, 1889 (1931).
39. C. Brosset. Chem. Abs., **37**, 24 (1943).
40. T. Ito, N. Yui. Chem. Abs., **48**; 6791 (1954).
41. L. N. Mulay, P. W. Selwood. J. Am. Chem. Soc., **77**, 2693 (1955).
42. R. Fricke, K. Meyring. Z. anorg. Chem., **176**, 329 (1928).
43. A. B. Garrett, A. E. Hirschler. J. Am. Chem. Soc., **60**, 299 (1938).
44. L. S. Darken, H. F. Meier. J. Am. Chem. Soc., **64**, 621 (1942).
45. M. Gorman. J. Am. Chem. Soc., **61**, 3342 (1939).
46. A. B. Garrett, R. E. Heins. J. Am. Chem. Soc., **63**, 562 (1941).
47. C. A. Colman-Porter, C. B. Monk. J. Chem. Soc., 1952, 1312.
48. R. Benoit. Bull. Soc. chim. France, 518 (1949); Chem. Abs., 8939 (1949).
49. C. E. Johnson. J. Am. Chem. Soc., **74**, 959 (1952).
50. K. A. Kraus, F. Nelson. J. Am. Chem. Soc., **77**, 3721 (1955).
51. S. C. Furman, C. S. Garner. J. Am. Chem. Soc., **72**, 1785 (1950).
52. I. A. Korshunov, E. F. Khrul'kova. J. Gen. Chem., **19**, 2045 (1949).*
53. M. Stackelberg, H. Freyhold. Z. Electrochem., **46**, 120 (1940).

Hydroperoxo complexes

Complex ion	Temperature, °C	Ionic strength	Method	k	pk	K	pK	Literature main	additional
$Fe(O_2H)^{2+}$	20	0,1	Spectr.	$5,0 \cdot 10^{-10}$	9,30	$5,0 \cdot 10^{-10}$	9,30	[1]	—
$TiO(H_2O_2)^{2+}$	Room	0,1	„	$1,0 \cdot 10^{-4}$	4,00	$1,0 \cdot 10^{-4}$	4,00	[2]	[3,4]

LITERATURE CITED

1. M. G. Evans, P. George, N. Uri. Trans. Farad. Soc., **45**, 230 (1949).
2. K. E. Kleiner. J. Gen. Chem., **22**, 17 (1952).*
3. A. K. Babko, A. I. Volkova. J. Gen. Chem., **21**, 1949 (1951).*
4. E. Gastinger. Z. anorg. Chem., **275**, 331 (1954).

Iodate complexes

Complex ion	Temperature, °C	Ionic strength	Method	k	pk	K	pK	Literature
$BaIO_3^+$	25	0	Electrocon. Sol.	$8,9 \cdot 10^{-2}$		1,05	$8,9 \cdot 10^{-2}$	1,05	[1]
$CaIO_3^+$	25	0	Sol.	0,129		0,89	0,129	0,89	[2]
KIO_3	25	0	Electrocon.	2,0		−0,30	2,0	−0,30	[3]
$MgIO_3^+$	25	0	Sol.	0,190		0,72	0,190	0,72	[4]
$SrIO_3^+$	25	0	Electrocon. Sol.	0,10		1,00	0,10	1,00	[5]
$ThIO_3^{3+}$	25	0,5	Distrib.	$1,32 \cdot 10^{-3}$		2,88	$1,32 \cdot 10^{-3}$	2,88	[6]
$Th(IO_3)_2^{2+}$	25	0,5	„	$1,23 \cdot 10^{-2}$		1,91	$1,62 \cdot 10^{-5}$	4,79	[6]
$Th(IO_3)_3^+$	25	0,5	„	$4,4 \cdot 10^{-3}$		2,36	$7,1 \cdot 10^{-8}$	7,15	[6]
$TlIO_3$	25	0	„	0,32		0,50	0,32	0,50	[4]

LITERATURE CITED

1. T. Macdougall, C. W. Davies. J. Chem. Soc., 1935, 1416.
2. C. W. Davies. J. Chem. Soc., 1938, 271.
3. C. W. Davies. Trans. Farad. Soc., **26**, 592 (1930).
4. C. W. Davies. J. Chem. Soc., 1930, 2410.
5. C. A. Colman-Porter, C. B. Monk. J. Chem. Soc., 1952, 1312.
6. R. A. Day, R. W. Stoughton. J. Am. Chem. Soc., **72**, 5662 (1950).

Iodide complexes

Complex ion	Temperature, °C	Ionic strength	Method	k	pk	K	pK	Literature main	Literature additional
Ag_3I^{2+}	Room	Variable	Sol.	—	—	$8 \cdot 10^{-15}$	14,15	[1]	—
AgI_3^{2-}	"	1,6	Potent.	—	—	$1,4 \cdot 10^{-14}$	13,95	[2]	[14,15]
AgI_4^{3-}	"	1,6	"	—	—	$1,8 \cdot 10^{-14}$	13,75	[2]	[16,17]
BiI_6^{3-}	20	Variable	Potent.	—	—	$3,1 \cdot 10^{-12}$	11,51	[3]	—
Cd_2I^{3+}	25	0,2—9,0	Sol.	—	—	$3,2 \cdot 10^{-3}$	2,49	[4]	—
CdI^+	25	0,0	Potent.	$5,2 \cdot 10^{-3}$	2,28	$5,2 \cdot 10^{-3}$	2,28	[5]	[4,18]
"	25	3,0	"	$8,3 \cdot 10^{-3}$	2,08	$8,3 \cdot 10^{-3}$	2,08	[6]	
CdI_2	25	0,0	"	$2,3 \cdot 10^{-2}$	1,64	$1,2 \cdot 10^{-4}$	3,92	[5]	[18]
"	25	3,0	"	(0,24)	(0,62)	$(2,0 \cdot 10^{-3})$	(2,70)	[6]	
CdI_3^-	25	0,0	"	$(8,3 \cdot 10^{-2})$	(1,08)	$(1,0 \cdot 10^{-5})$	(5,0)	[5]	[7,18]
"	25	3,0	"	$5,0 \cdot 10^{-3}$	2,30	$1,0 \cdot 10^{-5}$	5,0	[6]	
CdI_4^{2-}	25	0,0	"	$7,9 \cdot 10^{-2}$	1,10	$8 \cdot 10^{-7}$	6,10	[5]	[7,18, 19,20]
"	25	3,0	"	$3,2 \cdot 10^{-2}$	1,49	$3,0 \cdot 10^{-7}$	6,49	[6]	

Complex ion	Temperature, °C	Ionic strength	Method	k	pk	K	pK	Literature main	Literature additional
CdI_6^{4-}	25	0,05—2,5	Polarog.	—	—	$4,0\cdot10^{-6}$	6,0	[7]	—
CuI_2^-	25	0,02—0,5	Potent.	—	—	$1,75\cdot10^{-9}$	8,76	[8]	—
Hg_2I^{3+}	25	0,05—3	Sol.	—	—	$1,77\cdot10^{-14}$	13,75	[9]	—
HgI^+	25	0,5	Potent.	$1,35\cdot10^{-13}$	12,87	$1,35\cdot10^{-13}$	12,87	[10]	[9,21]
HgI_2	25	0,5	"	$1,12\cdot10^{-11}$	10,95	$1,51\cdot10^{-24}$	23,82	[10]	[22]
HgI_3^-	25	0,5	l Potent.	$1,66\cdot10^{-4}$	3,78	$2,5\cdot10^{-28}$	27,60	[10]	—
HgI_4^{2-}	25	0,5	"	$5,9\cdot10^{-3}$	2,23	$1,48\cdot10^{-30}$	29,83	[10]	[2,22,23]
InI^{2+}	25	1,0	Ion. exch.	0,5	0,30	0,5	0,30	[11]	[24]
Pb_2I^{3+}	25	0,3—3,6	Sol.	—	—	$2,2\cdot10^{-2}$	1,66	[4]	—
PbI^{2+}	25	0,3—3,6	"	$5,05\cdot10^{-3}$	2,30	$5,05\cdot10^{-3}$	2,30	[4]	[25]
PbJ_3^-	25	0,0	"	—	—	$2,22\cdot10^{-5}$	4,65	[12]	[17]
PbJ_4^{2-}	25	0,0	"	6,3	—0,80	$1,42\cdot10^{-4}$	3,85	[12]	[26]
ZnI^+	25	3,0	Potent.	20	—1,3	20	—1,3	[13]	—

111

LITERATURE CITED

1. K. B. Yatsimirskii. Proc. Acad. Sci. USSR, 77, 819 (1951); K. Hellwig. Z. anorg. Chem., 25, 157 (1900).
2. A. M. Golub. Ukr. Chem. J., 19, 467 (1953).
3. A. K. Babko, A. M. Golub. Collection of Articles on General Chemistry, Acad. Sci. USSR Press, 1953, Vol. I, p. 64.
4. K. B. Yatsimirskii, A. A. Shutov. J. Phys. Chem., 27, 782 (1953).
5. R. G. Bates, W. C. Vosburgh. J. Am. Chem. Soc., 60, 137 (1938).
6. J. Leden. Z. phys. Chem.. Abt. A, 188, 160 (1941).
7. I. A. Korshunov, N. I. Malyugina, O. M. Balabanova. J. Gen. Chem., 21, 620 (1951).*
8. G. Bodländer, O. Storbeck. Z. anorg. Chem., 31, 458 (1902).
9. K. B. Yatsimirskii, A. A. Shutov. J. Phys. Chem., 26, 842 (1952).
10. J. Quarfort, L. G. Sillen. Acta Chem. Scand. 3, 505 (1949).
11. J. A. Schuffe, H. M. Eiland. J. Am. Chem. Soc., 76, 960 (1954).
12. E. Lanford. J. Am. Chem. Soc., 63, 667 (1941).
13. L. G. Sillen, B. Liljeqvist. Chem. Abs., 40, 4588 (1946).
14. W. Erber. Z. anorg. Chem., 248, 36 (1941); Chem. Abs., 1943 (1947).
15. K. Schulz, B. Težak. Arhiv. Kemi., 23, 200 (1951).
16. G. Bodländer, W. Eberlein. Z. anorg. Chem., 39, 197 (1904).
17. I. M. Korenman. J. Gen. Chem., 16, 157 (1946).
18. H. L. Riley, B. Gallafent. J. Chem. Soc., 1931, 514.
19. A. T. Stromberg, I. E. Bykov. J. Gen. Chem., 19, 245 (1949).*
20. P. Job. Zbl., I, 2572 (1928).
21. H. Morze. Z. phys. Chem., 41, 709 (1902).
22. M. S. Scherill. Z. phys. Chem., 43, 475 (1903); 47, 103 (1904).
23. N. I. Malyugina, M. K. Shchennikova, I. A. Korshunov. J. Gen. Chem.. 16. 1573 (1946).
24. N. Sunden. Svenek. Kem. Tidsk., 66, 50 (1954); Chem. Abst. J., No, 10, 18547 (1955).
25. H. Fromherz, K. Lin. Z. phys. Chem., Abt. A, 153, 321 (1931).
26. I. A. Korshunov, V. A. Osipova. J. Gen. Chem., 19, 1816 (1949).*

Perchlorate complexes

Complex ion	Temperature, °C	Ionic strength	Method	k	pk	K	pK	Literature
$CeClO_4^{2+}$	25	0	Spectr.	$1,17.10^{-2}$	1,93	$1,17 \cdot 10^{-2}$	1,93	[1]
	25	4,5	Spectr.	1,16	−0,07	1,16	−0,07	[1]
$FeClO_4^{2+}$	25	0	Spectr.	2,10	−0,32	2,10	−0,32	[2]

LITERATURE CITED

1. L. J. Heidt, J. Berestecki. J. Am. Chem. Soc., 77, 2049 (1955).
2. J. Sutton. Nature, 169, 71 (1952).

Nitrate complexes

Complex ion	Temperature, °C	Ionic strength	Method	k	pk	K	pK	Literature main	additional
$BaNO_3^+$	25	0	Electrocon.	0,12	0,92	0,12	0,92	[1]	—
$BiNO_3^{2+}$	25	0,1	Sol.	$5,6\cdot10^{-3}$	2,25	$5,6\cdot10^{-3}$	2,25	[2]	—
$CaNO_3^+$	25	0	Electrocon.	0,52	0,28	0,52	0,28	[1]	—
$CdNO_3^+$	25	0	"	0,40	0,40	0,40	0,40	[1]	—
"	25	3,0	Potent.	0,77	0,11	0,77	0,11	[3]	—
$MgNO_3^+$	25	0	Electrocon.	1,00	0	1,00	0	[1,13]	—
$PbNO_3^+$	25	2,0	Polarog., potent.	0,33	0,48	0,33	0,48	[4]	[10]
$PuNO_3^{3+}$	25	2,0	Spectr.	0,34	0,47	0,34	0,47	[5]	[11]
$SrNO_3^+$	25	0	Electrocon.	0,15	0,82	0,15	0,82	[1]	—
$ThNO_3^{3+}$	25	0,5	Distrib.	0,21	0,68	0,21	0,68	[6]	—
"	25	5,97	"	0,35	0,45	0,35	0,45	[7]	—
$Th(NO_3)_2^{2+}$	25	5,97	"	2,00	—0,30	0,71	0,15	[7]	—
$TlNO_3^{2+}$	18	3,5	Spectr.	0,66	0,18	0,66	0,18	[8]	—
$UO_2NO_3^+$	25	2,0	"	4,8	—0,68	4,8	—0,68	[9]	[12]

LITERATURE CITED

1. E. C. R i g h e l a t o, C. W. D a v i e s. Trans. Farad. Soc., **26**, 592 (1930).
2. K. B. Y a t s i m i r s k i i. Collection of Articles on General Chemistry, Acad. Sci. USSR Press, 1953, Vol. I, p. 97; D. F. S w i n e h a r t, A. B. G a r r e t t. J. Am. Chem. Soc., **73**, 507 (1951).
3. J. L e d e n. Z. Phys. Chem., Abt. A, 188, 160 (1941).
4. H. M. H e r s h e n s o n, M. E. S m i t h, D. N. H u m e. J. Am. Chem. Soc., 75, 507 (1953).
5. J. C. H i n d m a n. Chem. Abs., **44**, 3831 (1950).
6. R. A. D a y, R. W. S t o u g h t o n. J. Am. Chem. Soc., **72**, 5662 (1950).
7. E. L. Z e b r o s k i, H. W. A l t e r, F. K. N e u m a n n. J. Am. Chem. Soc., 73, 5646 (1951).
8. D. P e s c h a n s k i. Compt. rend., **238**, 2077 (1954).
9. R. B e t t s, R. C. M i c h e l s. Chem. Abs., **44**, 8745 (1950).
10. G. H. N a n c o l l a s. J. Chem. Soc., 1955, 1458
11. S. W. R a b i d e a u, J. F. L a m o n s. J. Am. Chem. Soc., **73**, 2895 (1951).
12. S. A h r l a n d. Acta chem. Scand., **5**, 1271 (1951); Chem. Abs., **47**, 1528 (1953).
13 H. W. J o n e s, C. B. M o n k, C. W. D a v i e s. J. Chem. Soc., 1949, 2693.

Selenocyanate complexes

Complex ion	Temperature, °C	Ionic strength	Method	k	pk	K	pK
Ag $(SeCN)_2^-$	25	0,3	Potent.	—	—	$2,2 \cdot 10^{-12}$	11,66
Ag $(SeCN)_3^{2-}$	25	0,3	„	$6,0 \cdot 10^{-2}$	1,22	$1,32 \cdot 10^{-13}$	12,88
Cd $(SeCN)_4^{2-}$	25	0,3	Polarog.	—	—	$2,5 \cdot 10^{-4}$	3,60
Hg $(SeCN)_3^-$	25	0,3	Potent.	—	—	$3,8 \cdot 10^{-27}$	26,42
Hg $(SeCN)_4^{2-}$	25	0,3	„	$3,4 \cdot 10^{-3}$	2,47	$1,29 \cdot 10^{-29}$	28,89

LITERATURE CITED

V. F. T o r o p o v a. J. Inorg. Chem., **1**, 243 (1956).

Pyrophosphate complexes

Complex ion	Temperature, °C	Ionic strength	Method	k	pk	K	pK	Literature main	Literature additional
$CaP_2O_7^{2-}$	19	0,02	Indic. meas. pH	$1,00\cdot10^{-5}$	5,00	$1,00\cdot10^{-5}$	5,00	[1]	[8]
$CdP_2O_7^{2-}$	—	—	Polarog.		—	$2,7\cdot10^{-6}$	5,57	[2]	[9]
$CuP_2O_7^{2-}$	25	0,1	Sol.	$2,0\cdot10^{-7}$	6,70	$2,0\cdot10^{-7}$	6,70	[3]	[10, 11]
$Cu(P_2O_7)_2^{6-}$	25	0,1	"	$5\cdot10^{-3}$	2,30	$1,0\cdot10^{-9}$	9,00	[3]	[11, 12]
$MgP_2O_7^{2-}$	19	0,02	Indic. meas. pH	$2,0\cdot10^{-6}$	5,70	$2,0\cdot10^{-6}$	5,70	[4]	—
$NiP_2O_7^{2-}$	25	0,1	Sol.	$1,5\cdot10^{-6}$	5,82	$1,5\cdot10^{-6}$	5,82	[3]	—
$Ni(P_2O_7)_2^{6-}$	25	0,1	"	$4,3\cdot10^{-2}$	1,37	$6,5\cdot10^{-8}$	7,19	[3]	—
$Pb(P_2O_7)_2^{6-}$	25	—	Electrocon.		—	$4,74\cdot10^{-2}$	5,33	[5]	[13]
$TlP_2O_7^{3-}$	35	—	Polarog.	$2,0\cdot10^{-2}$	1,69	$2,0\cdot10^{-2}$	1,69	[6]	—
$Tl(P_2O_7)_2^{7-}$	35	—	"	0,66	0,18	$1,35\cdot10^{-2}$	1,87	[6]	—
$Zn(P_2O_7)_2^{6-}$	25	—	Cryoscop. polarog.		—	$3,4\cdot10^{-7}$	6,46	[2,7]	[12]
$CeP_2O_7^{-}$	25	0,5	Ion. exch.	$7,1\cdot10^{-18}$	17,15	$7,1\cdot10^{-18}$	17,15	[14]	—

LITERATURE CITED

1. K. B. Yatsimirskii, V. P. Vasil'ev. J. Phys. Chem., **30**, 28 (1956).
2. G. Sartory. Gazz. chim. ital., **64**, 3 (1934).
3. K. B. Yatsimirskii, V. P. Vasil'ev. J. Anal. Chem., **11**, 536 (1956).*
4. V. P. Vasil'ev. J. Phys. Chem. (in press).
5. B. C. Haldar. Current Sci, 19, 244 (1950); Zbl., I, 2856 (1951).
6. P. Senise, P. Delahay. J. Am. Chem. Soc., **74**, 6128 (1952).
7. B. C. Haldar. Current Sci, 19, 283 (1950); Chem. Abs., **45**, 9415 (1951).
8. R. Gosselin, E. Coghlan. Arch. Biochem. Biophys., **45**, 301 (1953).
9. P. Souchey, J. Fencherre. Bull. Soc. chim. France, 529 (1947); Chem. Abs., **42**, 810 (1948).
10. E. Erikson. Chem. Abs., **44**, 3392 (1950).
11. J. Watters, A. A. Aaron. J. Am. Chem. Soc., **75**, 611 (1953).
12. A. I. Stabrovskii. J. Phys. Chem., **26**, 949 (1952).
13. K. B. Yatsimirskii, V. P. Vasil'ev. J. Phys. Chem., **30**, 901 (1956).
14. S. W. Mayer, S. D. Schwartz. J. Am. Chem. Soc., **72**, 5106 (1950).

Thiocyanate complexes

Complex ion	Temperature, °C	Ionic strength	Method	k	pk	K	pK	Literature main	additional
$Ag(CNS)_2^-$	25	2,2	Sol.	—	—	$2.7 \cdot 10^{-8}$	7,57	[1]	[22, 23, 24]
$Ag(CNS)_3^{2-}$	25	2,2	"	$3,1 \cdot 10^{-3}$	2,51	$8,3 \cdot 10^{-10}$	9,08	[1]	[22, 24, 25]
$Ag(CNS)_4^{3-}$	25	2,2	"	0,10	1,00	$9,3 \cdot 10^{-11}$	10,08	[1]	[24, 25]
$Au(CNS)_2^-$	Room	—	Potent.	—	—	10^{-23}	23	[2]	—
$Au(CNS)_4^-$	"	—	"	—	—	10^{-42}	42	[2]	—
$BiCNS^{2+}$	20—25	Variable	Spectr.	$7,15 \cdot 10^{-2}$	1,15	$7,15 \cdot 10^{-2}$	1,15	[3]	—
$Bi(CNS)_2^+$	20—25	"	"	$7,7 \cdot 10^{-2}$	1,11	$5,5 \cdot 10^{-3}$	2,26	[3]	—
$Bi(CNS)_4^-$	20—25	"	"	—	—	$3,93 \cdot 10^{-4}$	3,41	[3]	[26]
$Bi(CNS)_6^{3+}$	20—25	"	"	—	—	$5,93 \cdot 10^{-5}$	4,23	[3]	—
$CdCNS^+$	30	2,0	Polarog.	$9,1 \cdot 10^{-2}$	1,04	$9,1 \cdot 10^{-2}$	1,04	[4]	[22]
"	25	3,0	Potent.	$4,1 \cdot 10^{-2}$	1,39	$4,1 \cdot 10^{-2}$	1,39	[5]	—
$Cd(CNS)_2$	30	2,0	Polarog.	0,195	0,71	$1,8 \cdot 10^{-2}$	1,75	[4]	—
"	25	3,0	Potent.	0,256	0,59	$1,05 \cdot 10^{-2}$	1,98	[5]	—
$Cd(CNS)_3^-$	30	2,0	Polarog.	(9,3)	(—0,97)	(0,167)	(0,78)	[4]	[6]
"	25	3,0	Potent.	0,25	0,60	$2,6 \cdot 10^{-3}$	2,58	[5]	—
$Cd(CNS)_4^{2-}$	30	2,0	Polarog.	0,10	1,00	$1,67 \cdot 10^{-2}$	1,78	[4]	[6]

Complex ion	Temperature, °C	Ionic strength	Method	k	pk	K	pK	Literature main	Literature additional
$Cd(CNS)_6^{4-}$	25	0,5—5,0	Polarog.	—	—	(1,033)	(−0,08)	[6]	—
$CoCNS^+$	25	—	Spectr.	1,08	−0,04	1,08	−0,04	[7]	—
$Co(CNS)_2$	25	—	"	4,6	−0,66	5,0	−0,70	[7]	—
$Co(CNS)_3^-$	25	—	"	0,2	0,70	1,00	0,00	[7]	—
$Co(CNS)_4^{2-}$	25	—	"	$5 \cdot 10^{-3}$	2,30	$1,00 \cdot 10^{-3}$	3,00	[7]	—
$CrCNS^{2+}$	25	1,0	Analysis	$1,35 \cdot 10^{-2}$	1,87	$1,35 \cdot 10^{-2}$	1,87	[8]	[27]
$Cr(CNS)_2^+$	25	1,0	"	$7,7 \cdot 10^{-2}$	1,11	$1,05 \cdot 10^{-3}$	2,98	[8]	—
$Cu(CNS)_2^-$	18	3,09	Potent.	—	—	$7,83 \cdot 10^{-13}$	12,11	[9]	—
$Cu(CNS)_3^-$	18	4,2	Spectr.	—	—	$6,5 \cdot 10^{-6}$	5,18	[10]	—
$FeCNS^{2+}$	25	0,0	"	$1,12 \cdot 10^{-3}$	2,95	$1,12 \cdot 10^{-3}$	2,95	[11]	[28,29,30,31]
"	25	1,28	"	$8,7 \cdot 10^{-3}$	2,06	$8,7 \cdot 10^{-3}$	2,06	[12]	—
$Fe(CNS)_2^+$	25	1,28	"	$5,0 \cdot 10^{-2}$	1,30	$4,4 \cdot 10^{-4}$	3,36	[12]	—
$Hg(CNS)_2$	25	0,35	"	—	—	$3,4 \cdot 10^{-18}$	17,47	[13]	—
$Hg(CNS)_4^{2-}$	25	0,3	Potent.	—	—	$5,9 \cdot 10^{-22}$	21,23	[14]	[32,33]
$InCNS^{2+}$	20	2,0	"	$2,6 \cdot 10^{-3}$	2,58	$2,6 \cdot 10^{-3}$	2,58	[15]	—
$In(CNS)_2^+$	20	2,0	"	0,38	0,42	$1,0 \cdot 10^{-3}$	3,00	[15]	—
$In(CNS)_3$	20	2,0	"	$2,3 \cdot 10^{-2}$	1,63	$2,3 \cdot 10^{-5}$	4,63	[15]	—
$NiCNS^+$	20	1,5	Ion. exch.	$6,7 \cdot 10^{-2}$	1,18	$6,7 \cdot 10^{-2}$	1,18	[16]	—
$Ni(CNS)_2$	20	1,5	Ion. exch.	0,35	0,46	$2,3 \cdot 10^{-2}$	1,64	[16]	—

Complex ion	Temperature, °C	Ionic strength	Method	k	pk	K	pK	Literature main	Literature additional
Ni(CNS)$_3^-$	20	1,5	Ion. exch.	0,68	0,17	$1,55 \cdot 10^{-2}$	1,81	[16]	—
Pb(CNS)$_6^{4-}$	25	3,0—7,5	Sol.	—	—	2,0	−0,30	[17]	—
RuCNS^{2+}	25	1,0	Spectr.	$1,17 \cdot 10^{-2}$	1,78	$1,17 \cdot 10^{-2}$	1,78	[18]	—
TlCNS	25	0,0	Sol.	0,160	0,80	0,160	0,80	[19]	—
UCNS^{3+}	25	2,00	Potent.	$3,2 \cdot 10^{-2}$	1,49	$3,2 \cdot 10^{-2}$	1,49	[20]	—
U(CNS)$_2^{2+}$	25	2,00	"	0,24	0,62	$7,7 \cdot 10^{-3}$	2,11	[20]	—
UO$_2$CNS$^+$	20	0,1	Spectr.	0,174	0,76	0,174	0,76	[21]	—
UO$_2$(CNS)$_2$	20	0,1	"	1,05	−0,02	0,182	0,74	[21]	—
U'O$_2$(CNS)$_3^-$	20	0,1	"	0,36	0,44	$6,6 \cdot 10^{-2}$	1,18	[21]	!
VCNS^{2+}	25	2,6	"	10^{-2}	2,0	10^{-2}	2,0	[11]	—
VOCNS$^+$	25	2,6	"	0,12	0,92	0,12	0,92	[11]	—
ZnCNS$^+$	18	0,1	Potent.	$2,4 \cdot 10^{-2}$	1,62	$2,4 \cdot 10^{-2}$	1,62	[22]	—

LITERATURE CITED

1. G. S. Cave, D. N. Hume. J. Am. Chem. Soc., 75, 2893 (1953).
2. N. Bjerrum, A. Kirschner. Kgl. Danske Videnskab. Math. phys., V, No 1 (1918).
3. W. D. Kingery, D. N. Hume. J. Am. Chem. Soc., 71, 2393 (1949).
4. D. N. Hume, D. D. De Ford, G. S. Cave. J. Am. Chem. Soc., 73, 5323 (1951).
5. J. Leden. Z. phys. Chem., Abt. A, 188, 160 (1941).
6. I.A. Korshunov, N.I. Malyugina, O.M. Balabanova. J. Gen. Chem., 21, 620 (1951).*
7. M. Lehne. Bull. Soc. chim. France, 76 (1951); Chem. Abs., 45, 6117 (1951).
8. K. G. Poulsen, J. Bjerrum, J. Poulsen. Acta Chem. Scand., 8, 921 (1954); Chem. Abs., 49, 2926 (1955).
9. A.I. Stabrovskii. J. Phys. Chem., 26, 949 (1952).
10. M. Oudinet, F. Gallais. Compt. rend., 373 (1953); Chem. Abs., 49, 13816 (1955).
11. S. C. Furman, S. C. Garner. J. Am. Chem. Soc., 73, 4528 (1951)
12. R. H. Betts, F. S. Dainton. J. Am. Chem. Soc., 75, 5721 (1953).
13. K.B. Yatsimirskii, B.D. Tukhlov. J. Gen. Chem., 26, 356 (1956).*
14. V.F. Toropova. J. Inorg. Chem., 1, 243 (1956).
15. N. Sunden. Svensk. Kem. Tidsk., 66, 50 (1954); 18547 (1955).
16. S. Fronaeus. Acta chem. Scand., 7, 21 (1953); Chem. Abs., 47, 8582 (1953).
17. K.B. Yatsimirskii. J. Phys. Chem., 25, 475 (1951).
18. R. P. Vaffe, A. Voigt. J. Am. Chem. Soc., 74, 2500 (1952).
19. R. P. Bell, J. H. B. George. Trans. Farad. Soc., 49, 619 (1953).
20. R. A. Day, R. N. Wilhite, F. D. Hamilton. J. Am. Chem. Soc., 77, 3180 (1955).
21. S. Ahrland. Chem. Abs., 44, 5256 (1950).
22. E. Ferrell, J. M. Ridgion, H. L. Riley. J. Chem. Soc., 1121 (1936).
23. G. Bodländer, W. Eberlein. Z. anorg. Chem., 39, 197 (1904).
24. I. Leden. Z. Naturforsch., No 1, 10a (1955).
25. J. Kratohvil. cit. in V. B. Vonk, J. Kratohvil, B. Težak Arhiv. Kemi., 25, 219 (1953).
26. F.S. Frum, M.N. Skobina, Chem. Abst. J., 28666 (1954).
27. N. Bjerrum. Z. anorg. Chem., 119, 189 (1921).
28. A.K. Babko. J. Gen. Chem., 16, 1549 (1946).
29. S. M. Edmonds, N. Birnbaum. J. Am. Chem. Soc., 63, 1471 (1941).
30. H. E. Bent, C. L. French. J. Am. Chem. Soc., 63, 568 (1941).
31. H. S. Frank, R. L. Oswalt. J. Am. Chem. Soc., 69, 1321 (1947).
32. I.A. Korshunov, M.K. Shchennikova. J. Gen. Chem., 19, 1820 (1949).*
33. F. Gallais, J. Monnier. Compt. rend., 223, 790 (1946).
34. S. Ahrland, R. Larsson. Acta chem. Scand., 8, 137 (1954); Chem. Abs., 48, 11969 (1954).

Sulfate complexes

Complex ion	Temperature, °C	Ionic strength	Method	k	pk	K	pK	Literature main	Literature additional
$AgSO_4^-$	25	3,0	Potent.	0,59	0,23	0,59	0,23	[1]	—
$Ag(SO_4)_2^{3-}$	25	3,0	"	1,0	0,00	0,59	0,23	[1]	—
$CaSO_4$	25	0	Sol.	$4,9 \cdot 10^{-3}$	2,31	$4,9 \cdot 10^{-3}$	2,31	[2]	[3]
$CdSO_4$	25	0	Electrocon.	$4,9 \cdot 10^{-3}$	2,31	$4,9 \cdot 10^{-3}$	2,31	[3]	—
$CeSO_4^+$	25	3,0	Potent.	$1,41 \cdot 10^{-2}$	0,85	$1,41 \cdot 10^{-2}$	0,85	[1]	[25]
$CeSO_4^+$	25		Sol., spectr.	$4,0 \cdot 10^{-4}$	3,40	$4,0 \cdot 10^{-4}$	3,40	[4]	[9, 25]
"	25	0,5—0,9	Ion. exch.	$1,66 \cdot 10^{-2}$	1,78	$1,66 \cdot 10^{-2}$	1,78	[5]	—
$CoSO_4$	25	0	Electrocon.	$3,4 \cdot 10^{-3}$	2,47	$3,4 \cdot 10^{-3}$	2,47	[3]	—
$CuSO_4$	25	0	Electrocon.	$4,5 \cdot 10^{-3}$	2,35	$4,5 \cdot 10^{-3}$	2,35	[6]	—
"	20	1,0	Potent.	0,112	0,95	0,112	0,95	[7]	—
"	25	4,0	Spectr.	0,42	0,38	0,42	0,38	[8]	—
$ErSO_4^+$	25	0	Electrocon.	$2,6 \cdot 10^{-4}$	3,58	$2,6 \cdot 10^{-4}$	3,58	[9]	—
$FeSO_4$	25	0	Calc.	$5 \cdot 10^{-3}$	2,30	$5 \cdot 10^{-3}$	2,30	[10]	—
$FeSO_4^+$	18	0	Kinetic	$6,8 \cdot 10^{-5}$	4,17	$6,8 \cdot 10^{-5}$	4,17	[11]	—
"	18	0,066	Ion. exch.	$1,0 \cdot 10^{-3}$	3,00	$1,0 \cdot 10^{-3}$	3,00	[11]	—
$Fe(SO_4)_2^-$	28	1,0	Spectr.	$9,3 \cdot 10^{-3}$	2,03	$9,3 \cdot 10^{-3}$	2,03	[12]	—
"	28	1,0	"	0,112	0,95	$1,05 \cdot 10^{-3}$	2,98	[12]	—
$GdSO_4^+$	25	0	Electrocon.	$2,2 \cdot 10^{-4}$	3,66	$2,2 \cdot 10^{-4}$	3,66	[9]	—
HSO_4^-	25	0	"	$7,6 \cdot 10^{-2}$	1,12	$7,6 \cdot 10^{-2}$	1,12	[13]	—
$HoSO_4^+$	25	0	"	$2,6 \cdot 10^{-4}$	3,58	$2,6 \cdot 10^{-4}$	3,58	[9]	—
$InSO_4^+$	20	2,0	Potent.	$1,66 \cdot 10^{-2}$	1,78	$1,66 \cdot 10^{-2}$	1,78	[14]	[27]
$In(SO_4)_2^-$	20	2,0	"	0,79	0,10	$1,32 \cdot 10^{-2}$	1,88	[14]	—
$In(SO_4)_3^{3-}$	20	2,0	"	0,32	0,48	$4,4 \cdot 10^{-3}$	2,36	[14]	—
	25		Electrocon.	0,11	0,96	0,11	0,96	[9]	—

Complex ion	Temperature, °C	Ionic strength	Method	k	pk	K	pK	Literature main	Literature additional
$LaSO_4^+$	25	0	Sol.	$2,3\cdot10^{-4}$	3,64	$2,3\cdot10^{-4}$	3,64	[15]	[9, 43, 16]
$MgSO_4$	25	0	Potent.	$4,4\cdot10^{-3}$	2,35	$4,4\cdot10^{-3}$	2,35	[16]	[3]
$MnSO_4$	25	0	Electrocon.	$5,2\cdot10^{-3}$	2,28	$5,2\cdot10^{-3}$	2,28	[10]	—
$NaSO_4^-$	25	0	"	0,19	0,72	0,19	0,72	[13]	—
$NdSO_4^+$	25	0	"	$2,3\cdot10^{-4}$	3,64	$2,3\cdot10^{-4}$	3,64	[9]	—
$NiSO_4$	25	0	"	$4,0\cdot10^{-3}$	2,40	$4,0\cdot10^{-3}$	2,40	[3]	—
$NpSO_4^{2+}$	25	2,0	Distrib.	$3,7\cdot10^{-3}$	2,43	$3,7\cdot10^{-3}$	2,43	[17]	—
$Np(SO_4)_2$	25	2,0	"	$9,1\cdot10^{-2}$	1,04	$3,4\cdot10^{-4}$	3,47	[17]	—
$PrSO_4^+$	25	2,0	Electrocon.	$2,4\cdot10^{-4}$	3,62	$2,4\cdot10^{-4}$	3,62	[9]	—
$PuSO_4^{2+}$	25	1,0	Potent.	$2,2\cdot10^{-4}$	3,66	$2,2\cdot10^{-4}$	3,66	[18]	—
$SmSO_4^+$	25	0	Electrocon.	$2,2\cdot10^{-4}$	3,66	$2,2\cdot10^{-4}$	3,66	[9]	—
$ThSO_4^{2+}$	25	2,0	Distrib.	$4,8\cdot10^{-4}$	3,32	$4,8\cdot10^{-4}$	3,32	[19, 20]	—
$Th(SO_4)_2$	25	2,0	"	$6,6\cdot10^{-3}$	2,18	$3,2\cdot10^{-6}$	5,50	[19, 20]	—
USO_4^{2+}	25	3,5	"	$5,8\cdot10^{-4}$	3,24	$5,8\cdot10^{-4}$	3,24	[21, 22]	—
$U(SO_4)_2$	25	3,5	"	$6,6\cdot10^{-3}$	2,18	$3,8\cdot10^{-6}$	5,42	[21, 22]	—
UO_2SO_4	20	1,0	Potent.	$2,0\cdot10^{-2}$	1,70	$2,0\cdot10^{-2}$	1,70	[23]	[29]
$UO_2(SO_4)_2^{2-}$	20	1,0	"	0,178	0,75	$2,8\cdot10^{-3}$	2,55	[23]	—
$UO_2(SO_4)_3^{4-}$	20	1,0	"	0,141	0,85	$4,0\cdot10^{-4}$	3,40	[23]	—
YSO_4^+	25	0	Electrocon.	$3,4\cdot10^{-4}$	3,47	$3,4\cdot10^{-4}$	3,47	[9]	—
$YbSO_4^+$	25	0	"	$2,6\cdot10^{-4}$	3,58	$2,6\cdot10^{-4}$	3,58	[9]	—
$ZnSO_4$	25	0	"	$4,9\cdot10^{-3}$	2,31	$4,9\cdot10^{-3}$	2,31	[6]	—
$ZrSO_4^{2+}$	25	2,0	Distrib.	$1,62\cdot10^{-4}$	3,79	$1,62\cdot10^{-4}$	3,79	[24]	—
$Zr(SO_4)_2$	25	2,0	"	$1,41\ 10^{-3}$	2,85	$2,3\cdot10^{-7}$	6,64	[24]	—
$Zr(SO_4)_3^{2-}$	25	2,0	"	$7,4\cdot10^{-2}$	1,13	$1,7\cdot10^{-8}$	7,77	[24]	—

LITERATURE CITED

1. I. L e d e n. Acta Chem. Scand., 6, 97 (1952); Chem. Abs., 47, 3747 (1953).
2. R. P. B e l l, J. H. B. G e o r g e. Trans. Farad. Soc., 49, 619 (1953).
3. T. O. D e n n e y, C. B. M o n k. Trans. Farad. Soc., 47, 992 (1951).
4. T. W. N e w t o n, G. M. A r c a n d. J. Am. Chem. Soc., 75, 2449 (1953).
5. R. E. C o n n i c k, S. W. M a y e r s. J. Am. Chem. Soc., 73, 1176 (1951).
6. B. B. O w e n, R. W. G u r r y. J. Am. Chem. Soc., 60, 3074 (1938).
7. S. F r o n a e u s. Acta Chem. Scand., 4, 72 (1950); Chem. Abs., 44, 8810 (1950).
8. R. N ä s ä n e n. Suomen Kemistileht, 67, 2613 (1953); Chem. Abs., 48, 11158 (1954).
9. F. H. S p e d d i n g, S. J a f f e. J. Am. Chem. Soc., 76, 882 (1954).
10. K. B. Y a t s i m i r s k i i. J. Gen. Chem., 24, 1498 (1954).*
11. K. W. S y k e s. J. Chem. Soc., 124 (1952).
12. R. A. W h i t e k e r, N. D a v i d s o n. J. Am. Chem. Soc., 75, 3081 (1953).
13. J. L. J e n k i n s, C. B. M o n k. J. Am. Chem. Soc., 72, 2695 (1950).
14. N. S u n d e n. Svensk. Kem. Tidsk., 65, 257 (1953); Chem. Abs. J., 18546 (1955).
15. C. W. D a v i e s. J. Chem. Soc., 1930, 2421.
16. H. W. J o n e s, C. B. M o n k. Trans. Farad. Soc., 48, 929 (1952).
17. J. C. S u l l i v a n, J. C. H i n d m a n. J. Am. Chem. Soc., 76, 5931 (1954).
18. S. W. R a b i d e a u, J. F. L a m o n s. J. Am. Chem. Soc., 73, 2895 (1951).
19. R. A. W h i t e k e r, N. D a v i d s o n. J. Am. Chem. Soc., 75, 3081 (1953).
20. E. L. Z e b r o s k i, H. W. A l t e r, F. K. N e u m a n n. J. Am. Chem. Soc., 73, 5646 (1951).
21. R. H. B e t t s, R. L e i g h. Canad. J. Res., B8, 514 (1950).
22. J. C. S u l l i v a n, J. C. H i n d m a n. J. Am. Chem. Soc., 74, 6091 (1952).
23. S. A h r l a n d. Acta Chem. Scand., 5, 1151 (1951); Chem. Abs., 46, 5480 (1952).
24. R. E. C o n n i c k, W. H. M c V e y. J. Am. Chem. Soc., 71, 3182 (1949).
25. I. L e d e n. Z. phys. Chem., Abt. A, 188, 160 (1941); Chem. Abs. 48, 9251 (1954).
26. I. M. K o r e n m a n. J. Gen. Chem., 24, 1910 (1954).*
27. N. S u n d e n. Svensk. Kem. Tidsk., 66, 173 (1954); Chem. Abs., 49, 1465 (1955).
28. R. A. D a y, R. N. W i l h i t e, F. D. H a m i l t o n. J. Am. Chem. Soc., 77, 3180 (1955).
29. R. H. B e t t s, R. K. M i c h e l s. Chem. Abs., 44, 8745 (1950).

Sulfite complexes

Complex ion	Temperature, °C	Ionic strength	Method	k	pk	K	pK	Literature	
								main	additional
$AgSO_3^-$	25	2,0	Potent.	$5,0 \cdot 10^{-6}$	5,30	$5,0 \cdot 10^{-6}$	5,30	[1]	—
$Ag(SO_3)_2^{3-}$	25	2,0	"	$8,9 \cdot 10^{-3}$	2,05	$4,5 \cdot 10^{-8}$	7,35	—	[3]
$CuSO_3^-$	20	1,0	Polarog.	$3,4 \cdot 10^{-8}$	7,47	$3,4 \cdot 10^{-8}$	7,47	[1]	—
$Cu(SO_3)_2^{3-}$	20	1,0	"	$9,1 \cdot 10^{-2}$	1,04	$3,1 \cdot 10^{-9}$	8,51	[1]	—
$Cu(SO_3)_3^{5-}$	20	1,0	"	0,209	0,68	$6,5 \cdot 10^{-10}$	9,19	[1]	—
$Hg(SO_3)_2^{2-}$	18	3,0	Potent.	—	—	$2,19 \cdot 10^{-23}$	22,66	[2]	—
$Hg(SO_3)_3^{4-}$	18	3,0	"	0,78	0,11	$1,70 \cdot 10^{-23}$	22,77	[2]	—
$Hg(SO_3)_4^{6-}$	18	3,0	"	0,85	0,07	$1,45 \cdot 10^{-23}$	22,84	[2]	—

LITERATURE CITED

1. V.F. Toropova, I.A. Sirotina, V.B. Rotanova. Sci. Rep. V.I. Ul'yanov-Lenin State University, Kazan, 115, No. 3, 53 (1955).

2. V.F. Toropova, E.A. Belaya. Sci. Rep. V.I. Ul'yanov-Lenin State University, Kazan', 115, No. 3, 61 (1955).

3. E.L. Jahn, H. Stande, Z. Naturforsch., 6A, 385 (1951).

Tetrametaphosphate complexes

Complex ion	Temperature, °C	Ionic strength	Method	k	pk	K	pK	Literature
$BaP_4O_{12}^{2-}$	25	0	Electrocon.	$1,02 \cdot 10^{-5}$	4,99	$1,02 \cdot 10^{-5}$	4,99	[1]
$CaP_4O_{12}^{2-}$	25	0	"	$3,4 \cdot 10^{-6}$	5,47	$3,4 \cdot 10^{-6}$	5,47	[1]
$CuP_4O_{12}^{2-}$	30	1,0	Potent.	$7,6 \cdot 10^{-4}$	3,12	$7,6 \cdot 10^{-4}$	3,12	[2]
$Cu(P_4O_{12})_2^{6-}$	30	1,0	"	$3,0 \cdot 10^{-2}$	1,52	$2,3 \cdot 10^{-5}$	4,64	[2]
$LaP_4O_{12}^{-}$	25	0	Electrocon.	$2,2 \cdot 10^{-7}$	6,66	$2,2 \cdot 10^{-7}$	6,66	[3]
$MgP_4O_{12}^{2-}$	25	0	"	$6,8 \cdot 10^{-6}$	5,17	$6,8 \cdot 10^{-6}$	5,17	[1]
$MnP_4O_{12}^{2-}$	25	0	"	$3,3 \cdot 10^{-6}$	5,48	$3,3 \cdot 10^{-6}$	5,48	[1]
$NaP_4O_{12}^{3-}$	30	0	Potent.	0,15	0,81	0,15	0,81	[2]
$NiP_4O_{12}^{2-}$	25	0	Electrocon.	$1,12 \cdot 10^{-5}$	4,95	$1,12 \cdot 10^{-5}$	4,95	[1]
$NiP_4O_{12}^{2-}$	30	1,0	Potent.	$2,3 \cdot 10^{-3}$	2,63	$2,3 \cdot 10^{-3}$	2,63	[2]
$Ni(P_4O_{12})_2^{6-}$	30	1,0	"	0,14	0,85	$3,3 \cdot 10^{-4}$	3,48	[2]
$SrP_4O_{12}^{2-}$	25	0	Electrocon. Sol.	$7,8 \cdot 10^{-6}$	5,11	$7,8 \cdot 10^{-6}$	5,11	[4]

LITERATURE CITED

1. H. W. Jones, C. B. Monk. J. Chem. Soc., 1950, 3475.
2. R. J. Gross, J. W. Gryder. J. Am. Chem. Soc., 77, 3695 (1955).
3. C. B. Monk. J. Chem. Soc., 1952, 1317.
4. C. B. Monk. J. Chem. Soc., 1952, 1314.

Thiourea complexes

Complex ion	Temperature, °C	Ionic strength	Method	k	pk	K	pK	Literature main	Literature addit.
Ag $(CSN_2H_4)_3^+$	Room	0,01	Potent.	—	—	$7,0\cdot10^{-14}$	13,14	[1]	[7]
Bi $(CSN_2H_4)_6^{3+}$	"	1,0	Polarog.	—	—	$1,1\cdot10^{-12}$	11,94	[2]	—
Cd $(CSN_2H_4)^{2+}$	25	0,2	"	$2,63\cdot10^{-2}$	1,58	$2,63\cdot10^{-2}$	1,58	[3]	—
Cd $(CSN_2H_4)_2^{2+}$	25	0,2	"	$8,9\cdot10^{-2}$	1,05	$2,3\cdot10^{-3}$	2,63	[3]	—
Cd $(CSN_2H_4)_3^{2+}$	25	0,1	"	—	—	$1,2\cdot10^{-3}$	2,92	[4]	[8]
Cu $(CSN_2H_4)_3^{2+}$	Room	0,01—0,03	Potent.	—	—	$1,5\cdot10^{-13}$	12,82	[1]	—
Cu $(CSN_2H_4)_4^{2+}$	25	0,1	Polarog.	—	—	$4,1\cdot10^{-16}$	15,39	[5]	—
Hg $(CSN_2H_4)_2^{2+}$	25	1,0	"	—	—	$1,2\cdot10^{-22}$	21,9	[6]	—
Hg $(CSN_2H_4)_3^{2+}$	25	1,0	"	$2\cdot10^{-3}$	2,7	$3,2\cdot10^{-25}$	24,6	[6]	—
Hg $(CSN_2H_4)_4^{2+}$	Room	0,01	Potent.	—	—	$1,1\cdot10^{-28}$	27,96	[1]	—
Hg $(CSN_2H_4)_4^{2+}$	25	1,0	Polarog.	$2\cdot10^{-2}$	1,7	$3,2\cdot10^{-27}$	26,3	[6]	—
Pb $(CSN_2H_4)_3^{2+}$	25	0,1	"	—	1,7	$1,7\cdot10^{-2}$	1,77	[4]	—

LITERATURE CITED

1. A. T. Pilipenko, T. S. Lisetskaya. Ukr. Chem. J., 19, 81 (1953).
2. O. S. Fedorova. J. Gen. Chem., 24, 62 (1954).
3. C. L. Rulfs, E. R. Przybylowicz, C. E. Skinner. Anal. Chem., 26, 408 (1954).
4. O. S. Fedorova. Collection on General Chemistry, Acad. Sci. USSR Press, 1953, Vol. I, p. 206.
5. E. I. Onstott, H. A. Laitinen. J. Am. Chem. Soc., 72, 4724 (1950).
6. V. F. Toropova. J. Inorg. Chem., 1, 930 (1956).
7. F. G. Pawelka. Z. Elektrochem., 30, 180 (1924).
8. W. S. Fyfe. J. Chem. Soc., 1955, 1032.

Thiosulfate complexes

Complex ion	Temperature, °C	Ionic strength	Method	k	pk	K	pK	main	additional
								Literature	
$AgS_2O_3^-$	20	—	Potent.	$1,5 \cdot 10^{-9}$	8,82	$1,5 \cdot 10^{-9}$	8,82	[1]	—
$Ag(S_2O_3)_2^{3-}$	20	—	"	$2,3 \cdot 10^{-5}$	4,64	$3,5 \cdot 10^{-14}$	13,46	[1]	[10]
BaS_2O_3	25	0	Sol.	$4,7 \cdot 10^{-3}$	2,33	$4,7 \cdot 10^{-3}$	2,33	[2]	[11]
CaS_2O_3	25	0	"	$1,04 \cdot 10^{-2}$	1,98	$1,04 \cdot 10^{-2}$	1,98	[2]	[11]
CdS_2O_3	25	0	"	$1,21 \cdot 10^{-4}$	3,92	$1,21 \cdot 10^{-4}$	3,92	[2]	—
$Cd(S_2O_3)_2^{2-}$	18	0,11	Kinetic	$1,26 \cdot 10^{-3}$	2,90	$1,26 \cdot 10^{-7}$	2,90	[3]	—
"	25	0	"	$3,0 \cdot 10^{-3}$	2,52	$3,6 \cdot 10^{-7}$	6,44	[2]	[10]
$Cd(S_2O_3)_3^{4-}$	25	0,3—9,0	Polarog.	—	—	$4,7 \cdot 10^{-7}$	6,33	[4]	[10]
CoS_2O_8	25	0	Sol.	$9,0 \cdot 10^{-3}$	2,05	$9,0 \cdot 10^{-3}$	2,05	[2]	—
$CuS_2O_3^-$	25	2,0	Polarog., potent.	$5,4 \cdot 10^{-11}$	10,27	$5,4 \cdot 10^{-11}$	10,27	[5]	—
$Cu(S_2O_3)_2^{3-}$	25	2,0	"	$1,12 \cdot 10^{-2}$	1,95	$6,0 \cdot 10^{-13}$	12,22	[5]	[12]
$Cu(S_2O_3)_3^{5-}$	25	2,0	"	$2,4 \cdot 10^{-2}$	1,62	$1,44 \cdot 10^{-14}$	13,84	[5]	—
FeS_2O_3	6,1	0	Kinetic	$6,8 \cdot 10^{-3}$	2,17	$6,8 \cdot 10^{-3}$	2,17	[6]	—
$FeS_2O_3^+$	6,1	0,48	Spectr.	0,12	0,92	0,12	0,92	[6]	[13]
"	6,1	0	"	$5,59 \cdot 10^{-4}$	3,25	$5,59 \cdot 10^{-4}$	3,25	[6]	—
"	6,1	0,47	"	$2,55 \cdot 10^{-2}$	1,59	$2,55 \cdot 10^{-2}$	1,59	[6]	—
"	25	0,47	"	$7,9 \cdot 10^{-3}$	2,10	$7,9 \cdot 10^{-3}$	2,10	[6]	—
$Hg(S_2O_3)_2^{2-}$	25	0	Potent.	—	—	$3,6 \cdot 10^{-30}$	29,44	[7]	—
$Hg(S_2O_3)_3^{4-}$	25	0	"	$3,5 \cdot 10^{-3}$	2,45	$1,26 \cdot 10^{-32}$	31,90	[7]	—

Complex ion	Temperature, °C	Ionic strength	Method	k	pk	K	pK	Literature main	Literature additional
$Hg(S_2O_3)_4^{6-}$	25	0	Potent.	$4,6 \cdot 10^{-2}$	1,34	$2,8 \cdot 10^{-34}$	33,24	[7]	—
$KS_2O_3^-$	25	0	Sol.	0,12	0,92	0,12	0,92	[2]	—
MgS_2O_3	25	0	"	$1,45 \cdot 10^{-2}$	1,84	$1,45 \cdot 10^{-2}$	1,84	[2]	—
MnS_2O_3	25	0	"	$1,12 \cdot 10^{-2}$	1,95	$1,12 \cdot 10^{-2}$	1,95	[2]	—
$NaS_2O_3^-$	25	0	"	**0,21**	0,68	0,21	0,68	[2]	—
NiS_2O_3	25	0	"	$8,7 \cdot 10^{-3}$	2,06	$8,7 \cdot 10^{-3}$	2,06	[2]	—
$Pb(S_2O_3)_2^{2-}$	25	0,07—0,75	"	$7,41 \cdot 10^{-6}$	5,13	$7,41 \cdot 10^{-6}$	5,13	[8]	—
$Pb(S_2O_3)_3^{4-}$	25	0,07—0,75	"	$6,0 \cdot 10^{-22}$	1,22	$4,48 \cdot 10^{-7}$	6,35	[8]	—
SrS_2O_3	25	0	"	$9,2 \cdot 10^{-3}$	2,04	$9,2 \cdot 10^{-3}$	2,04	[2]	—
$TlS_2O_3^-$	Room	0,1—0,2	Polarog.	$1,23 \cdot 10^{-2}$	1,91	$1,23 \cdot 10^{-2}$	1,91	[9]	—
ZnS_2O_3	25	0	"	$4,0 \cdot 10^{-3}$	2,40	$4,0 \cdot 10^{-3}$	2,40	[2]	[10]

LITERATURE CITED

1. H. Chateau, J. Pouradier. Compt. rend, 240, 1882 (1955).
2. T.O. Denney, C. B. Monk. Trans. Farad. Soc., 47, 992 (1951).
3. K.B. Yatsimirskii. J. Anal. Chem., 6, 344 (1955).*
4. A.G. Stromberg, I.E. Bykov. J. Gen. Chem., 19, 245 (1949).*
5. V.F. Toropova, I.A. Sirotina, T.I. Lisova. Sci. Rep. V.I. Ul'yanov-Lenin State University, Kazan', 115, No. 3, 43 (1955).
6. F.M. Page. Trans. Farad. Soc., 50, 120 (1954).
7. V.F. Toropova. J. Gen. Chem., 24, 423 (1954).*
8. K.B. Yatsimirskii. J. Phys. Chem., 25, 475 (1951).
9. M.S. Novakovskii, T.M. Shmaeva. Ukr. Chem.J., 20, 615 (1954).
10. E. Ferell, J. M. Ridgion, H. L. Riley, J. Chem. Soc., 1936, 1121.
11. C. W. Davies, P. A. H. Wyatt. Trans. Farad. Soc., 45, 770 (1949).
12. A.I. Stabrovskii. J. Phys. Chem., 26, 949 (1952).
13. B.C. Haldar, S. Banerjee. Chem. Abs., 43, 6536 (1949).

127

Trimetaphosphate complexes

Complex ion	Temperature, °C	Ionic strength	Method	k	pk	K	pK	Literature
$BaP_3O_9^-$	25	0	Electrocon.	$5,6 \cdot 10^{-4}$	3,25	$5,6 \cdot 10^{-4}$	3,25	[1]
$CaP_3O_9^-$	25	0	Sol.	$3,4 \cdot 10^{-4}$	3,47	$3,4 \cdot 10^{-4}$	3,47	[1,2]
LaP_3O_9	25	0	Electrocon.	$2,0 \cdot 10^{-6}$	5,70	$2,0 \cdot 10^{-6}$	5,70	[3]
$MgP_3O_9^-$	25	0	Electrocon.	$3,9 \cdot 10^{-4}$	3,31	$3,9 \cdot 10^{-4}$	3,31	[1,2]
$MnP_3O_9^-$	25	0	»	$2,8 \cdot 10^{-4}$	3,56	$2,8 \cdot 10^{-4}$	3,56	[1]
$NaP_3O_9^{2-}$	25	0	Sol.	$6,8 \cdot 10^{-2}$	1,17	$6,8 \cdot 10^{-2}$	1,17	[2]
$NiP_3O_9^-$	25	0	Electrocon.	$6,0 \cdot 10^{-4}$	3,22	$6,0 \cdot 10^{-4}$	3,22	[1]
$SrP_3O_9^-$	25	0	Sol.\nElectrocon.	$3,5 \cdot 10^{-4}$	3,35	$3,5 \cdot 10^{-4}$	3,35	[4]

LITERATURE CITED

1. W. H. Jones, C. B. Monk, C. W. Davies. J. Chem. Soc., 1949, 2693.
2. C. W. Davies, C. B. Monk. J. Chem. Soc., 1949, 413.
3. C. B. Monk. J. Chem. Soc., 1952, 1317.
4. C. B. Monk. J. Chem. Soc., 1952, 1314.

Phosphate complexes

Complex ion	Temperature, °C	Ionic strength	Method	k	pk	K	pK	Literature
$CaHPO_4$	Room	0	Potent.	$4,0 \cdot 10^{-3}$	2,40	$4,0 \cdot 10^{-3}$	2,40	[1]
$FeHPO_4^+$	30	0,665	Spectr.	$3,5 \cdot 10^{-10}$	9,35	$3,5 \cdot 10^{-10}$	9,35	[2]
$MgHPO_4$	Room	0	Potent.	$3,2 \cdot 10^{-3}$	2,50	$3,2 \cdot 10^{-3}$	2,50	[1]
$ThH_3PO_4^{4+}$	25	2,0	Distrib.	$1,29 \cdot 10^{-2}$	1,89	$1,29 \cdot 10^{-2}$	1,89	[3]
$ThH_2PO_4^{3+}$	25	2,0	,,	$5,0 \cdot 10^{-5}$	4,30	$5,0 \cdot 10^{-5}$	4,30	[3]
$Th(H_2PO_4)_2^{2+}$	25	2,0	,,	$1,41 \cdot 10^{-4}$	3,85	$7,1 \cdot 10^{-9}$	8,15	[3]

LITERATURE CITED

1. I. Greenwald, J. Redish, A. C. Kibrick, J. Biol. Chem., 135, 65 (1940); Chem. Abs., 34, 7703 (1940).
2. O. E. Lanford, S. J. Kiehl, J. Am. Chem. Soc., 64, 291 (1942); Chem. Abs., 36, 1836 (1942).
3. E. L. Zebroski, H. W. Alter, F. K. Neumann, J. Am. Chem. Soc., 73, 5646 (1951).

Fluoride complexes

Complex ion	Temperature, °C	Ionic strength	Method	k	pk	K	pK	Literature main	Literature additional
AlF^{2+}	25	0,53	Potent	$7,4 \cdot 10^{-7}$	6,13	$7,4 \cdot 10^{-7}$	6,13	[1]	[15]
AlF_2^+	25	0,53	"	$9,5 \cdot 10^{-6}$	5,02	$7,1 \cdot 10^{-12}$	11,15	[1]	—
AlF_3	25	0,53	"	$1,4 \cdot 10^{-4}$	3,85	$1,0 \cdot 10^{-15}$	15,00	[1]	—
AlF_4^-	25	0,53	"	$1,8 \cdot 10^{-3}$	2,75	$1,8 \cdot 10^{-18}$	17,75	[1]	—
AlF_5^{2-}	25	0,53	"	$2,4 \cdot 10^{-2}$	1,62	$4,3 \cdot 10^{-20}$	19,37	[1]	—
AlF_6^{3-}	25	0,53	"	$3,4 \cdot 10^{-1}$	0,47	$1,44 \cdot 10^{-20}$	19,84	[1]	—
BeF^+	25	0,01 — 6	Sol.	$5,1 \cdot 10^{-5}$	4,29	$5,1 \cdot 10^{-5}$	4,29	[2]	[10, 16]
BeF_2	25	0,01 — 6	"	$1,0 \cdot 10^{-2}$	2,00	$5,1 \cdot 10^{-7}$	6,29	[2]	—
CeF^{2+}	25	0	Potent.	$6,3 \cdot 10^{-4}$	3,20	$6,3 \cdot 10^{-4}$	3,20	[3]	[17]
CrF^{2+}	25	0,5	Spectr.	$3,9 \cdot 10^{-5}$	4,41	$3,9 \cdot 10^{-5}$	4,41	[4]	—
CrF_2^+	25	0,5	"	$4,0 \cdot 10^{-4}$	3,40	$1,5 \cdot 10^{-8}$	7,81	[4]	—
CrF_3	25	0,5	"	$3,3 \cdot 10^{-3}$	2,48	$5,1 \cdot 10^{-11}$	10,29	[4]	—
FeF^{2+}	25	0,5	Potent.	$5,2 \cdot 10^{-6}$	5,28	$5,2 \cdot 10^{-6}$	5,28	[5]	[17, 18, 19]
FeF_2^+	25	0,5	"	$9,5 \cdot 10^{-5}$	4,02	$5,0 \cdot 10^{-10}$	9,30	[5]	[18]
FeF_3	25	0,5	"	$1,7 \cdot 10^{-3}$	2,76	$8,7 \cdot 10^{-13}$	12,06	[5]	—
GaF^{2+}	25	0,5	Spectr.	$8,34 \cdot 10^{-6}$	5,08	$8,34 \cdot 10^{-6}$	5,08	[4]	—
GdF^{2+}	25	0,5	Potent.	$3,5 \cdot 10^{-4}$	3,46	$3,5 \cdot 10^{-4}$	3,46	[3]	—
HF	25	0	"	$1,0 \cdot 10^{-3}$	3,0	$1,0 \cdot 10^{-3}$	3,0	[10]	—
InF^{2+}	20	1,0	"	$2,0 \cdot 10^{-4}$	3,70	$2,0 \cdot 10^{-4}$	3,70	[6]	[20, 21]
InF_2^+	20	1,0	"	$2,8 \cdot 10^{-3}$	2,55	$5,6 \cdot 10^{-7}$	6,25	[6]	[21, 22]
InF_3	20	1,0	"	$4,5 \cdot 10^{-3}$	2,35	$2,5 \cdot 10^{-9}$	8,60	[6]	[21]
InF_4^-	20	1,0	"	$7,9 \cdot 10^{-2}$	1,10	$2,0 \cdot 10^{-10}$	9,70	[6]	—

Complex ion	Temperature, °C	Ionic strength	Method	h	pk	K	pK	Literature	
								main	additional
LaF^{2+}	25	0,0	Potent.	$1,7\cdot10^{-3}$	2,77	$1,7\cdot10^{-3}$	2,77	[3]	—
MgF^{+}	25	0,5	"	$5,0\cdot10^{-2}$	1,30	$5,0\cdot10^{-2}$	1,30	[7]	—
MnF^{2+}	25,2	2,0	Kinetic	$3,3\cdot10^{-6}$	5,48	$3,3\cdot10^{-6}$	5,48	[8]	—
PuF^{3+}	25	2,0	Potent.	$1,7\cdot10^{-7}$	6,77	$1,7\cdot10^{-7}$	6,77	[9]	—
ScF_6^{3-}	—	—	—	—	—	$5\cdot10^{-18}$	17,3	[10]	—
ThF^{3+}	25	0,5	Potent.	$2,2\cdot10^{-8}$	7,65	$2,2\cdot10^{-8}$	7,65	[5]	[22, 23]
ThF_2^{2+}	25	0,5	"	$1,5\cdot10^{-6}$	5,81	$3,5\cdot10^{-14}$	13,46	[5]	[22, 23]
ThF_3^{+}	25	0,5	Spectr.	$3,1\cdot10^{-5}$	4,51	$1,1\cdot10^{-16}$	17,97	[5]	—
$TiOF^{+}$	18	0,1	Sol.	$3,6\cdot10^{-7}$	6,44	$3,6\cdot10^{-7}$	6,44	[11]	—
TlF	25	0,0	Potent.	$0,8$	0,1	$0,8$	0,1	[12]	—
UO_2F^{+}	20	—	"	$2,6\cdot10^{-5}$	4,59	$2,6\cdot10^{-5}$	4,59	[13]	—
UO_2F_2	20	—	"	$4,6\cdot10^{-4}$	3,34	$1,2\cdot10^{-8}$	7,93	[13]	—
$UO_2F_3^{-}$	20	—	"	$2,9\cdot10^{-3}$	2,54	$3,4\cdot10^{-11}$	10,47	[13]	—
$UO_2F_4^{2-}$	20	—	Distrib.	$4,3\;10^{-2}$	1,37	$1,4\cdot10^{-2}$	11,84	[13]	—
ZrF^{3+}	25	2,0	"	$1,6\cdot10^{-9}$	8,80	$1,6\cdot10^{-9}$	8,80	[14]	—
ZrF_2^{2+}	25	2,0	"	$4,8\cdot10^{-8}$	7,32	$7,6\cdot10^{-17}$	16,12	[14]	—
ZrF_3^{+}	25	2,0	"	$1,5\cdot10^{-6}$	5,82	$1,2\cdot10^{-22}$	24,94	[14]	—

131

LITERATURE CITED

1. C. Brosset, J. Orring. Svensk. Kem. Tidsk., 55, 101 (1943); Chem. Abs., 37, 24 (1945).
2. I.V. Tananaev, E.N. Deichman. Bull. Acad. Sci. USSR, Div. Chem. Sci., 144 (1949).
3. J. W. Kury. Chem. Abs., 48, 3833 (1954).
4. A. S. Wilson, H. Taube. J. Am. Chem. Soc., 74, 3509 (1952).
5. H. W. Dodgen, G. K. Rollefson. J. Am. Chem. Soc., 71, 2600 (1949).
6. N. Sunden. Svensk. Kem. Tidsk., 66, 50 (1954); Chem. Abst. J., 18547 (1955).
7. R. E. Connick, Maak-Sang Tsao. J. Am. Chem. Soc., 76, 5311 (1954).
8. H. Taube. J. Am. Chem. Soc., 70, 3928 (1948).
9. C. K. Mc Lane. Chem. Abs., 44. 3831 (1950).
10. W.M. Latimer. Oxidation States of Elements and their Potentials in Aqueous Solutions. Foreign Lit. Press, 1954. [Russian translation].
11. K.E. Kleiner. J. Gen. Chem., 22, 17 (1952).*
12. R. P. Bell, J. H. B. George. Trans. Farad. Soc., 49, 619 (1953).
13. S. Ahrland, R. Larsson. Acta Chem. Scand., 8, 354 (1954); Chem. Abs., 48, 11970 (1954).
14. R. E. Connick, W. H. Mc Vev. J. Am. Chem. Soc., 71, 3182 (1949).
15. K.E. Kleiner. J. Gen. Chem., 20, 1747 (1950).*
16. K.E. Kleiner. J. Gen. Chem., 21, 18 (1951).*
17. S. W. Mayer, S. D. Schwartz. J. Am. Chem. Soc., 73, 390 (1951).
18. A.K. Babko, K.E. Kleiner. J. Gen. Chem., 17, 1259 (1947).
19. C. Brosset. Chem. Abs., 37, 24 (1943).
20. G. Saini. Gazz. Chim. ital., 83, 677 (1953); Chem. Abs., 48, 6899 (1954).
21. L. G. Hepler, J. W. Kury, Z. Z. Hugus. J. phys. Chem., 58, 26 (1954).
22. J. A. Schufle, H. M. Eiland. J. Am. Chem. Soc., 76, 960 (1954).
23. R. A. Day, R. W. Stoughton. J. Am. Chem. Soc., 72, 5662 (1950).
24. E. L. Zebroski, H. W. Alter, F. K. Neuman. J. Am. Chem. Soc., 73, 5646 (1951).

Chlorate complexes

Complex ion	Temperature, °C	Ionic strength	Method	k	pk	K	pK	Literature
$BaClO_3^+$	25	0	Electrocon.	0,20	0,70	0,20	0,70	[1]
$ThClO_3^{3+}$	25	0,5	Distrib.	0,55	0,26	0,55	0,26	[2]

LITERATURE CITED

1. T. Macdougall, C. W. Davies. J. Chem. Soc., 1935, 1416.
2. R. A. Day, R. W. Stoughton. J. Am. Chem. Soc., 72, 5662 (1950).

Chloride complexes

Complex ion	Temperature, °C	Ionic strength	Method	k	pk	K	pK	Literature main	Literature additional
Ag_2Cl^+	Room	—	Sol.	—	—	$2 \cdot 10^{-7}$	6,70	[1]	[33]
$AgCl$	25	0,0	»	$2,04 \cdot 10^{-9}$	2,69	$2,04 \cdot 10^{-3}$	2,69	[2]	[3,33]
$AgCl_2^-$	25	0,0	»	$8,7 \cdot 10^{-8}$	2,06	$1,76 \cdot 10^{-5}$	4,75	[2]	[34,35,36]
$AgCl_3^{2-}$	25	5,0	Potent.	—	—	$4,0 \cdot 10^{-6}$	5,40	[3]	[37]
$AgCl_4^{3-}$	25	0,0	Sol.	—	—	$1,2 \cdot 10^{-6}$	5,92	[4]	[38]
»	25	5,0	Potent.	1,2	−0,08	$4,8 \cdot 10^{-6}$	5,32	[3]	[37]
$AuCl_4^-$	25	—	»	—	—	$5 \cdot 10^{-22}$	21,30	[5]	—
$BiCl^{2+}$	25	1,0—2,0	Раств	$3,6 \cdot 10^{-3}$	2,44	$3,6 \cdot 10^{-3}$	2,44	[6]	[39]
$BiCl_2^+$	25	1,0—2,0	»	0,22	0,66	$7,9 \cdot 10^{-4}$	3,10	[6]	[39]
$BiCl_3$	25	1,0—2,0	»	0,23	0,64	$1,8 \cdot 10^{-4}$	3,74	[6]	[39]
$BiCl_4^-$	25	1,0—2,0	»	0,94	0,03	$1,7 \cdot 10^{-4}$	3,77	[6]	[7,39]
$BiCl_5^{2-}$	18	2,5	Potent.	—	—	$(2 \cdot 10^{-6})$	(5,7)	[7]	—
$BiCl_6^{3-}$	18	1,6	»	—	—	$(3,8 \cdot 10^{-7})$	(6,4)	[7]	—
$CdCl^+$	25	1,0	»	$4,5 \cdot 10^{-2}$	1,35	$4,5 \cdot 10^{-2}$	1,35	[8]	[11,40,41]
»	25	3,0	Polarog.	$2,86 \cdot 10^{-2}$	1,54	$2,86 \cdot 10^{-2}$	1,54	[9]	[42]
$CdCl_2$	25	1,0	Potent.	$3,7 \cdot 10^{-1}$	0,43	$1,67 \cdot 10^{-2}$	1,78	[8]	[11,40,41]
»	25	3,0	Polarog.	$3,0 \cdot 10^{-1}$	0,52	$8,71 \cdot 10^{-3}$	2,06	[9]	[42]
$CdCl_3^-$	25	3,0	Polarog.	0,41	0,40	$3,40 \cdot 10^{-3}$	2,46	[9]	[40,41,42,43]
$CdCl_4^{2-}$	18	1,0—1,6	Sol.	—	—	$(9,3 \cdot 10^{-3})$	(2,0)	[10]	[41,42,43]
$CdCl_6^{4-}$	25	0,0	Polarog.	—	—	$(3,8 \cdot 10^{-3})$	(2,58)	[11]	[43]

Complex ion	Temperature, °C	Ionic strength	Method	k	pk	K	pK	Literature main	Literature additional
$CeCl^{2+}$	18	0,0	Ion. exch.	0,33	0,48	0,33	0,48	[12]	—
$CrCl_2^+$	Room	0,0	Electrocon.	—	—	$1,26 \cdot 10^{-2}$	1,90	[13]	[44]
$CuCl_3^{2-}$	18	0,67	Potent.	—	—	$5,01 \cdot 10^{-6}$	5,30	[14]	[23, 45]
$CuCl^+$	25,2	1,0	Spectr.	0,77	0,11	0,77	0,11	[15]	[46—51]
$CuCl_2$	25,2	1,0	"	4,3	-0,63	3,3	-0,52	[15]	[46—48, 51]
$FeCl^{2+}$	25	0,0	"	$3,3 \cdot 10^{-2}$	1,48	$3,3 \cdot 10^{-2}$	1,48	[16]	[52]
"	26,7	1,0	"	0,24	0,62	0,24	0,62	[16]	[53, 54]
"	20	2,0	"	0,175	0,76	0,175	0,76	[17]	—
$FeCl_2^+$	25	0,0	"	0,22	0,65	$7,4 \cdot 10^{-3}$	2,13	[6]	—
"	26,7	1,0	"	0,76	0,12	$1,8 \cdot 10^{-1}$	0,74	[16]	—
"	20	2,0	"	0,50	0,30	$8,7 \cdot 10^{-2}$	1,06	[17]	[17]
$FeCl_3$	25	0,0	"	10	-1,00	$7,4 \cdot 10^{-2}$	1,13	[16]	[17]
"	26,7	1,0	"	25	-1,40	4,6	-0,66	[16]	—
$GaCl^{2+}$	—	0,5	—	1	0	1	0	[18]	—
$HgCl^+$	25	0,5	Potent.	$5,4 \cdot 10^{-6}$	5,27	$5,4 \cdot 10^{-6}$	5,27	[19]	[55]
$H Cl_2$	25	0,5	"	$3,1 \cdot 10^{-8}$	7,54	$1,7 \cdot 10^{-18}$	12,78	[19]	[55, 56]
$HgCl_3^-$	25	0,5	"	$7,2 \cdot 10^{-2}$	1,14	$1,2 \cdot 10^{-14}$	13,92	[19]	[55, 57]
$HgCl_4^{2-}$	25	0,5	"	0,10	1,0	$1,2 \cdot 10^{-15}$	14,92	[19]	[56]
$InCl^{2+}$	25	1,0	Ion. exch.	$3,8 \cdot 10^{-2}$	1,42	$3,8 \cdot 10^{-2}$	1,42	[20]	[58]
$InCl_2^+$	25	1,0	"	0,15	0,81	$5,9 \cdot 10^{-3}$	2,23	[20]	[58]
$InCl_3$	25	1,0	"	0,10	1,00	$5,9 \cdot 10^{-4}$	3,23	[20]	—
$MnCl^{2+}$	25,2	2,0	Kinetic	0,11	0,96	0,11	0,96	[21]	—
$PbCl^+$	25	0,0	Polarog.	$2,3 \cdot 10^{-2}$	1,64	$2,3 \cdot 10^{-2}$	1,64	[11]	[59, 60, 67]

Complex ion	Temperature, °C	Ionic strength	Method	k	pk	K	pK	Literature main	Literature additional
$PbCl_3^-$	25	0,0	Polarog.	—	—	$1,4 \cdot 10^{-2}$	1,85	[11]	[43]
$PdCl_4^{2-}$	25	1,0—4,0	Potent.	—	—	$6 \cdot 10^{-14}$	13,22	[22]	[23]
$PtCl_4^{2-}$	—	—	"	—	—	10^{-16}	16	[23]	—
$PuCl_4^{3+}$	25	2,00	Spectr.	2,5	—0,40	2,5	—0,40	[24]	[61,62]
$SnCl^+$	25	3,00	Potent.	$8,9 \cdot 10^{-2}$	1,05	$8,9 \cdot 10^{-2}$	1,05	[25]	[62]
$SnCl_2$	25	3,0	"	0,22	0,65	$2,0 \cdot 10^{-2}$	1,70	[25]	[62]
$SnCl_3^-$	25	3,0	"	1,05	0,02	$2,1 \cdot 10^{-2}$	1,68	[25]	[62]
$ThCl^{3+}$	25	0,5	Distrib.	0,57	0,25	0,57	0,25	[26]	—
"	25	4,0	"	0,77	0,12	0,77	0,12	[27]	[63]
$ThCl_2^{2+}$	25	4,0	Distrib.	10,5	—1,02	8,00	—0,90	[27]	[63]
$ThCl_3^+$	25	4,0	"	3,4	—0,53	27	—1,43	[27]	[63]
$ThCl_4$	25	4,0	"	2,6	—0,42	71	—1,85	[27]	[63]
$TlCl$	25	0,0	Sol.	0,21	0,68	0,21	0,68	[28]	[67]
$TlCl^{2+}$	25	0,1—0,2	Potent.	$8,0 \cdot 10^{-9}$	8,1	$8,0 \cdot 10^{-9}$	8,10	[29]	—
$TlCl_2^+$	25	0,1—0,2	"	$3,2 \cdot 10^{-6}$	5,5	$2,5 \cdot 10^{-11}$	13,60	[29]	—
$TlCl_8$	25	0,1—0,2	"	$6,3 \cdot 10^{-3}$	2,2	$1,6 \cdot 10^{-16}$	15,80	[29]	—
$TlCl_4^-$	25	0,1—0,2	"	$2,5 \cdot 10^{-3}$	2,6	$4 \cdot 10^{-19}$	18,40	[29]	—
UCl^{3+}	25	0,0	Spectr.	0,143	0,85	0,143	0,85	[30]	[65]
"	25	0,5	"	1,6	—0,20	1,6	—0,20	[30]	[67]
UO_2Cl^+	20	—	Potent.ⁱ	2,0	—0,30	2,0	—0,30	[31]	—
$ZnCl^+$	25	3,0	"	1,54	—0,19	1,54	—0,19	[32]	[68]
$ZnCl_2$	25	3,0	"	2,6	—0,41	4,00	—0,60	[32]	—
$ZnCl_3^-$	25	3,0	"	0,18	0,75	0,71	0,15	[32]	—

LITERATURE CITED

1. K.B. Yatsimirskii. Proc. Acad. Sci. USSR, 77, 819 (1951); K. Hellwig. Z. anorg. Chem., 25, 157 (1900).
2. J. H. Jonte, D. S. Martin. J. Am. Chem. Soc., 74, 2052 (1952).
3. E. Berne, I. Leden. Svensk. Kem. Tidsk., 65, 88 (1953); Chem. Abs., 47, 10392 (1953).
4. W. Erber, A. Schüly. Chem. Abs., 35, 7801 (1941); J. prakt. Chem., 158, 176 (1941).
5. N. Bjerrum, A. Kirschner. Kgl. Danske Videnskab., V, N I (1918).
6. K.B. Yatsimirskii. Collection of Articles on General Chemistry, Acad. Sci. USSR Press, 1953, Vol. I, p. 97.
7. A.K. Babko, A.M. Golub. Collection of Articles on General Chemistry, Acad. Sci. USSR Press, 1953, Vol. I, p. 64.
8. C. E. Vanderzee, H. J. Dawson. J. Am. Chem. Soc., 75, 5659 (1953).
9. L. Eriksson. Acta Chem. Scand., 7, 1146 (1953); Chem. Abs., 48, 13366 (1954).
10. I.M. Korenman. J. Gen. Chem., 18, 1233 (1948).
11. A.M. Vasil'ev, V.I. Proukhina. J. Anal. Chem., 6, 218 (1951).
12. S. W. Mayer, S. D. Schwartz. J. Am. Chem. Soc., 73, 222 (1951).
13. A. B. Lamb, G. R. Fonda. J. Am. Chem. Soc., 43, 1155 (1921).
14. A.I. Stabrovskii. J. Phys. Chem., 26, 949 (1952).
15. H. Mc Connell, N. Davidson. J. Am. Chem. Soc., 72, 3164 (1950).
16. E. Rabinowitch, W. Stockmayer. J. Am. Chem. Soc., 64, 335 (1942).
17. G. A. Gamlen, D. O. Jordan. J. Chem. Soc., 1953, 1435.
18. H. Taube, A.S. Wilson. Cited in W.M. Latimer's book "Oxidation States of Elements and their Potentials in Aqueous Solutions." Foreign Lit. Press, 1954. [Russian translation].
19. A. Johnson, J. Quarfort, L. G. Sillen. Chem. Abs., 42, 2161 (1948).
20. J. A. Schuffe, H. M. Eiland. J. Am. Chem. Soc., 76, 960 (1954).
21. H. Taube. J. Am. Chem. Soc., 70, 3928 (1948).
22. D. H. Templeton, G. W. Watt, C. S. Garner. J. Am. Chem. Soc., 65, 1608 (1943).
23. W.M. Latimer. Oxidation States of Elements and their Potentials in Aqueous Solutions. Foreign Lit. Press, 1954. [Russian translation].
24. J. C. Hindman. Chem. Abs., 44, 3831 (1950).
25. C. E. Vanderzee, D. E. Rhodes. J. Am. Chem. Soc., 74, 3552 (1952).
26. R. A. Day, R. W. Stoughton. J. Am. Chem. Soc., 72, 5662 (1950).
27. E. L. Zebroski, H. W. Alter, F. K. Neumann. J. Am. Chem. Soc., 73, 5646 (1951).
28. R. P. Bell, J. H. B. George. Trans. Farad. Soc., 49, 619 (1953).
29. R. Benoit. Bull. Soc. Chim. France, 518 (1949); Chem. Abs., 43, 8939 (1949).

30. K. A. Kraus, F. Nelson. J. Am. Chem. Soc., **72**, 3901 (1950).

31. S. Ahrland. Chem. Abs., **47**, 1528 (1953).

32. L. G. Sillen, B. Liljeqvist. Chem. Abs., **40**, 4588 (1946).

33. A. Pinkus, S. Frederik, R. Schepmans. Bull. Soc. Chim. Belges, 47, 304 (1937); Zbl., II, 1382 (1938).

34. I. M. Korenman. J. Gen. Chem., **16**, 157 (1946).

35. J. E. Barney, W. J. Argersinger, C. A. Reynolds. J. Am. Chem. Soc., **73**, 3785 (1951).

36. G. S. Forbes. J. Am. Chem. Soc., **33**, 1937 (1911).

37. I. Leden. Svensk. Kem. Tidskr., **64**, 249 (1952); Chem. Abs., **48**, 3114 (1954).

38. G. Bodländer, W. Eberlein. Z. anorg. Chem., **39**, 197 (1904).

39. A. K. Babko. Sci. Rep KDU, **4**, 81 (1939).

40. E. L. King. J. Am. Chem. Soc., **71**, 319 (1949).

41. H. L. Riley, V. Gallafent. J. Chem. Soc., 514 (1932).

42. I. Leden. Z. Phys. Chem., Abt. A, **188**, 160 (1941).

43. I. A. Korshunov, N. I. Malyugina, O. M. Balabanova. J. Gen. Chem., **21**, 620 (1951).*

44. S. G. Shuttleworth. J. Soc. Leather Trades Chemists, **38**, 110 (1954); Chem. Abst. J., 23513 (1955).

45. A. A. Noyes, M. J. Show. J. Am. Chem. Soc., **40**, 739 (1948).

46. J. Bjerrum. Kgl. Dansk. Vidensk. Selskab., No 18, 22 (1946).

47. A. K. Babko. Sci. Rep. KDU, **4**, 81 (1939).

48. H. L. Riley, H. C. Smith. J. Chem. Soc., 1448. (1934).

49. C. B. Monk. Trans. Farad. Soc., **47**, 285 (1951).

50. R. Nasanen. Suom. Kem. B **26**, 37 (1953); Chem. Abst. J., 11487 (1955).

51. R Kruh. J. Am. Chem. Soc., **76**, 4865 (1954).

52. W. C. Bray, A. V. Hershey. J. Am. Chem. Soc., **56**, 1889 (1931).

53. C. Brosset. Svensk. Kem. Tidsk., **53**, 434 (1941).

54. J. Badoz-Lambling. Bull. Soc. Chim. France, 552 (1950).

55. H. Morze. Z. Phys. Chem., **41**, 709 (1902).

56. M. S. Scherill. Z. Phys. Chem., **43**, 705 (1903); **47**, 103 (1904).

57. D. Peschanski. J. Chim. phys., **50**, 640 (1953); Chem. Abs., **48**, 4939 (1954).

58. N. Sunden. Svensk. Kem. Tidsk., **66**, 20 (1954); **66**, 173 (1954); Chem. Abs., **48**, 9252 (1954); **49**, 1465 (1955).

59. M. Cavigli. Chem. Abs., **46**, 3832 (1952).

60. H. Fromherz. Z. phys. Chem., **153**, 382 (1931).

61. F. R. Duke, R. C. Pinkerton. J. Am. Chem. Soc., **73**, 3045 (1951)

62. F. R. Duke, W. G. Courtenay. cit. in J. Am. Chem. Soc., **74**, 3552 (1952).

63. W. C. Waggener, R. W. Stoughton. J. phys. Chem., **56**, 1 (1952).

64. Kuo-Hao Hu, A. B. Scott. J. Am. Chem. Soc., **77**, 1380 (1955).

65. S. Ahrland, R. Larsson Acta Chem. Scand.; 8, 137 (1954); Chem. Abs., **48**, 11969 (1954).

66. R. A. Day, R. N. Wilhite, F. D. Hamilton. J. Am. Chem. Soc., **77**, 3180 (1955).

67. G. H. Nancollas. J. Chem. Soc., 1955, 1458.

68. E. Ferrell. J. Chem. Soc., 1936, 1124.

Cyanide complexes

Complex ion	Temperature, °C	Ionic strength	Method	k	pk	K	pK	Literature main	Literature additional
$Ag(CN)_2^-$	18°	0,3	Potent.	—	—	$8 \cdot 10^{-22}$	21,1	[1]	[4,10,11[
$Ag(CN)_3^{2-}$	25	0,1—1	Spectr.	0,113	0,95	—	—	[2]	[10]
"	25	0	"	0,20	0,70	$1,6 \cdot 10^{-22}$	21,8	[2]	—
$Ag(CN)_4^{3-}$	25	0,1—1	"	3,18	—0,50	—	—	[2]	—
"	25	0	"	13,4	—1,13	$2,1 \cdot 10^{-21}$	20,68	[2]	—
$Au(CN)_2^-$	—	—	Potent.	—	—	$5,0 \cdot 10^{-39}$	38,3	[3,4]	—
$CdCN^+$	25	3,0	"	$2,9 \cdot 10^{-6}$	5,54	$2,9 \cdot 10^{-6}$	5,54	[5]	—
$Cd(CN)_2$	25	3,0	"	$8,7 \cdot 10^{-6}$	5,06	$2,5 \cdot 10^{-11}$	10,60	[5]	—
$Cd(CN)_3^-$	25	3,0	"	$2,0 \cdot 10^{-5}$	4,70	$5,0 \cdot 10^{-16}$	15,30	[5]	[9,12]
$Cd(CN)_4^{2-}$	25	3,0	"	$2,8 \cdot 10^{-4}$	3,55	$1,41 \cdot 10^{-19}$	18,85	[5]	[9,10,13,14]
$Cu(CN)_2^-$	25	0	"	—	—	$1 \cdot 10^{-24}$	24,0	[6]	[4]

Complex ion	Temperature, °C	Ionic strength	Method	k	pk	K	pK	Literature	
								main	additional
$Cu(CN)_3^{2-}$	25	0	Spectr.	$2,6 \cdot 10^{-5}$	4,59	$2,6 \cdot 10^{-29}$	28,59	[7]	[15]
$Cu(CN)_4^{3-}$	25	0	"	$2 \cdot 10^{-2}$	1,70	$5,0 \cdot 10^{-32}$	30,30	[7]	[13]
$Fe(CN)_6^{4-}$	18	—	Potent.	—	—	10^{-35}	35	[4]	—
$Fe(CN)_6^{3-}$	18	—	"	—	—	10^{-42}	42	[4]	—
$Hg(CN)_4^{2-}$	25	0,05—0,20	"	—	—	$4,0 \cdot 10^{-42}$	41,4	[8]	—
$Zn(CN)_4^{4-}$	18	0,1—0,2	"	—	—	$1,3 \cdot 10^{-17}$	16,89	[9]	[12,13,15,16]

LITERATURE CITED

1. R. Gaugin. J. Chim. phys., **42**, 28 (1945).
2. L. H. Jones, R. A. Penneman. J. Chem. phys., **22**, 965 (1954).
3. G. Bodländer. Ber., **36**, 3933 (1903).
4. W.M. Latimer. Oxidation States of Elements and their Potentials in Aqueous Solutions. Foreign Lit. Press, 1954. [Russian translation].
5. I. Leden. Svensk. Kem. Tidsk., 56, 31 (1944); Chem. Abs., 40, 3070 (1946).
6. M.G. Vladimirov, I.A. Kakovskii. J. Appl. Chem., **23**, 580 (1950).*
7. R. A. Penneman, L. H. Jones. J. Chem. Phys., **24**, 293 (1956).
8. M.S. Sherill. Z. Phys. Chem. Chem., **43**, 705 (1903); **47**, 103, (1904).
9. H. Euler. Ber., **36**, 3400 (1903).
10. E. Ferrell a. oth. J. Chem. Soc., 1936, 1121.
11. R. Gaugin. Ann. chim., **4**, 832 (1949); Chem. Abs., **44**, 4757 (1950).
12. J. Héyrovsky. Polarographic Method [In Russian], United Sci. Tech. Press, 1937.
13. S. Suzuki. Chem. Abs., **48**, 7491 (1954).
14. F. Hirata. Chem. Abs., **46**, 1382 (1952).
15. A.I. Stabrovskii. J. Phys. Chem., **26**, 949 (1952).
16. F. Kunschert. Z. anorg. Chem., **41**, 341 (1904).

139

II. COMPLEXES WITH ORGANIC ADDENDS

1. COMPLEXES WITH AMINES

Complexes with dipyridyl ⟨ ⟩—N N—⟨ ⟩ Dip

Complex ion	Temperature, °C	Ionic strength	Method	k	pk	K	pK	Literature main	Literature addit.
Cd (Dip)$_3^{2+}$	25	0,1	Polarog.	—	—	$3,4 \cdot 10^{-11}$	10,47	[1]	[1]
Cu (Dip)$_2^+$	25	0,1	"	—	—	$6,3 \cdot 10^{-15}$	14,2	[2]	—
Cu (Dip)$_2^{2+}$	25	0,1	"	—	—	$1,4 \cdot 10^{-18}$	17,85	[2]	—
Fe Dip^{2+}	25	0,025	Kinetic	$6,1 \cdot 10^{-5}$	4,21	$6,1 \cdot 10^{-5}$	4,21	[3]	[4,6]
Fe (Dip)$_2^{2+}$	25	0,025	"	$1,0 \cdot 10^{-5}$	5,0	$6,1 \cdot 10^{-9}$	9,21	[3]	—
Fe (Dip)$_3^{2+}$	25	0,33	"	—	—	$2,6 \cdot 10^{-18}$	17,58	[4]	[7]
Mg Dip^{2+}	25	0,5	Spectr.	$3,16 \cdot 10^{-1}$	0,5	$3,16 \cdot 10^{-1}$	0,5	[5]	—
Mn Dip^{2+}	27	0,5	"	$3,16 \cdot 10^{-3}$	2,5	$3,16 \cdot 10^{-3}$	2,5	[5]	—
Pb Dip^{2+}	27	0,5	"	$1,0 \cdot 10^{-3}$	3,0	$1,0 \cdot 10^{-3}$	3,0	[5]	—

LITERATURE CITED

1. B. E. Douglas, H. A. Laitinen, J. C. Bailar, Jr., J. Am. Chem. Soc., 72, 2484 (1950).
2. E. I. Onstott, H. A. Laitinen J. Am. Chem. Soc., 72, 4724 (1950).
3. J. H. Baxendall, P. George, Nature, 163, 725 (1949); cit. in Chem. Abs., 43, 6056 (1949). cit. in
4. P. Krumholz. Nature, 163, 724 (1949); cit. in Chem. Abs., 43, 6056 (1949).
5. K. Sone, P. Krumholz, H. Stammreich. J. Am. Chem. Soc., 77, 777 (1955).
6 F. P. Dwyer, R. S. Nyholm. J. Proc. Roy. Soc. N. S. Wales, 80, 28 (1946); cit. in Chem. Abs., 42, 19 (1948).
7. J. H. Baxendall, P. George, Nature, 162, 777 (1948); cit. in Chem. Abs., 43, 3695 (1949).

Complexes with diethylenetriamine $H_2N(CH_2)_2NH(CH_2)_2NH_2$ (Deta)

Complex ion	Temperature, °C	Ionic strength	Method	k	pk	K	pK	Literature main	Literature additional
$AgDeta^+$	20	0,1	pH-potent.	$8,0\cdot10^{-7}$	6,1	$8,0\cdot10^{-7}$	6,1	[1]	—
$CdDeta^{2+}$	20	0,1	„	$3,54\cdot10^{-9}$	8,45	$3,54\cdot10^{-9}$	8,45	[1]	—
$Cd(Deta)_2^{2+}$	20	0,1	„	$4,0\cdot10^{-6}$	5,40	$1,40\cdot10^{-14}$	13,85	[1]	[3]
$Co\,Deta^{2+}$	20	0,1	„	$8,0\cdot10^{-9}$	8,1	$8,0\cdot10^{-9}$	8,1	[1]	[2]
$Co\,(Deta)_2^{2+}$	20	0,1	„	$1,0\cdot10^{-6}$	6,0	$1,0\cdot10^{-15}$	14,1	[1]	[2]
$Cu\,Deta^{2+}$	20	0,1	„	$1,0\cdot10^{-16}$	16,0	$1,0\cdot10^{-16}$	16,0	[1]	—
$Cu\,(Deta)_2^{2+}$	20	0,1	„	$5,0\cdot10^{-6}$	5,3	$5,0\cdot10^{-22}$	21,3	[2]	—
$Fe\,Deta^{2+}$	30	1,5	„	$5,9\cdot10^{-7}$	6,23	$5,9\cdot10^{-7}$	6,23	[2]	—
$Fe\,(Deta)_2^{2+}$	30	1,5	„	$7,4\cdot10^{-5}$	4,13	$4,4\cdot10^{-11}$	10,36	[1]	—
$HgDeta^{2+}$	20	0,5	„	$1,6\cdot10^{-22}$	21,8	$1,6\cdot10^{-22}$	21,8	[1]	—
$Hg\,(Deta)_2^{2+}$	30	1,5	„	$1,0\cdot10^{-7}$	7,0	$1,6\cdot10^{-29}$	28,8	[2]	—
$Mn\,Deta^{2+}$	30	1,5	„	$1,02\cdot10^{-4}$	4,0	$1,02\cdot10^{-4}$	3,99	[2]	[2]
$Mn\,(Deta)_2^{2+}$	30	1,5	„	$1,48\cdot10^{-3}$	2,83	$1,51\cdot10^{-7}$	6,82	[2]	—
$Ni\,Deta^{2+}$	20	0,1	„	$2,0\cdot10^{-11}$	10,7	$2,0\cdot10^{-11}$	10,7	[1]	[2]
$Ni\,(Deta)_2^{2+}$	20	0,1	„	$5,6\cdot10^{-9}$	8,25	$1,12\cdot10^{-19}$	18,95	[1]	[2]
$Zn\,Deta^{2+}$	20	0,1	„	$1,26\cdot10^{-9}$	8,9	$1,26\cdot10^{-9}$	8,9	[1]	[2]
$Zn\,(Deta)_2^{2+}$	20	0,1	„	$3,16\cdot10^{-6}$	5,5	$4,0\cdot10^{-15}$	14,4	[1]	—

LITERATURE CITED

1. J. E. Prue, G. Schwarzenbach. Helv. chim. Acta, 33, 985 (1950).
2. H. B. Jonassen, G. G. Hurst, R. B. Le Blanc, A. W. Meibohm. J. Phys. Chem., 56, 16 (1952).
3. B. E. Douglas, H. A. Laitinen, J. C. Bailar. J. Am. Chem. Soc., 72, 2484 (1950).

Complexes with imidazole $\underset{N\,=\,CH}{\overset{HC\,=\,CH}{\big|\quad\big\rangle}}NH$ Im

Complex ion	Temperature, °C	Ionic strength	Method	k	pk	K	pK	Literature main	Literature addit.
$CdIm^{2+}$	25	0,15	pH-potent.	$1,58\cdot10^{-3}$	2,80	$1,58\cdot10^{-3}$	2,80	[1]	[1]
$Cd(Im)_2^{2+}$	25	0,15	"	$8,0\cdot10^{-3}$	2,10	$1,26\cdot10^{-5}$	4,90	[1]	[1]
$Cd(Im)_3^{2+}$	25	0,15	"	$2,8\cdot10^{-2}$	1,55	$3,5\cdot10^{-7}$	6,45	[1]	[1]
$Cd(Im)_4^{2+}$	25	0,15	"	$7,4\cdot10^{-2}$	1,13	$2,6\cdot10^{-8}$	7,58	[1]	[1]
$CuIm^{2+}$	22,5	0,16	"	$4,4\cdot10^{-5}$	4,36	$4,4\cdot10^{-5}$	4,36	[2]	[2]
$Cu(Im)_2^{2+}$	22,5	0,16	"	$2,7\cdot10^{-4}$	3,57	$1,17\cdot10^{-8}$	7,93	[2]	[2]
$Cu(Im)_3^{2+}$	22,5	0,16	"	$1,4\cdot10^{-3}$	2,85	$1,65\cdot10^{-11}$	10,78	[2]	[2]
$Cu(Im)_4^{2+}$	22,5	0,16	"	$8,7\cdot10^{-2}$	2,06	$1,45\cdot10^{-13}$	12,84	[2]	[2]
$NiIm^{2+}$	25	0,15	"	$5,4\cdot10^{-4}$	3,27	$5,4\cdot10^{-4}$	3,27	[3]	—
$Ni(Im)_2^{2+}$	25	0,15	"	$2,1\cdot10^{-3}$	2,68	$1,12\cdot10^{-6}$	5,95	[3]	—
$Ni(Im)_3^{2+}$	25	0,15	"	$7,1\cdot10^{-3}$	2,15	$8,0\cdot10^{-9}$	3,10	[3]	—
$Ni(Im)_4^{2+}$	25	0,15	"	$2,2\cdot10^{-2}$	1,65	$1,8\cdot10^{-10}$	9,75	[3]	—
$Ni(Im)_5^{2+}$	25	0,15	"	$7,6\cdot10^{-2}$	1,12	$1,35\cdot10^{-11}$	10,87	[3]	—
$Ni(Im)_6^{2+}$	25	0,15	"	$3,0\cdot10^{-1}$	0,52	$4,1\cdot10^{-12}$	11,39	[3]	[2]
$ZnIm^{2+}$	24	0,16	"	$2,6\cdot10^{-3}$	2,58	$2,6\cdot10^{-3}$	2,58	[2]	[2]
$Zn(Im)_2^{2+}$	24	0,16	"	$4,26\cdot10^{-3}$	2,37	$1,12\cdot10^{-5}$	4,95	[2]	[2]
$Zn(Im)_3^{2+}$	24	0,16	"	$5,9\cdot10^{-3}$	2,23	$6,6\cdot10^{-8}$	7,18	[2]	[2]
$Zn(Im)_4^{2+}$	24	0,16	"	$9,5\cdot10^{-3}$	2,02	$6,3\cdot10^{-10}$	9,20	[2]	[2]

LITERATURE CITED

1. C. Tanford, M. L. Wagner. J. Am. Chem. Soc., 75, 434 (1953).
3. N. C. Li, T. L. Chu, C. T. Fujii, J. M. White. J. Am. Chem. Soc., 77, 859 (1955).
2. J. T. Edsall, G. Felsenfeld, D. W. S. Goodman, F. R. N. Gurd, J. Am. Chem. Soc., 76, 3054 (1954).

Complexes with pyridine $\langle\ \rangle_N$ (Pyt)

Complex ion	Temperature, °C	Ionic strength	Method	k	pk	K	pK	Literature main	additional
AgPyr+	25	—	Sol.	$1,0\cdot10^{-2}$	2,0	$1,0\cdot10^{-2}$	2,0	[1]	[4]
Ag(Pyr)$_2^+$	25	—	,,	$7,8\cdot10^{-3}$	2,11	$7,8\cdot10^{-5}$	4,11	[1]	[4]
Cd(Pyr)$_2^{2+}$	25	0,1	Polarog.	—	—	$7,2\cdot10^{-3}$	2,14	[2]	—
Cd.Pyr$_4^{2+}$	25	0,1	,,	—	—	$3,2\cdot10^{-3}$	2,49	[2]	—
Cu(Pyr)$_2^+$	25	0,01	,,	—	—	$4,6\cdot10^{-4}$	3,34	[3]	—
Cu(Pyr)$_3^+$	25	0,01	,,	$6,75\cdot10^{-2}$	1,17	$3,1\cdot10^{-5}$	4,51	[3]	—
Cu(Pyr)$_4^+$	25	0,01	,,	$1,17\cdot10^{-1}$	0,93	$3,6\cdot10^{-6}$	5,44	[3]	—
Cu(Pyr)$_6^+$	25	0,01	,,	—	—	$1,3\cdot10^{-7}$	6,89	[3]	—
CuPyr^{2+}	25	0,5	pH-potent.	$3,02\cdot10^{-3}$	2,52	$3,02\cdot10^{-3}$	2,52	[4]	—
Cu(Pyr)$_2^{2+}$	25	0,5	,,	$1,38\cdot10^{-2}$	1,86	$4,16\cdot10^{-5}$	4,38	[4]	—
Cu(Pyr)$_3^{2+}$	25	0,5	,,	$4,90\cdot10^{-2}$	1,31	$2,04\cdot10^{-6}$	5,69	[4]	—
Cu(Pyr)$_4^{2+}$	25	0,5	,,	0,141	0,85	$2,88\cdot10^{-7}$	6,54	[4]	—
Cu(Pyr)$_6^{2+}$	25	0,01	Polarog.	—	—	0,1	1,0	[3]	—

LITERATURE CITED

1. W. C. Vosburgh, S. A. Cogswell. J. Am. Chem. Soc., 65, 2412 (1943).
2. B. E. Douglas, H. A. Laitinen, J. C. Bailar. J. Am. Chem. Soc., 72, 2484 (1950).
3. I. A. Korshunov, N. I. Malyugina. J. Gen. Chem., 20, 402 (1950).*
4. R. J. Bruehlman, F. H. Verhoek. J. Am. Chem. Soc., 70, 1401 (1948).

Complexes with propylenediamine $H_2NCHCH_2NH_2$ (Pn)
$$\underset{\quad CH_3}{}$$

Complex ion	Temperature, °C	Ionic strength	Method	k	pk	K	pK	Literature main	Literature additional
CdPn²⁺	30	0,5	pH-potent.	$3,80 \cdot 10^{-6}$	4,52	$3,80 \cdot 10^{-6}$	5,42	[1]	—
Cd(Pn)₂²⁺	30	0,5	"	$2,82 \cdot 10^{-5}$	4,55	$1,07 \cdot 10^{-10}$	9,97	[1]	—
Cd(Pn)₃²⁺	30	0,5	"	$7,08 \cdot 10^{-3}$	2,15	$7,59 \cdot 10^{-13}$	12,12	[1]	[2]
CuPn²⁺	30	0,5	"	$2,63 \cdot 10^{-11}$	10,58	$2,63 \cdot 10^{-11}$	10,58	[1]	—
Cu(Pn)₂²⁺	30	0,5	"	$8,31 \cdot 10^{-10}$	9,08	$2,19 \cdot 10^{-20}$	19,66	[1]	—
NiPn²⁺	30	0,5	"	$3,90 \cdot 10^{-8}$	7,41	$3,90 \cdot 10^{-8}$	7,41	[1]	—
Ni(Pn)₂²⁺	30	0,5	"	$5,00 \cdot 10^{-7}$	6,30	$1,95 \cdot 10^{-14}$	13,71	[1]	—
Ni(Pn)₃²⁺	30	0,5	"	$5,13 \cdot 10^{-5}$	4,29	$1,0 \cdot 10^{-18}$	18,00	[1]	—
ZnPn²⁺	30	0,5	"	$1,29 \cdot 10^{-6}$	5,89	$1,29 \cdot 10^{-6}$	5,89	[1]	—
Zn(Pn)₂²⁺	30	0,5	"	$1,05 \cdot 10^{-5}$	4,98	$1,35 \cdot 10^{-11}$	10,87	[1]	—
Zn(Pn)₃²⁺	30	0,5	"	$2,00 \cdot 10^{-2}$	1,70	$2,70 \cdot 10^{-13}$	12,57	[1]	—

LITERATURE CITED

1: G. A. Carlson, J. P. McReynolds, F. H. Verhoek. J. Am. Chem. Soc., 67, 1334 (1945). 2. B. E. Douglas, H. A. Laitinen, J. C. Bailar, Jr. J. Am. Chem. Soc., 72, 2484 (1950).

Complexes with 1,2,3-triaminopropane $C_3H_5(NH_2)_3$ (Ptn)

Complex ion	Temperature, °C	Ionic strength	Method	k	pk	K	pK
$AgPtn^+$	20	0,1	pH-potent.	$2,24 \cdot 10^{-6}$	5,65	$2,24 \cdot 10^{-6}$	5,65
$CdPtn^{2+}$	20	0,1	"	$3,55 \cdot 10^{-7}$	6,45	$3,55 \cdot 10^{-7}$	6,45
$CoPtn^{2+}$	20	0,1	"	$1,6 \cdot 10^{-7}$	6,8	$1,6 \cdot 10^{-7}$	6,8
$CuPtn^{2+}$	20	0,1	"	$8,0 \cdot 10^{-12}$	11,1	$8,0 \cdot 10^{-12}$	11,1
$Cu(Ptn)_2^{2+}$	20	0,1	"	$1,0 \cdot 10^{-9}$	9,0	$8,0 \cdot 10^{-21}$	20,1
$HgPtn^{2+}$	20	0,5	"	$2,5 \cdot 10^{-20}$	19,6	$2,5 \cdot 10^{-20}$	19,6
$NiPtn^{2+}$	20	0,1	"	$5,0 \cdot 10^{-10}$	9,3	$5,0 \cdot 10^{-10}$	9,3
$ZnPtn^{2+}$	20	0,1	"	$1,78 \cdot 10^{-7}$	6,75	$1,78 \cdot 10^{-7}$	6,75

LITERATURE CITED

J. E. Prue, G. Schwarzenbach. Helv. chim. Acta, 33, 995 (1950).

Complexes with methylamine CH_3NH_2

Complex ion	Temperature, °C	Ionic strength	Method	k	pk	K	pK
$Cd(CH_3NH_2)^{2+}$	25	1,0	pH-potent.	$1,80 \cdot 10^{-3}$	2,745	$1,80 \cdot 10^{-3}$	2,745
$Cd(CH_3NH_2)_2^{2+}$	25	1,0	"	$8,66 \cdot 10^{-3}$	2,063	$1,56 \cdot 10^{-5}$	4,808
$Cd(CH_3NH_2)_3^{2+}$	25	1,0	"	$7,40 \cdot 10^{-2}$	1,131	$1,15 \cdot 10^{-6}$	5,939
$Cd(CH_3NH_2)_4^{2+}$	25	1,0	"	0,245	0,611	$2,82 \cdot 10^{-7}$	6,550

LITERATURE CITED

C. G. Spike, R. W. Parry. J. Am. Chem. Soc., 75, 2726 (1953).

Complexes with triaminotriethylamine N (CH₂CH₂NH₂)₃ (Tate)

Complex ion	Temperature, °C	Ionic strength	Method	k	pk	K	pK
Ag Tate⁺	20	0,1	pH-potent.	$1,58 \cdot 10^{-8}$	7,8	$1,58 \cdot 10^{-8}$	7,8
Cd Tate²⁺	20	0,1	"	$5,0 \cdot 10^{-13}$	12,3	$5,0 \cdot 10^{-13}$	12,3
Co Tate²⁺	20	0,1	"	$1,58 \cdot 10^{-13}$	12,8	$1,58 \cdot 10^{-13}$	12,8
Cu Tate²⁺	20	0,1	"	$1,58 \cdot 10^{-19}$	18,8	$1,58 \cdot 10^{-19}$	18,8
Fe Tate²⁺	20	0,1	"	$1,58 \cdot 10^{-9}$	8,8	$1,58 \cdot 10^{-9}$	8,8
Hg Tate²⁺	20	0,5	"	$1,58 \cdot 10^{-23}$	22,8	$1,58 \cdot 10^{-23}$	22,8
Mn Tate²⁺	20	0,1	"	$1,58 \cdot 10^{-6}$	5,8	$1,58 \cdot 10^{-6}$	5,8
Ni Tate²⁺	20	0,1	"	$1,58 \cdot 10^{-15}$	14,8	$1,58 \cdot 10^{-15}$	14,8
Zn Tate²⁺	20	0,1	"	$2,24 \cdot 10^{-15}$	14,65	$2,24 \cdot 10^{-15}$	14,65

LITERATURE CITED

J. E. Prue, G. Schwarzenbach. Helv. chim. Acta, 33, 963 (1950).

Complexes with trimethylenediamine H₂NCH₂CH₂CH₂NH₂ (Tmen)

Complex ion	Temperature, °C	Ionic strength	Method	k	pk	K	pK
CuTmen²⁺	25	1,0	pH-potent.	$1,05 \cdot 10^{-10}$	9,98	$1,05 \cdot 10^{-10}$	9,98
Cu (Tmen)₂²⁺	25	1,0	"	$6,45 \cdot 10^{-8}$	7,19	$6,75 \cdot 10^{-18}$	17,17
NiTmen²⁺	25	1,0	"	$4,07 \cdot 10^{-7}$	6,39	$4,07 \cdot 10^{-7}$	6,39
Ni (Tmen)₂²⁺	25	1,0	"	$4,07 \cdot 10^{-5}$	4,39	$1,66 \cdot 10^{-11}$	10,78
Ni (Tmen)₃²⁺	25	1,0	"	$5,90 \cdot 10^{-2}$	1,23	$9,80 \cdot 10^{-13}$	12,01

LITERATURE CITED

I. Poulsen, J. Bjerrum. Acta Chem. Scand., 9, 1407 (1955); Cit. in

Complexes with triethylenetetramine $NH_2(CH_2)_2NH(CH_2)_2NH(CH_2)_2NH_2$ (Teta)

Complex ion	Temperature, °C	Ionic strength	Method	k	pk	K	pK	Literature
Ag Teta⁺	20	0,1	pH-potent.	$2,0 \cdot 10^{-8}$	7,7	$2,0 \cdot 10^{-8}$	7,7	[1]
Cd Teta²⁺	20	0,1	"	$1,78 \cdot 10^{-11}$	10,75	$1,78 \cdot 10^{-11}$	10,75	[1]
Cd (Teta)$_2^{2+}$	25	0,3	Polarog.	—	—	$1,2 \cdot 10^{-14}$	13,9	[2]
Co Teta²⁺	20	0,1	pH-potent.	$1,0 \cdot 10^{-11}$	11,0	$1,0 \cdot 10^{-11}$	11,0	[1]
Cu Teta²⁺	20	0,1	"	$4,0 \cdot 10^{-21}$	20,4	$4,0 \cdot 10^{-21}$	20,4	[1]
Fe Teta²⁺	20	0,1	"	$1,6 \cdot 10^{-8}$	7,8	$1,6 \cdot 10^{-8}$	7,8	[1]
Hg Teta²⁺	20	0,5	"	$5,5 \cdot 10^{-26}$	25,26	$5,5 \cdot 10^{-26}$	25,26	[1]
Mn Teta²⁺	20	0,1	"	$1,26 \cdot 10^{-5}$	4,9	$1,26 \cdot 10^{-5}$	4,9	[1]
Ni Teta²⁺	20	0,1	"	$1,0 \cdot 10^{-14}$	14,0	$1,0 \cdot 10^{-14}$	14,0	[1]
Zn Teta²⁺	20	0,1	"	$8,0 \cdot 10^{-13}$	12,1	$8,0 \cdot 10^{-13}$	12,1	[1]

LITERATURE CITED

1. G. Schwarzenbach. Helv. chim. Acta, 33, 974 (1950).
2. B. E. Douglas, H. A. Laitinen, J. C. Bailar, Jr. J. Am. Chem. Soc., 72, 2484 (1950).

Complexes with phenanthroline

(Ph)

Complex ion	Temperature, °C	Ionic strength	Method	k	pk	K	pK	Literature	
								main	addit.
$CaPh^{2+}$	27	0,5	Spectr.	$3,2\cdot10^{-1}$	0,5	$3,2\cdot10^{-1}$	0,5	[1]	—
$Cd(Ph)_2^{2+}$	25	0,03*	Polarog.	—	—	$7,0\cdot10^{-14}$	13,16	[2]	—
$Cd(Ph)_3^{2+}$	25	0,02	»	—	—	$6,4\cdot10^{-16}$	15,20	[2]	—
$FePh^{3+}$	25	0,7	Spectr.	$1,3\cdot10^{-6}$	5,89	$1,3\cdot10^{-6}$	5,89	[3]	—
$Fe(Ph)_3^{2+}$	25	0	Potent.	—	—	$5,0\cdot10^{-22}$	21,3	[4]	[6,7]
$MgPh^{2+}$	27	0,5	Spectr.	$3,2\cdot10^{-2}$	1,5	$3,2\cdot10^{-2}$	1,5	[1]	—
$ZnPh^{2+}$	25	0,1	Spectr.	$3,7\cdot10^{-7}$	6,43	$3,7\cdot10^{-7}$	6,43	[5]	—
$Zn(Ph)_2^{2+}$	25	0,1	Distrib.	$1,9\cdot10^{-6}$	5,72	$7\cdot10^{-18}$	12,15	[5]	—
$Zn(Ph)_3^{2+}$	25	0,1	»	$1,6\cdot10^{-5}$	4,8	$1\cdot10^{-17}$	17,0	[5]	—

* 28.5% ethanol.

LITERATURE CITED

1. K. Sone, P. Krumholz, H. Stammerich. J. Am. Chem. Soc., 77, 777 (1955).
2. B. E. Douglas, H. A. Laitinen, J. C. Bailar, Jr. J. Am. Chem. Soc., 72, 2484 (1950).
3. I. M. Kolthoff, D. L. Leussing, T. S. Lee. J. Am. Chem. Soc., 72, 2173 (1950).
4. T. S. Lee, I. M. Kolthoff, D. L. Leussing. J. Am. Chem. Soc., 70, 2348 (1948).
5. I. M. Kolthoff, D. L. Leussing, T. S. Lee. J. Am. Chem. Soc., 73, 390 (1951).
6. C. M. Cook, F. A. Long. J. Am. Chem. Soc., 73, 4119 (1951).
7. F. P. Dwyer, R. S. Nyholm. J. Proc. Roy. Soc. N. S. Wales, 80, 28 (1946); cit. in Chem. Abs., 43, 19 (1948).

Complexes with ethylenediamine $H_2NCH_2CH_2NH_2$ (En)

Complex ion	Temperature, °C	Ionic strength	Method	k	pk	K	pK	Literature main	Literature addit.
$AgEn^+$	16	—	Spectr.	$1 \cdot 10^{-5}$	$5,0$	$1 \cdot 10^{-5}$	$5,0$	[1]	—
$Ag(En)_2^+$	16	—	»	$1,45 \cdot 10^{-3}$	$2,84$	$1,45 \cdot 10^{-8}$	$7,84$	[1]	—
$CdEn^{2+}$	30	0,5	pH-potent.	$3,40 \cdot 10^{-6}$	$5,47$	$3,40 \cdot 10^{-6}$	$5,47$	[2]	[6]
$Cd(En)_2^{2+}$	30	0,5	»	$2,82 \cdot 10^{-5}$	$4,55$	$2,60 \cdot 10^{-11}$	$10,02$	[2]	[6]
$Cd(En)_3^{2+}$	30	0,5	»	$8,50 \cdot 10^{-3}$	$2,07$	$8,15 \cdot 10^{-13}$	$12,09$	[2]	[6]
$CoEn^{2+}$	30	1,2	»	$1,29 \cdot 10^{-6}$	$5,89$	$1,29 \cdot 10^{-6}$	$5,89$	[3]	—
$Co(En)_2^{2+}$	30	1,2	»	$1,48 \cdot 10^{-5}$	$4,88$	$1,91 \cdot 10^{-11}$	$10,72$	[3]	—
$Co(En)_3^{2+}$	30	1,2	»	$7,95 \cdot 10^{-4}$	$3,10$	$1,52 \cdot 10^{-14}$	$13,82$	[3]	—
$Co(En)_3^{3+}$	30	1,0	»	—	—	$2,04 \cdot 10^{-49}$	$48,69$	[3]	—
$CuEn^{2+}$	30	0,5	»	$2,82 \cdot 10^{-11}$	$10,55$	$2,82 \cdot 10^{-11}$	$10,55$	[2]	[4,7]
$Cu(En)_2^{2+}$	30	0,5	»	$8,92 \cdot 10^{-10}$	$9,05$	$2,52 \cdot 10^{-20}$	$19,60$	[2]	[4,5,7]
$FeEn^{2+}$	30	1,2	»	$5,25 \cdot 10^{-5}$	$4,28$	$5,25 \cdot 10^{-5}$	$4,28$	[3]	—
$Fe(En)_2^{2+}$	30	1,2	»	$5,62 \cdot 10^{-4}$	$3,25$	$2,95 \cdot 10^{-8}$	$7,53$	[3]	—
$Fe(En)_3^{2+}$	30	1,2	»	$1,02 \cdot 10^{-2}$	$1,99$	$3,01 \cdot 10^{-10}$	$9,52$	[3]	—

149

Continuation

Complex ion	Temperature, °C	Ionic strength	Method	k	pk	K	pK	Literature main	Literature addit.
MnEn²⁺	30	1,2	pH-potent.	$1,86 \cdot 10^{-3}$	2,73	$1,86 \cdot 10^{-3}$	2,73	[3]	—
Mn(En)₂²⁺	30	1,2	»	$8,7 \cdot 10^{-3}$	2,06	$1,62 \cdot 10^{-5}$	4,79	[3]	—
Mn(En)₃²⁺	30	1,2	»	$1,32 \cdot 10^{-1}$	0,88	$2,14 \cdot 10^{-6}$	5,67	[3]	—
NiEn²⁺	30	1,2	»	$2,18 \cdot 10^{-8}$	7,66	$2,18 \cdot 10^{-8}$	7,66	[3]	[2,4]
Ni(En)₂²⁺	30	1,2	»	$3,98 \cdot 10^{-7}$	6,40	$8,70 \cdot 10^{-15}$	14,06	[3]	[2,4]
Ni(En)₃²⁺	30	1,2	»	$2,95 \cdot 10^{-5}$	4,53	$2,57 \cdot 10^{-19}$	18,59	[3]	[2,4]
ZnEn²⁺	30	1,0	»	$1,95 \cdot 10^{-6}$	5,71	$1,95 \cdot 10^{-6}$	5,71	[2]	[7]
Zn(En)₂²⁺	30	1,0	»	$2,19 \cdot 10^{-5}$	4,66	$4,26 \cdot 10^{-11}$	10,37	[2]	[7]
Zn(En)₃²⁺	30	1,0	»	$1,91 \cdot 10^{-2}$	1,72	$8,12 \cdot 10^{-13}$	12,08	[2]	—

LITERATURE CITED

1. P. Job. Ann. chim., [10] **9**, 113; cit. in Zbl., I, 2572 (1928).
2. G. A. Carlson, J. P. Mc Reynolds, F. H. Verhoek. J. Am. Chem. Soc., **67**, 1334 (1945).
3. J. Bjerrum. Metalammine formation in aqueous solutions. Copenhagen, 1941; cit. in Chem. Abs., 6527 (1941).
4. F. Basolo, R. K. Murman. J. Am. Chem. Soc., **74**, 5243 (1952).
5. E. I. Onstott, H. A. Laitinen. J. Am. Chem. Soc., **72**, 4724 (1950).
6. C. G. Spike, R. W. Parry. J. Am. Chem. Soc., **75**, 2726 (1953).
7. C. G. Spike, R. W. Parry. J. Am. Chem. Soc., **75**, 3770 (1953).

2. COMPLEXES WITH ANIONS OF ORGANIC ACIDS

Acetate complexes

Complex ion	Temperature, °C	Ionic strength	Method	k	pk	K	pK	Literature main	addit.
AgCH$_3$COO	25	2,95	Potent.	0,183	0,74	0,183	0,74	[1]	—
Ag(CH$_3$COO)$_2^-$	25	2,95	»	1,26	0,10	0,230	0,64	[1]	—
BaCH$_3$COO$^+$	25	0	Sol.	0,39	0,41	0,39	0,41	[2]	[16]
»	—	0,20	Potent.	0,42	0,38	0,42	0,38	[3]	—
CaCH$_3$COO$^+$	25	0	Sol.	0,17	0,77	0,17	0,77	[2]	[16, 17]
»	25	0,20	Potent.	0,29	0,53	0,29	0,53	[3]	—
CdCH$_3$COO$^+$	—	—	»	1,7·10^{-2}	1,77	1,7·10^{-2}	1,77	[4]	—
Cd (CH$_3$COO)$_2$	—	—	»	1,0·10^{-1}	1,0	1,7·10^{-3}	2,77	[4]	—
CeCH$_3$COO^{2+}	20	1,00	Ion. exch.	2,1·10^{-2}	1,68	2,7·10^{-2}	1,68	[5]	—
Ce (CH$_3$COO)$_2^+$	20	1,00	»	0,107	0,97	2,2·10^{-3}	2,65	[5]	—
Ce (CH$_3$COO)$_3$	20	1,0	»	0,21	0,68	5,9·10^{-4}	3,23	[5]	—
CuCH$_3$COO$^+$	25	0	Sol.	5,7·10^{-3}	2,24	5,7·10^{-3}	2,24	[6]	—
Cu (CH$_3$COO)$_2$	—	—	Potent.	0,125	0,90	5,0·10^{-4}	3,30	[7]	[7]
Hg (CH$_3$COO)$_2$	—	—	Sol.	—	—	3,75·10^{-9}	8,43	[8]	—
InCH$_3$COO^{2+}	—	—	Potent.	3,12·10^{-4}	3,51	3,12·10^{-4}	3,51	[9]	—

Complex ion	Temperature, °C	Ionic strength	Method	h	$p\kappa$	K	pK	Literature main	addit.
In $CH_3COO)_2^+$	—	—	Potent.	$3,6\cdot10^{-3}$	2,44	$1,11\cdot10^{-6}$	5,95	[9]	—
In $(CH_3COO)_3$	—	—	"	$1,12\cdot10^{-2}$	1,95	$1,25\cdot10^{-8}$	7,90	[9]	—
In $(CH_3COO)_4^-$	—	—	"	$6,6\cdot10^{-2}$	1,18	$8,3\cdot10^{-10}$	9,08	[9]	—
In $(CH_3COO)_5^{2-}$	—	—	"	0,71	0,15	$5,9\cdot10^{-10}$	9,23	[9]	—
In $(CH_3COO)_6^{3-}$	—	—	"	$8,5\cdot10^{-2}$	1,07	$5,0\cdot10^{-11}$	18,30	[9]	—
$MgCH_3COO^+$	25	0	"	0,165	0,82	0,165	0,82	[2]	[16]
$MnCH_3COO^+$	25	0	Calc.	$6\cdot10^{-2}$	1,2	$6\cdot10^{-2}$	1,2	[10]	—
$NiCH_3COO^+$	25	0	"	$1,6\cdot10^{-2}$	1,8	$1,6\cdot10^{-2}$	1,8	[10]	[18]
"	20	1,0	Potent.	0,22	0,67	0,22	0,67	[11]	—
$Ni(CH_3COO)_2$	20	1,0	"	0,26	0,59	$5,5\cdot10^{-2}$	1,26	[11]	—
$PbCH_3COO^+$	25	1,0	Sol.	$9\cdot10^{-3}$	2,05	$9,0\cdot10^{-3}$	2,05	[12]	[19]
"	20	2,0	Polarog.	$1,6\cdot10^{-2}$	1,80	$1,6\cdot10^{-2}$	1,80	[13,14]	—
$Pb(CH_3COO)_2$	20	2,0	"	0,58	0,24	$0,92\cdot10^{-2}$	2,04	[13,14]	—
$Pb(CH_3COO)_3^-$	20	2,0	"	1,35	-0,13	$1,2\cdot10^{-2}$	1,91	[13,14]	—
$Pb(CH_3COO)_4^{2-}$	20	2,0	"	3,16	-0,50	$3,8\cdot10^{-2}$	-1,41	[13,14]	—
$SrCH_3COO^+$	25	0	Sol.	0,36	0,44	0,36	0,44	[2]	[16,17]
$ZnCH_3COO^+$	18	0,1	Potent.	$2\cdot10^{-2}$	1,70	$2\cdot10^{-2}$	1,70	[15]	[3]

LITERATURE CITED

1. F. H. Mac Dougall, L. E. Topol. J. phys. Chem., 56, 1090 (1952).
2. C. A. Colman Porter C. B. Monk J. Chem. Soc., 1952, 4363.
3. R. K. Cannan, A. Kibrick. J. Am. Chem. Soc., 60, 2314 (1938).
4. S. Aditya, B. Prasad. J. Indian. Chem. Soc., 30, 255 (1953); Chem. Abs., 48, 488 (1954).
5. S. Fronaeus. Svenck. Kem. Tidsk., 65, 19 (1953); Chem. Abs., 47, 8459 (1953).
6. M. Lloyd, V. Wycherley, C. B. Monk. J. Chem. Soc., 1951, 1786.
7. S. S. Sorcar, S. Aditya, B. Prasad. J. Indian. Chem. Soc. 30, 255 (1953).
8. P. Mahapatra, S. Aditya, B. Prasad. J. Indian. Chem. Soc., 30, 509 (1953).
9. N. Sunden. Svenck. Kem. Tidsk., 65, 257 (1953); Chem. Abst. J., 13786 (1955).
10. K.B. Yatsimirskii. J. Gen. Chem., 24, 1498 (1954).*
11. S. Fronaeus. Acta Chem. Scand., 6, 1200 (1952); Chem. Abs., 47, 5292 (1953).
12. S. M. Edmonds, N. Birnbaum. J. Am. Chem. Soc., 62, 2367 (1940).
13. V.F. Toropova, F.M. Batorgshina. J. Anal. Chem., 4, 337 (1949).*
14. K.B. Yatsimirskii. Coll. of Work on General Chemistry, Acad. Sci. USSR Press, 1953, Vol. I, p. 193.
15. E. Ferrell, J. M. Ridgion, H. L. Riley. J. Chem. Soc., 1936, 1121.
16. G. H. Nancollas. J. Chem. Soc., 1956, 744.
17. J. Schubert, A. Lindenbaum. J. Am. Chem. Soc., 74, 3529 (1952).
18. P. K. Jena, S. A. Aditya, B. Prasad, J. Indian. Chem. Soc., 30, 735 (1953); Chem. Abs., 48, 9161 (1954).
19. N. K. Das, S. Aditya, B. Prasad. Chem. Abs., 46, 10802 (1952).

Malate complexes - $^-OOCCHOHCH_2COO^-(Mal^{2-})$

Complex ion	Temperature, °C	Ionic strength	Method	k	pk	K	pK	Literature main	Literature addit.
BaMal	—	0,2	pH-potent.	$5 \cdot 10^{-2}$	1,30	$5 \cdot 10^{-2}$	1,30	[1]	[2]
CaMal	—	0,2	"	$1,6 \cdot 10^{-2}$	1,80	$1,6 \cdot 10^{-2}$	1,80	[1]	[2,3]
MgMal	—	0,2	"	$2,8 \cdot 10^{-2}$	1,55	$2,8 \cdot 10^{-2}$	1,55	[1]	[2]
SrMal	—	0,2	"	$3,5 \cdot 10^{-2}$	1,45	$3,5 \cdot 10^{-2}$	1,45	[1]	[3]
ZnMal	—	0,2	"	$1,6 \cdot 10^{-3}$	2,80	$1,6 \cdot 10^{-3}$	2,80	[1]	[2]

LITERATURE CITED

1. R. K. Cannan, A. Kibrick. J. Am. Chem. Soc., 60, 2314 (1938).
2. C. B. Monk. Trans. Farad. Soc., 47, 297 (1951).
3. J. Schubert, A. Lindenbaum. J. Am. Chem. Soc., 74, 3529 (1952).

Glycolate complexes $HOCH_2COO^-$ ($Glyc^-$)

Complex ion	Temperature, °C	Ionic strength	Method	h	ph	K	pK	Literature
BaGlyc$^+$	—	0,2	pH-potent.	$2,18 \cdot 10^{-1}$	0,66	$2,18 \cdot 10^{-1}$	0,66	[1]
CaGlyc$^+$	—	0,2	"	$7,76 \cdot 10^{-2}$	1,11	$7,76 \cdot 10^{-2}$	1,11	[1]
MgGlyc$^+$	—	0,2	"	$1,2 \cdot 10^{-1}$	0,92	$1,2 \cdot 10^{-1}$	0,92	[1]
SrGlyc$^+$	—	0,2	"	$1,58 \cdot 10^{-1}$	0,80	$1,58 \cdot 10^{-1}$	0,80	[1]
UO_2 Glyc$^+$	—	—	"	$3,8 \cdot 10^{-3}$	2,42	$3,8 \cdot 10^{-3}$	2,42	[2]
UO_2 (Glyc)$_2$	—	—	"	$2,9 \cdot 10^{-2}$	1,54	$1,1 \cdot 10^{-4}$	3,96	[2]
UO_2 (Glyc)$_3^-$	—	—	"	$5,7 \cdot 10^{-2}$	1,24	$6,3 \cdot 10^{-6}$	5,20	[2]
ZnGlyc$^+$	—	0,2	"	$1,2 \cdot 10^{-2}$	1,92	$1,2 \cdot 10^{-2}$	1,92	[1]

LITERATURE CITED

1. R. K. Cannan, A. Kibrick. J. Am. Chem. Soc., **60**, 2314 (1938).
2. S. Ahrland. Acta Chem. Scand., **7**, 485 (1953).

Glycerate complexes $CH_2OHCHOHCOO^-$ ($Glac^-$)

Complex ion	Temperature, °C	Ionic strength	Method	k	pk	K	pK
BaGlac$^+$	—	0,2	pH-potent.	$1,6 \cdot 10^{-1}$	0,80	$1,6 \cdot 10^{-1}$	0,80
CaGlac$^+$	—	0,2	"	$6,6 \cdot 10^{-2}$	1,18	$6,6 \cdot 10^{-2}$	1,18
MgGlac$^+$	—	0,2	"	$1,4 \cdot 10^{-1}$	0,86	$1,4 \cdot 10^{-1}$	0,86
SrGlac$^+$	—	0,2	"	$1,3 \cdot 10^{-1}$	0,89	$1,3 \cdot 10^{-1}$	0,89
ZnGlac$^+$	—	0,2	"	$1,6 \cdot 10^{-2}$	1,80	$1,6 \cdot 10^{-2}$	1,80

LITERATURE CITED

R. K. Cannan, A. Kibrick. J. Am. Chem. Soc., **60**, 2314 (1938).

Complexes with gluconic acid $CH_2OH(CHOH)_4COO^-$ Glu⁻

Complex ion	Temperature, °C	Ionic strength	Method	k	pk	K	pK	Literature	
								main	additional
BaGlu⁺	—	0,2	pH-potent.	$1,12 \cdot 10^{-1}$	0,95	$1,12 \cdot 10^{-1}$	0,95	[1]	—
CaGlu⁺	25	0,16	Ion. exch.	$6,03 \cdot 10^{-2}$	1,22	$6,03 \cdot 10^{-2}$	1,22	[2]	[1]
MgGlu⁺	—	0,2	pH-potent.	$2,0 \cdot 10^{-1}$	0,70	$2,0 \cdot 10^{-1}$	0,70	[1]	—
SrGlu⁺	25	0,16	Ion. exch.	$9,8 \cdot 10^{-2}$	1,01	$9,8 \cdot 10^{-2}$	1,01	[2]	[1]
ZnGlu⁺	—	0,2	pH-potent.	$2,0 \cdot 10^{-2}$	1,70	$2,0 \cdot 10^{-2}$	1,70	[1]	—

LITERATURE CITED

1. R. K. Cannan, A. Kibrick. J. Am. Chem. Soc., 60, 2314 (1938).
2. J. Schubert, A. Lindenbaum. J. Am. Chem. Soc., 74, 3529 (1952).

Complexes with kojic acid *

$$CH_2OH \ \ \text{—O—} \ \text{O—} \ \text{—O}^- \quad (Koj^-)$$

Complex ion	Temperature, °C	Ionic strength	Method	k	pk	K	pK
CaKoj⁺	30	—	pH-potent.	$4,0 \cdot 10^{-5}$	4,4	$4,0 \cdot 10^{-5}$	4,4
Ca (Koj)₂	30	—	»	$2,0 \cdot 10^{-3}$	2,7	$8,0 \cdot 10^{-8}$	7,1
CdKoj⁺	30	—	»	$2,5 \cdot 10^{-7}$	6,6	$2,5 \cdot 10^{-7}$	6,6
Cd (Koj)₂	30	—	»	$2,0 \cdot 10^{-5}$	4,7	$5,0 \cdot 10^{-12}$	11,3
CoKoj⁺	30	—	»	$1,6 \cdot 10^{-7}$	6,8	$1,6 \cdot 10^{-7}$	6,8
Co (Koj)₂	30	—	»	$6,3 \cdot 10^{-6}$	5,2	$1,0 \cdot 10^{-12}$	12,0
CuKoj⁺	30	—	»	$5,0 \cdot 10^{-10}$	9,3	$5,0 \cdot 10^{-10}$	9,3
Cu (Koj)₂	30	—	»	$6,3 \cdot 10^{-8}$	7,2	$3,2 \cdot 10^{-17}$	16,5
NiKoj⁺	30	—	»	$8,0 \cdot 10^{-8}$	7,1	$8,0 \cdot 10^{-8}$	7,1
Ni (Koj)₂	30	—	»	$3,16 \cdot 10^{-6}$	5,5	$2,5 \cdot 10^{-13}$	12,6
UO₂Koj⁺	30	—	»	$8,0 \cdot 10^{-11}$	10,1	$8,0 \cdot 10^{-11}$	10,1
UO₂ (Koj)₂	30	—	»	$4,0 \cdot 10^{-8}$	7,4	$3,2 \cdot 10^{-18}$	17,5
ZnKoj⁺	30	—	»	$4,0 \cdot 10^{-8}$	7,4	$4,0 \cdot 10^{-8}$	7,4
Zn (Koj)₂	30	—	P	$1,6 \cdot 10^{-6}$	5,8	$6,3 \cdot 10^{-14}$	13,2

*In a 50% dioxane—water mixture

LITERATURE CITED

B. E. Bryant. W. C. Fernelius. J. Am. Chem. Soc., 76, 5351 (1954).

Lactate complexes $CH_3CHOHCOO^-$ (Lac^-)

Complex ion	Temperature, °C	Ionic strength	Method	k	pk	K	pK	Literature main	Literature additional
BaLac+	—	0,2	pH-potent.	$2,8 \cdot 10^{-1}$	0,55	$2,8 \cdot 10^{-1}$	0,55	[1]	—
CaLac+	25	0,15	"	$1,5 \cdot 10^{-1}$	0,82	$1,5 \cdot 10^{-1}$	0,82	[2]	[1,5,6]
Co (Lac)₂	—	—	Spectr.	—	—	$2,08 \cdot 10^{-2}$	1,68	[3]	—
Cu (Lac)₂	—	—	"	—	—	$2,05 \cdot 10^{-3}$	2,69	[4]	—
MgLac+	—	0,2	pH-potent.	$1,17 \cdot 10^{-1}$	0,93	$1,17 \cdot 10^{-1}$	0,93	[1]	[6]
SrLac+	—	0,2	"	$2,0 \cdot 10^{-1}$	0,70	$2,0 \cdot 10^{-1}$	0,70	[1]	—
ZnLac+	—	0,2	"	$1,38 \cdot 10^{-2}$	1,86	$1,38 \cdot 10^{-2}$	1,86	[1]	—

LITERATURE CITED

1. R. K. Cannan, A. Kibrick. J. Am. Chem. Soc., 60, 2314 (1938).
2. C. B. Monk. Trans. Farad. Soc., 47, 297 (1951).
3. M. Bobtelsky, J. Bar-Gadda. Bull. Soc. chim. France, No. 7—8, 687 (1953), cit. in Chem. Abst. J., 16142 (1955).
4. M. Bobtelsky, J. Bar-Gadda. Bull. Soc. chim. France, No. 3, 276 (1953), cit. in Chem. Abst. J., 16141 (1955).
5. C. W. Davies. J. Chem. Soc., 1938, 277.
6. J. Schubert, A. Lindenbaum. J. Am. Chem. Soc., 74, 3529 (1952).

Malonate complexes $HOOCC\,H_2COOHCH_2(COO)_2^{2-}$ (Mal^{2-})

Complex ion	Temperature, °C	Ionic strength	Method	k	pk	K	pK	Literature main	Literature addit.
BaMal	—	0,2	pH-potent.	$5,9\cdot10^{-2}$	1,23	$5,9\cdot10^{-2}$	1,23	[1]	[3]
CaMal	—	0,2	pH-potent.	$3,46\cdot10^{-2}$	1,46	$3,46\cdot10^{-2}$	1,46	[1]	[3,8]
CdMal	25	0	Electrocon.	$5,1\cdot10^{-4}$	3,29	$5,1\cdot10^{-4}$	3,29	[2]	[3,10]
CoMal	—	0,04	pH-color.	$1,9\cdot10^{-4}$	3,72	$1,9\cdot10^{-4}$	3,72	[3]	—
Co(Mal)$_2^{2-}$	—	—	Spectr.	—	—	$7,28\cdot10^{-4}$	3,14	[4]	—
CuMal	25	0	Electrocon.	$2,5\cdot10^{-6}$	5,60	$2,5\cdot10^{-6}$	5,60	[2]	[3,9,10]
Cu(Mal)$_2^{2-}$	Room	0,03	pH-potent.	—	—	$5,4\cdot10^{-8}$	7,27	[5]	[11]
FeMal	—	1,0	Polarog.	$1,58\cdot10^{-3}$	2,8	$1,58\cdot10^{-3}$	2,8	[6]	—
Fe(Mal)$_2^{2-}$	25	0,5	"	—	—	$6\cdot10^{-3}$	2,22	[7]	—
Fe(Mal)$_3^{3-}$	25	0,5	"	—	—	$2,2\cdot10^{-16}$	15,66	[7]	—
MgMal	25	0	Electrocon.	$1,6\cdot10^{-3}$	2,80	$1,6\cdot10^{-3}$	2,80	[2]	[1,3,10]
MnMal	—	0,04	pH-color.	$5,1\cdot10^{-4}$	3,29	$5,1\cdot10^{-4}$	3,29	[3]	—
NiMal	18	0	Electrocon.	$7,3\cdot10^{-5}$	4,14	$7,3\cdot10^{-5}$	4,14	[2]	[3,9]
SrMal	25	0,16	Ion exch.	$5,37\cdot10^{-2}$	1,27	$5,37\cdot10^{-2}$	1,27	[8]	[1]
ZnMal	25	—	Electrocon.	$4,5\cdot10^{-4}$	3,35	$4,5\cdot10^{-4}$	3,35	[9]	[1,2,10]

LITERATURE CITED

1. R. K. Cannan, A. Kibrick. J. Am. Chem. Soc., 60, 2314 (1938).
2. R. W. Money, C. W. Davies. Trans. Farad. Soc., 28, 609 (1932).
3. D. I. Stock, C. W. Davies. J. Chem. Soc., 1949, 1371.
4. M. Bobtelsky, J. Bar-Gadda. Bull. Soc. chim. France, No. 7–8, 687 (1953); cit. in Chem. Abst. J., 16142 (1955).
5. H. L. Riley. J. Chem. Soc., 1307 (1929); cit. in Zbl., I, 957 (1930).
6. A. E. Martell, M. Calvin. Chemistry of the metal chelate compounds. New York, 1953.
7. W. B. Schaap, H. A. Laitinen, J. C. Bailar. J. Am. Chem. Soc., 76, 5868 (1954).
8. J. Schubert, A. Lindenbaum. J. Am. Chem. Soc., 74, 3529 (1952).
9. D. J. G. Ives, H. L. Riley. J. Chem. Soc., 1931, 1998.
10. H. L. Riley, N. J. Fischer. J. Chem. Soc., 1929, 2006; cit. in Zbl., II, 3110 (1929).
11. M. Bobtelsky, J. Bar-Gadda. Bull. soc. chim. France, No. 3, 276 (1953); cit. in Chem. Abst. J., 16141 (1955).

Complexes with butyric acid $C_3H_7COO^-$ (Bu^-)

Complex ion	Temperature, °C	Ionic strength	Method	h	ph	K	pK
BaBu$^+$	—	0,2	pH-potent.	$4,90 \cdot 10^{-1}$	0,31	$4,90 \cdot 10^{-1}$	0,31
CaBu$^+$	—	0,2	—	$3,10 \cdot 10^{-1}$	0,51	$3,10 \cdot 10^{-1}$	0,51
MgBu$^+$	—	0,2	»	$2,95 \cdot 10^{-1}$	0,53	$2,95 \cdot 10^{-1}$	0,53
SrBu$^+$	—	0,2	»	$4,35 \cdot 10^{-1}$	0,36	$4,35 \cdot 10^{-1}$	0,36
ZnBu$^+$	—	0,2	»	$1,0 \cdot 10^{-1}$	1,00	$1,0 \cdot 10^{-1}$	1,00

LITERATURE CITED

R. K. Cannan, A. Kibrick. J. Am. Chem. Soc., **63**, 2314 (1951).

Nitroacetate complexes $O_2NCH_2COO^-$ (Nac^-)

Complex ion	Temperature, °C	Ionic strength	Method	$[h$	ph	K	pK
AlNac^{2+}	18	0,6	Kinetic	$3,3 \cdot 10^{-1}$	0,48	$3,3 \cdot 10^{-1}$	0,48
BeNac$^+$	18	0,6	»	$5,5 \cdot 10^{-1}$	0,26	$5,5 \cdot 10^{-1}$	0,26
CaNac$^+$	18	0,6	»	2,0	−0,30	2,0	−0,30
CdNac$^+$	18	0,6	»	$6,5 \cdot 10^{-1}$	0,19	$6,5 \cdot 10^{-1}$	0,19
CoNac$^+$	18	0,6	»	1,0	0,0	1,0	0,0
CuNac$^+$	18	0,6	»	$3,6 \cdot 10^{-1}$	0,44	$3,6 \cdot 10^{-1}$	0,44
MgNac$^+$	18	0,6	»	1,55	−0,19	1,55	−0,19
NiNac$^+$	18	0,6	»	$8,7 \cdot 10^{-1}$	0,06	$8,7 \cdot 10^{-1}$	0,06
PbNac$^+$	18	0,6	»	$7,2 \cdot 10^{-1}$	0,14	$7,2 \cdot 10^{-1}$	0,14
ZnNac$^+$	18	0,6	»	$9,3 \cdot 10^{-1}$	0,03	$9,3 \cdot 10^{-1}$	0,03

LITERATURE CITED

K. J. Pedersen. Acta Chem. Scand., **3**, 656 (1949); cit. in Chem. Abs., **44**, 2341 (1950).

Oxalate complexes $C_2O_4^{2-}$ (Ox^{2-})

Complex ion	Temperature, °C	Ionic strength	Method	k	pk	K	pK	Literature main	Literature addit.
$Al(Ox)_2^-$	—	$>$0,01	pH-potent.	—	—	$1 \cdot 10^{-13}$	13,0	[1]	—
$Al(Ox)_3^{3-}$	—	$>$0,01		$1,6 \cdot 10^{-3}$	3,8	$1,6 \cdot 10^{-17}$	16,8	[1]	—
$BaOx$	18	0	Electrocon.	$4,7 \cdot 10^{-3}$	2,31	$4,7 \cdot 10^{-3}$	2,31	[2]	—
$CaOx$	18	0		$1,0 \cdot 10^{-3}$	3,0	$1,0 \cdot 10^{-3}$	3,0	[2]	—
$CdOx$	25	0	Sol.	$3,0 \cdot 10^{-4}$	3,52	$3,0 \cdot 10^{-4}$	3,52	[3]	[2]
$Cd(Ox)_2^{2-}$	25	0		$1,4 \cdot 10^{-2}$	1,85	$4,2 \cdot 10^{-6}$	5,37	[3]	[9]
$CeOx^+$	25	0		$3,0 \cdot 10^{-7}$	6,52	$3,0 \cdot 10^{-7}$	6,52	[4]	—
$Ce(Ox)_2^-$	25	0		$1,1 \cdot 10^{-4}$	3,96	$3,3 \cdot 10^{-11}$	10,5	[4]	—
$Ce(Ox)_3^{3-}$	25	0		$1,5 \cdot 10^{-1}$	0,82	$5,0 \cdot 10^{-12}$	11,3	[4]	—
$CoOx$	18	0	Electrocon.	$2,0 \cdot 10^{-5}$	4,70	$2,0 \cdot 10^{-5}$	4,70	[2]	—
$Co(Ox)_2^{2-}$	25	$>$0,1	Thermody.	$3,9 \cdot 10^{-8}$	2,41	$7,8 \cdot 10^{-8}$	7,11	[5]	[9]
$Co(Ox)_3^{4-}$	25	0,1	Sol.	—	—	$1,1 \cdot 10^{-8}$	7,96	[5]	—
$CuOx$	18	0	Electrocon.	$7,0 \cdot 10^{-7}$	6,16	$7,0 \cdot 10^{-7}$	6,16	[6]	—
$Cu(Ox)_2^{2-}$	25	$>$0,1	Thermody.	—	—	$9,1 \cdot 10^{-9}$	8,04	[5]	[13]
$FeOx$	18	0	Electrocon.	$2 \cdot 10^{-4}$	4,7	$2,0 \cdot 10^{-4}$	4,7	[2]	—
$Fe(Ox)_2^{2-}$	25	0,5	Polarog.	—	—	$3,0 \cdot 10^{-5}$	4,52	[7]	[5]

Complex ion	Temperature, °C	Ionic strength	Method	k	pk	K	pK	Literature	
								main	addit.
Fe(Ox)$_3^{4-}$	25	0,5	Polarog.	$2 \cdot 10^{-1}$	0,70	$6 \cdot 10^{-6}$	5,22	[7]	—
FeOx$^+$	—	—	pH-potent.	$4,0 \cdot 10^{-10}$	9,4	$4,0 \cdot 10^{-10}$	9,4	[8]	—
Fe(Ox)$_2^-$	—	—	"	$1,6 \cdot 10^{-7}$	6,8	$6,3 \cdot 10^{-17}$	16,2	[8]	—
Fe(Ox)$_3^{3-}$	—	—	pH-potent.	$1 \cdot 10^{-4}$	4,0	$6,3 \cdot 10^{-21}$	20,2	[8]	[7]
MgOx	18	0	Electrocon.	$3,7 \cdot 10^{-4}$	3,43	$3,7 \cdot 10^{-4}$	3,43	[2]	[14]
Mg(Ox)$_2^{2-}$	25	0,02	Sol.	—	—	$4,2 \cdot 10^{-5}$	4,38	[9]	—
MnOx	18	θ	Electrocon.	$1,3 \cdot 10^{-4}$	3,89	$1,3 \cdot 10^{-4}$	3,89	[2]	—
Mn(Ox)$_2^{2-}$	25	>0,1	Thermody.	—	—	$1,6 \cdot 10^{-6}$	5,80	[5]	—
MnOx$^+$	25,2	2,0	Kinetic	$1,05 \cdot 10^{-10}$	9,98	$1,05 \cdot 10^{-10}$	9,98	[10]	—
Mn(Ox)$_2^-$	25,2	2,0	"	$2,6 \cdot 10^{-7}$	6,59	$2,72 \cdot 10^{-17}$	16,57	[10]	—
Mn(Ox)$_3^{3-}$	25,2	2,0	"	$1,4 \cdot 10^{-8}$	2,85	$3,82 \cdot 10^{-20}$	19,42	[10]	—
NdOx$^+$	25	0	Sol.	$6,2 \cdot 10^{-8}$	7,21	$6,2 \cdot 10^{-8}$	7,21	[4]	—
Nd(Ox)$_2^-$	25	0	"	$5,0 \cdot 10^{-5}$	4,3	$3,1 \cdot 10^{-12}$	11,5	[4]	—
NiOx	18	0	Electrocon.	$5 \cdot 10^{-6}$	5,3	$5 \cdot 10^{-6}$	5,3	[2]	—
Ni(Ox)$_2^{2-}$	25	>0,1	Thermody.	—	—	$2,3 \cdot 10^{-8}$	7,64	[5]	[9]
NpO$_2$Ox$^-$	25	0,5	Spectr.	$5 \cdot 10^{-4}$	3,30	$5 \cdot 10^{-4}$	3,30	[11]	—
NpO$_2$(Ox)$_2^{3-}$	25	0,5	"	$1,7 \cdot 10^{-4}$	3,77	$8,5 \cdot 10^{-8}$	7,07	[11]	—
SrOx	18	0	Electrocon.	$2,9 \cdot 10^{-3}$	2,54	$2,9 \cdot 10^{-3}$	2,54	[2]	—
Th(Ox)$_4^{4-}$	30	—	pH-potent.	—	—	$3,3 \cdot 10^{-25}$	24,48	[12]	—
YbOx$^+$	25	0	Sol.	$5,0 \cdot 10^{-8}$	7,30	$5,0 \cdot 10^{-8}$	7,30	[4]	—
Yb(Ox)$_2^-$	25	0	"	$2,6 \cdot 10^{-5}$	4,41	$2,0 \cdot 10^{-12}$	11,7	[4]	—
ZnOx	18	0	Electrocon.	$1,3 \cdot 10^{-5}$	4,89	$1,3 \cdot 10^{-5}$	4,89	[2]	[3]
Zn(Ox)$_2^{2-}$	25	>0,1	Thermody.	—	—	$2,5 \cdot 10^{-8}$	7,60	[5]	—

LITERATURE CITED

1. S. Lacroix. Bull. Soc. chim. France, 408 (1947); cit. in Chem. Abs., **42**, 1842 (1948).
2. R. W. Money, C. W. Davies. Trans. Farad. Soc., **28**, 609 (1932).
3. W. J. Clayton, W. C. Vosburgh. J. Am. Chem. Soc., **59**, 2414 (1937).
4. C. E. Crouthamel, D. S. Martin, Jr. J. Am. Chem. Soc., **73**, 569 (1951).
5. E. K. Zolotarev. Study of Oxalate Complexes in Solution. Dissertation, Chemicotechnological Institute, Ivanovo, 1956.
6. J. M. Peacock, J. C. James. J. Chem. Soc. 1951, 2233.
7. W. B. Schaap, H. A. Laitinen, J. C. Bailar. Jr. J. Am. Chem. Soc., **76**, 5868 (1954).
8. J. Badoz-Lambling. Ann. chim., 8, № 12, 586 (1953); cit. in Chem. Abst. J., 13790/(1955).
9. E. Barney, W. J. Argersinger, C. A. Reynolds. J. Am. Chem. Soc., **73**, 3785 (1951).
10. H. Taube. J. Am. Chem. Soc., **70**, 3928 (1948).
11. D. M. Gruen, J. J. Katz. J. Am. Chem. Soc., **75**, 3772 (1953).
12. M. Bose, D. M. Chowdhury. J. Indian Chem. Soc., **31**, № 2, 111 (1954); cit. in Chem. Abst. J., 16166 (1955).
13. H. T. S. Britton, M. E. Jarret. J. Chem. Soc., 1936, 1489.
14. R. K. Cannan, A. Kibrick. J. Am. Chem. Soc., **60**, 2314 (1938).

Complexes with oxaloacetic acid

$$\begin{array}{l} COO^- \\ | \\ CO \\ | \qquad (Oxac^{2-}) \\ CH_2 \\ | \\ COO^- \end{array}$$

Complex ion	Temperature, °C	Ionic strength	Method	k	pk	K	pK
DyOxac$^+$	25	0	pH-potent.	$2,2\cdot10^{-6}$	5,66	$2,2\cdot10^{-6}$	5,66
Dy (Oxac)$_2^-$	25	0	"	$3,3\cdot10^{-5}$	4,48	$7,2\cdot10^{-11}$	10,14
GdOxac$^+$	25	0	"	$2,9\cdot10^{-6}$	5,54	$2,9\cdot10^{-6}$	5,54
Gd (Oxac)$_2^-$	25	0	"	$3,0\cdot10^{-5}$	4,53	$8,5\cdot10^{-11}$	10,07
LaOxac$^+$	25	0	"	$5,6\cdot10^{-6}$	5,25	$5,6\cdot10^{-6}$	5,25
LuOxac$^+$	25	0	"	$1,35\cdot10^{-6}$	5,87	$1,35\cdot10^{-6}$	5,87
Lu (Oxac)$_2^-$	25	0	"	$1,9\cdot10^{-5}$	4,72	$2,6\cdot10^{-11}$	10,59
Y Oxac$^+$	25	0	"	$2,34\cdot10^{-6}$	5,63	$2,34\cdot10^{-6}$	5,63
Y (Oxac)$_2^-$	25	0	"	$6,3\cdot10^{-5}$	4,20	$1,5\cdot10^{-10}$	9,83

LITERATURE CITED

E. Gelles, G. H. Nancollas. Trans. Farad. Soc., **52**, 98 (1956).

Salicylate complexes $C_6H_4(COO)O^{2-}$ (Sal^{2-})

Complex ion	Temperature, °C	Ionic strength	Method	k	pk	K	pK	Literature main	Literature addit.
AlSal+	—	—	Spectr.	$8 \cdot 10^{-15}$	14,10	$8 \cdot 10^{-15}$	14,10	[1]	—
CaSal	25	0,15	Potent.	$7,25 \cdot 10^{-1}$	0,14	$7,25 \cdot 10^{-1}$	0,14	[2]	[6]
CuSal	—	—	Spectr.	$2,3 \cdot 10^{-11}$	10,6	$2,3 \cdot 10^{-11}$	10,6	[3]	—
Cu(Sal)₂²⁻	—	—	"	$5 \cdot 10^{-7}$	6,3	$1,26 \cdot 10^{-17}$	16,9	[3]	[7]
FeSal+	—	—	"	$4,0 \cdot 10^{-17}$	16,4	$4,0 \cdot 10^{-17}$	16,4	[4]	—
Fe(Sal)₂⁻	—	—	"	$3,5 \cdot 10^{-12}$	11,46	$1,4 \cdot 10^{-28}$	27,85	[4]	—
Fe(Sal)₃³⁻	—	—	"	$2 \cdot 10^{-6}$	5,7	$2,8 \cdot 10^{-34}$	33,55	[4]	—
UO₂Sal	—	—	"	$4 \cdot 10^{-14}$	13,4	$4 \cdot 10^{-14}$	13,4	[5]	—

LITERATURE CITED

1. A.K. Babko, T.N. Rychkova. J. Gen. Chem., 18, 1617 (1948).
2. N.R. Joseph. J. Biol. Chem., 164, 529 (1946); cit. in Chem. Abs., 40, 6321 (1946).
3. A.K. Babko. J. Gen. Chem., 17, 443 (1947).
4. A.K. Babko. J. Gen. Chem., 15, 745 (1945).
5. A.K. Babko, L.S. Kotelyanskaya. Chem. Coll. Kiev State University, No. 5, 1949, 75.
6. C. W. Davies. J. Chem. Soc., 1938, 277.
7. M. Bobtelsky, J. Bar-Gadda. Bull. Soc. chim. France, No. 3, 276 (1953); cit. in Chem. Abst. J., 16141 (1955).

Succinate complexes $\begin{array}{c} CH_2COO^- \\ | \\ CH_2COO^- \end{array}$ (Suc²⁻)

Complex ion	Temperature, °C	Ionic strength	Method	k	pk	K	pK	Literature main	Literature addit.
BaSuc	25	0,15	Potent.	$1,07 \cdot 10^{-1}$	0,97	$1,07 \cdot 10^{-1}$	0,97	[1]	[3,5]
CaSuc	25	0,15	"	$6,9 \cdot 10^{-2}$	1,16	$6,9 \cdot 10^{-2}$	1,16	[1]	[3,5,6]
CoSuc	—	—	Spectr.	$7,2 \cdot 10^{-1}$	0,14	$7,2 \cdot 10^{-1}$	0,14	[2]	—
MgSuc	—	0,2	pH-potent.	$6,3 \cdot 10^{-2}$	1,20	$6,3 \cdot 10^{-2}$	1,20	[3]	[5]
RaSuc	25	0,02	Ion. exch.	$1 \cdot 10^{-1}$	1,0	$1 \cdot 10^{-1}$	1,0	[4]	—
SrSuc	—	0,2	pH-potent.	$8,7 \cdot 10^{-2}$	1,06	$8,7 \cdot 10^{-2}$	1,06	[3]	[6]
ZnSuc	—	0,2	"	$1,66 \cdot 10^{-2}$	1,78	$1,66 \cdot 10^{-2}$	1,78	[3]	[5]

LITERATURE CITED

1. N. R. Joseph. J. Biol. Chem., 164, 529 (1946).
2. M. Bobtelsky, J. Bar-Gadda. Bull. Soc. chim. France, No. 7–8, 687 (1953); cit. in Chem. Abst.
3. R. K. Cannan, A. Kibrick. J. Am. Chem. Soc., 60, 2314 (1938).
4. A. E. Martell, M. Calvin. Chemistry of the metal chelate compounds, New York, 1953.
5. C. B. Monk. Trans. Farad. Soc., 47, 297 (1951).
6. J. Schubert, A. Lindenbaum. J. Am. Chem. Soc., 74, 3529 (1952).

Tartrate complexes $^-OOCCHOHCHOHCOO^-$ $(Tart^{2-})$

Complex ion	Temperature, °C	Ionic strength	Method	k	pk	K	pK	Literature main	Literature addit.
BaTart	—	0,2	pH-potent.	$2,4 \cdot 10^{-2}$	1,62	$2,4 \cdot 10^{-2}$	4,62	[1]	[9]
Bi (HTart)$_4^-$	—	—	pH-potent.	—	—	$5 \cdot 10^{-9}$	8,30	[2]	—
Bi (OH)$_3$Tart^{2-}	—	—	"	—	—	$1 \cdot 10^{-31}$	31,0	[2]	—
CaTart	25	0,16	Ion. exch.	$1,66 \cdot 10^{-2}$	1,78	$1,66 \cdot 10^{-2}$	1,78	[3]	[1]
CuTart	25	—	Potent.	$9,3 \cdot 10^{-4}$	3,03	$9,3 \cdot 10^{-4}$	3,03	[4]	[10]
Cu (HTart)$_2$	—	—	Spectr.	—	—	$5 \cdot 10^{-4}$	3,3	[5]	—
Cu (OH)$_2$ (Tart)$_2^{4-}$	25	>1,0	Polarog.	—	—	$1,4 \cdot 10^{-10}$	9,85	[6]	—
Cu (OH) Tart$^-$	—	—	Sol.	—	—	$3,6 \cdot 10^{-13}$	12,44	[5]	—
Cu (OH)$_2$Tart^{2-}	—	—	"	—	—	$7,3 \cdot 10^{-20}$	19,14	[5]	—
MgTart	—	0,2	pH-potent.	$4,4 \cdot 10^{-2}$	1,36	$4,4 \cdot 10^{-2}$	1,36	[1]	—
Pb (HTart)$_3^-$	—	—	Polarog.	—	—	$2 \cdot 10^{-5}$	4,7	[7]	—
Pb (OH)$_2$Tart^{2-}	—	—	"	—	—	$8 \cdot 10^{-15}$	14,1	[7]	—
SrTart	25	0,16	Ion. exch.	$2,56 \cdot 10^{-2}$	1,59	$2,56 \cdot 10^{-2}$	1,59	[3]	[1,9,11]
ZnTart	—	0,2	pH-potent.	$2,1 \cdot 10^{-3}$	2,68	$2,1 \cdot 10^{-3}$	2,68	[1]	[4]
Zn (OH)Tart$^-$	18	—	Polarog.	—	—	$2,4 \cdot 10^-$	7,62	[8]	—

165

LITERATURE CITED

1. R. K. C a n n a n, A. K i b r i c k. J. Am. Chem. Soc., **60**, 2314 (1938).
2. A.S. T i k h o n o v. J. Gen. Chem., **24**, 37 (1954).*
3. J. S c h u b e r t, A. L i n d e n b a u m. J. Am. Chem. Soc., *74*, 3529 (1952).
4. S u z u k i. J. Chem. Soc. Japan, Pure Chem. Sect., **72**, 524 (1951); cit. in Chem. Abs.. **46**, 3444 (1952).
5. A.S. T i k h o n o v, V.P. B e l 's k a y a. Collection of Articles on General Chemistry, 1953, Vol. II, 1211.
6. L. M e i t e s. J. Am. Chem. Soc., **71**, 3269 (1949).
7. A.S. T i k h o n o v. Trans. Voronezh University, **32**, 113 (1953); cited in Chem. Abst. J., 20995 (1955).
8. N.K. V i t c h e n k o, A.S. T i k h o n o v. Trans. Voronezh University, **32**, 129 (1953); cit. in Chem. Abst. J., 20994 (1955).
9. N. R. J o s e p h. J. Biol. Chem., **164**, 529 (1946); cit. in Chem. Abs., **40**, 6321 (1946).
10. R. N. S e n S a r m a. J. Indian. Chem. Soc., **27**, 683 (1950); cit. in Chem. Abs., **45**, 7907 (1951).
11. J. S c h u b e r t, J. W. R i c h t e r. J. Phys. Colloid. Chem., **52**, 350 (1948); cit. in Chem. Abs., **43**, 5301 (1948).

Complexes with propionic acid
$C_2H_5COO^-$ (Pr$^-$)

Complex ion	Temperature °C	Ionic strength	Method	k	pk	K	pK
BaPr$^+$	—	0,2	pH-potent.	$4,07 \cdot 10^{-1}$	0,39	$4,07 \cdot 10^{-1}$	0,39
CaPr$^+$	—	0,2	"	$2,95 \cdot 10^{-1}$	0,53	$2,95 \cdot 10^{-1}$	0,53
MgPr$^+$	—	0,2	"	$3,10 \cdot 10^{-1}$	0,51	$3,10 \cdot 10^{-1}$	0,51
SrPr$^+$	—	0,2	"	$3,72 \cdot 10^{-1}$	0,43	$3,72, 10^{-1}$	0,43
ZnPr$^+$	—	0,2	"	$9,35 \cdot 10^{-2}$	1,03	$9,35 \cdot 10^{-2}$	1,03

LITERATURE CITED

R. K. C a n n a n, A. K i b r i c k. J. Am. Chem. Soc., **60**, 2314 (1938).

o-Phthalate complexes

$$\langle\!\!\!\!\begin{array}{c} COO^- \\ COO^- \end{array} \quad (Pht^{2-})$$

Complex ion	Temperature, °C	Ionic strength	Method	k	pk	K	pK	Literature main	Literature addit.
BaPht	25	0,15	Potent.	$1,2\cdot10^{-1}$	0,92	$1,2\cdot10^{-1}$	0,92	[1]	—
CaPht	25	0,15	"	$8,5\cdot10^{-2}$	1,07	$8,5\cdot10^{-2}$	1,07	[1]	—
CoPht	—	—	Spectr.	$1,55\cdot10^{-2}$	1,81	$1,55\cdot10^{-2}$	1,81	[2]	—
Co$(Pht)_2^{2-}$	Room	0,03	Potent.	—	—	$3,1\cdot10^{-5}$	4,51	[3]	[4]

LITERATURE CITED

1. N. R. Joseph. J. Biol. Chem., **164**, 529 (1946); cit. in Chem. Abs., **40**, 6321 (1946).
2. M. Bobtelsky, J. Bar-Gadda. Bull. Soc. chim. France, No. 7—8, 687 (1953); cit. in Chem. Abst. J., 16142 (1955).
3. H. L. Riley. J. Chem. Soc., 1929, 1307; cit. in Zbl., II, 957 (1930).
4. M. Bobtelsky, J. Bar-Gadda. Bull. soc. chim. France, No. 3, 276 (1953); cit. in Chem. Abst. J., 16141 (1955).

Citrate complexes $C_3H_4OH(COO)_3^{3-}$ (Cit^{3-})

Complex ion	Temperature, °C	Ionic strength	Method	k	pk	K	pK	Literature main	Literature addit.
BaCit⁻	25	0,16	Ion. exch.	$5 \cdot 10^{-3}$	,3	$5 \cdot 10^{-3}$	2,3	[1]	[1,3]
BeCit⁻	34	0,15	"	$3 \cdot 10^{-5}$	4,52	$3 \cdot 10^{-5}$	4,52	[2]	—
BeHCit	34	0,15	"	$6 \cdot 10^{-3}$	2,22	$6 \cdot 10^{-3}$	2,22	[2]	—
BH₂Cit⁺	34	0,15	"	$4 \cdot 10^{-2}$	1,40	$4 \cdot 10^{-2}$	1,40	[2]	—
CaCit⁻	25	0,15	Potent.	$6,75 \cdot 10^{-4}$	3,17	$6,75 \cdot 10^{-4}$	3,17	[3]	[4,12]
CaHCit	25	0	Ion. exch.	$8,1 \cdot 10^{-4}$	3,09	$8,1 \cdot 10^{-4}$	3,09	[4]	—
CaH₂Cit⁺	25	0	"	$8 \cdot 10^{-2}$	1,90	$8 \cdot 10^{-2}$	1,90	[4]	—
CdCit⁻	25	0,1	Polarog.	$6 \cdot 10^{-5}$	4,22	$6 \cdot 10^{-5}$	4,22	[5]	—
CdCitOH²⁻	25	0,1	"	$9 \cdot 10^{-6}$	5,05	$5 \cdot 10^{-10}$	9,30	[5]	—
Ce(H₂Cit)₃	25	0,5	Ion. exch.	—	—	$6,3 \cdot 10^{-4}$	3,2	[6]	—
CuCit⁻	25	>0,5	Polarog.	$6,2 \cdot 10^{-15}$	14,21	$6,2 \cdot 10^{-15}$	14,21	[7]	—
Cu(OH)₂(Cit)₂⁶⁻	25	>0,5	"	—	—	$5 \cdot 10^{-20}$	19,30	[7]	—
Cu(H₂Cit)(HCit)⁻	Room	—	Spectr.	—	—	$1 \cdot 10^{-4}$	4,0	[8]	—
Cu(OH)(Cit)²⁻	"	—	Sol.	—	—	$4,5 \cdot 10^{-17}$	16,35	[8]	—

Complex ion	Temperature, °C	Ionic strength	Method	k	pk	K	pK	Literature main	Literature addit.
$Cu(OH)_2(Cit)_2^{6-}$	*	—	Sol.	$3,8 \cdot 10^{-3}$	2,42	$1,7 \cdot 10^{-19}$	18,77	[8]	—
$MgCit^-$	25	0,16	Biolog.	$6,3 \cdot 10^{-4}$	3,2	$6,3 \cdot 10^{-4}$	3,2	[9]	—
$PbCit^-$	25	0,16	Potent.	$1,8 \cdot 10^{-6}$	5,74	$1,8 \cdot 10^{-6}$	5,74	[10]	—
$Pr(H_2Cit)_3$	25	0,5	Ion. exch.	—	—	$4,4 \cdot 10^{-4}$	3,4	[6]	—
$RaCit^-$	25	0,16	Ion. exch.	$1 \cdot 10^{-2}$	2,0	$1 \cdot 10^{-2}$	2,0	[11]	—
$SrCit^-$	25	0,15	Potent.	$1,2 \cdot 10^{-3}$	2,92	$1,2 \cdot 10^{-3}$	2,92	[3]	[1,12,13]
$Y(H_2Cit)_3$	25	0,5	Ion. exch.	—	—	$2,3 \cdot 10^{-4}$	3,6	[6]	—

LITERATURE CITED

1. J. Schubert, J. W. Richter. J. Am. Chem. Soc., 70, 4259 (1948).
2. I. Feldman, T. Y. Toribara, J. R. Havill, W. F. Neuman. J. Am. Chem. Soc., 77, 878 (1955).
3. N. R. Joseph. J. Biol. Chem., 164, 529 (1946); cit. in Chem. Abs., 40, 6321 (1946).
4. C. W. Davies, B. E. Hoyle. J. Chem. Soc. 1955, 1038
5. L. Meites. J. Am. Chem. Soc., 73, 3727 (1951).
6. E. R. Tompkins, S. W. Mayer. J. Am. Chem. Soc., 69, 2859 (1947).
7. L. Meites. J. Am. Chem. Soc., 72, 180 (1950).
8. O. D. Talalaeva, A. S. Tikhonov. J. Gen. Chem., 23, 2067 (1953).*

9. A. B. Hastings and oth. J. Biol. Chem., 107, 351 (1934); cit. in A. E. Martell, M. Calvin. Chemistry of the metal chelate compounds. New York, 1953.
10. S. S. Kety. J. Biol. Chem., 142, 181 (1942).
11. A. E. Martell, M. Calvin. Chemistry of the metal chelate compounds, New York, 1953.
12. J. Schubert, A. Lindenbaum. J. Am. Chem. Soc., 74, 3529 (1952).
13. J. Schubert, J. W. Richter. J. Phys. Colloid. Chem., 52, 350 (1948); cit. in Chem. Abs., 42, 5301 (1948).

3. COMPLEXES WITH AMINO ACIDS

Complexes with alanine $CH_3(NH_2)CHCOO^-$ (Alan⁻)

Complex ion	Temperature, °C	Ionic strength	Method	k	pk	K	pK	Literature main	Literature addit.
Ag Alan	25	0	Sol.	$2,3 \cdot 10^{-4}$	3,64	$2,3 \cdot 10^{-4}$	3,64	[1]	[5]
Ag(Alan)₂⁻	25	0	»	$2,7 \cdot 10^{-4}$	3,57	$6,2 \cdot 10^{-8}$	7,21	[1]	—
Ba Alan⁺	25	0	—	$1,7 \cdot 10^{-1}$	0,77	$1,7 \cdot 10^{-1}$	0,77	[1]	—
Ca Alan⁺	25	0	Electrocon.	$5,75 \cdot 10^{-2}$	1,24	$5,75 \cdot 10^{-2}$	1,24	[2]	—
Co Alan⁺	25	0	pH-potent.	$1,51 \cdot 10^{-5}$	4,82	$1,51 \cdot 10^{-5}$	4,82	[1]	—
Co (Alan)₂	25	0	»	$2,2 \cdot 10^{-4}$	3,66	$3,3 \cdot 10^{-9}$	8,48	[1]	[4]
Cu Alan⁺	25	0	»	$3,1 \cdot 10^{-9}$	8,51	$3,1 \cdot 10^{-9}$	8,51	[1]	[6]
Cu (Alan)₂	25	0,01	»	$1,35 \cdot 10^{-7}$	6,87	$4,2 \cdot 10^{-16}$	15,38	[1]	[4, 6, 7]
Fe (Alan)₂	20	—	»	—	—	$5,0 \cdot 10^{-8}$	7,3	[3]	—
Mg Alan⁺	25	0	»	$1,1 \cdot 10^{-2}$	1,96	$1,1 \cdot 10^{-2}$	1,96	[1]	—
Mn Alan⁺	25	0	»	$9,5 \cdot 10^{-4}$	3,02	$9,5 \cdot 10^{-4}$	3,02	[1]	—
Mn (Alan)₂	25	—	»	$9,3 \cdot 10^{-4}$	3,03	$8,9 \cdot 10^{-7}$	6,05	[4]	—
Ni Alan⁺	25	0	Sol.	$1,1 \cdot 10^{-6}$	5,96	$1,1 \cdot 10^{-6}$	5,96	[1]	—
Ni (Alan)₂	25	0	»	$2,0 \cdot 10^{-5}$	4,70	$2,2 \cdot 10^{-11}$	10,66	[1]	—
Pb Alan⁺	25	0	pH-potent.	$1,0 \cdot 10^{-5}$	5,00	$1,0 \cdot 10^{-5}$	5,00	[1]	[5]
Pb (Alan)₂	25	0	»	$5,75 \cdot 10^{-4}$	3,24	$5,75 \cdot 10^{-9}$	8,24	[1]	—
Zn Alan⁺	25	0	»	$6,2 \cdot 10^{-6}$	5,21	$6,2 \cdot 10^{-6}$	5,21	[1]	—
Zn (Alan)₂	25	0	»	$4,7 \cdot 10^{-5}$	4,33	$2,9 \cdot 10^{-10}$	9,54	[1]	—

LITERATURE CITED

1. C. B. Monk. Trans. Farad. Soc., 47, 285, 292, 297 (1951).
2. C. W. Davies, G. M. Waind. J. Chem. Soc., 1950, 305.
3. A. E. Martell, M. Calvin. Chemistry of the metal
5. R. M. Keefer, H. R. Reiber. J. Amer. Chem. Soc., 63, 689 (1941).
6. R. M. Keefer. J. Amer. Chem. Soc., 68, 2329 (1946); 70, 476 (1948).
7. N. C. Li, E. Doody. J. Am. Chem. Soc., 72, 1891

Complexes with aminobarbituric, N,N-diacetic acid (Amac^{3-})

Complex ion	Temperature, °C	Ionic strength	Method	k	pk	K	pK	Literature
Ba Amac$^-$	20	0	pH-potent.	$1{,}65 \cdot 10^{-7}$	6,78	$1{,}65 \cdot 10^{-7}$	6,78	[1]
Ca Amac$^-$	20	0	"	$1{,}70 \cdot 10^{-9}$	8,77	$1{,}70 \cdot 10^{-9}$	8,77	[1]
Ca (Amac)$_2^{4-}$	Room	$\sim 0{,}01$	"	$6{,}3 \cdot 10^{-6}$	5,2	—	—	[2]
Cd (Amac)$_2^{4-}$	"	$\sim 0{,}01$	"	$2{,}0 \cdot 10^{-7}$	6,7	—	—	[2]
Ce (Amac)$_2^{3-}$	"	$\sim 0{,}01$	"	10^{-10}	10	—	—	[2]
Co (Amac)$_2^{4-}$	"	$\sim 0{,}01$	"	$6{,}3 \cdot 10^{-4}$	3,2	—	—	[2]
La (Amac)$_2^{3-}$	"	$\sim 0{,}01$	"	10^{-10}	10	—	—	[2]
Li Amac^{2-}	20	0	"	$4{,}00 \cdot 10^{-6}$	5,40	$4{,}00 \cdot 10^{-6}$	5,40	[1]
Mg Amac$^-$	20	0	"	$1{,}45 \cdot 10^{-9}$	8,84	$1{,}45 \cdot 10^{-9}$	8,84	[1]
Mg (Amac)$_2^{4-}$	Room	$\sim 0{,}01$	"	$8{,}0 \cdot 10^{-4}$	3,1	$8{,}0 \cdot 10^{-4}$	3,1	[1]
Mn (Amac)$_2^{4-}$	"	$\sim 0{,}01$	"	$1{,}0 \cdot 10^{-4}$	4,0	—	—	[2]
Na Amac^{2-}	20	0	"	$4{,}80 \cdot 10^{-4}$	3,32	$4{,}80 \cdot 10^{-4}$	3,32	[1]
Ni (Amac)$_2^{4-}$	Room	$\sim 0{,}01$	"	$5{,}0 \cdot 10^{-4}$	3,3	—	—	[2]
Sr Amac$^-$	20	0	"	$2{,}24 \cdot 10^{-8}$	7,65	$2{,}24 \cdot 10^{-8}$	7,65	[1]
Zn (Amac)$_2^{4-}$	Room	$\sim 0{,}01$	"	$6{,}3 \cdot 10^{-4}$	3,2	—	—	[2]

LITERATURE CITED

1. G. Schwarzenbach, E. Kampitsch, R. Steiner. Helv. chim. Acta, **29**, 364 (1946).
2. G. Schwarzenbach, W. Biederman. Helv. chim. Acta, 31, 456 (1948).

171

Complexes with asparagine

$$NH_2$$
$$|$$
$$H_2NOCCH_2CHCOO^- \ (Asp^-)$$

Complex ion	Temperature, °C	Ionic strength	Method	k	pk	K	
Cd (Asp)$_2$	20	0,01	pH-potent.	—	—	$1,6 \cdot 10^{-7}$	6,8
Co (Asp)$_2$	20	0,01	„	—	—	$4,0 \cdot 10^{-9}$	8,4
Cu (Asp)$_2$	20	0,01	„	—	—	$1,25 \cdot 10^{-15}$	14,9
Fe (Asp)$_2$	20	0,01	„	—	—	$3,16 \cdot 10^{-7}$	6,5
Mg (Asp)$_2$	20	0,01	„	—	—	$1 \cdot 10^{-4}$	4,0
Mn (Asp)$_2$	20	0,01	„	—	—	$3 \cdot 10^{-5}$	4,5
Ni (Asp)$_2$	20	0,01	„	—	—	$2,5 \cdot 10^{-11}$	10,6
Zn (Asp)$_2$	20	0,01	„	—	—	$2,0 \cdot 10^{-9}$	8,7

LITERATURE CITED

A. E. Martell, M. Calvin. Chemistry of the metal chelate compounds, New York, 1953.

Complexes with N-hydroxyethylethylenediaminotriacetic acid

$$H_2C - N \Big\langle {CH_2COO^- \atop CH_2COO^-}$$
$$|$$
$$H_2C - N \Big\langle {CH_2COO^- \atop CH_2CH_2OH} \qquad (Hed^{3-})$$

Complex ion	Temperature °C	Ionic strength	Method	k	pk	K	pK
CaHed$^-$	29,6	0,1	pH-potent.	$1,0 \cdot 10^{-8}$	8,0	$1,0 \cdot 10^{-8}$	8,0
CdHed$^-$	29,6	0,1	„	$1,0 \cdot 10^{-13}$	13,0	$1,0 \cdot 10^{-13}$	13,0
CoHed$^-$	29,6	0,1	„	$4,0 \cdot 10^{-15}$	14,4	$4,0 \cdot 10^{-15}$	14,4
CuHed$^-$	29,6	0,1	„	$4,0 \cdot 10^{-18}$	17,4	$4,0 \cdot 10^{-18}$	17,4
FeHed$^-$	29,6	0,1	„	$2,5 \cdot 10^{-12}$	11,6	$2,5 \cdot 10^{-12}$	11,6
MnHed$^-$	29,6	0,1	„	$2,0 \cdot 10^{-11}$	10,7	$2,0 \cdot 10^{-11}$	10,7
NiHed$^-$	29,6	0,1	„	$1,0 \cdot 10^{-17}$	17,0	$1,0 \cdot 10^{-17}$	17,0
ZnHed$^-$	29,6	0,1	„	$3,2 \cdot 10^{-15}$	14,5	$3,2 \cdot 10^{-15}$	14,5

LITERATURE CITED

S. Chabereck, Jr., A. E. Martell. J. Am. Chem. Soc., 77, 1477 (1955).

Complexes with aspartic acid $-OOCCH_2\underset{|}{\overset{|}{C}HCOO^-}$ with NH_2 ($Aspa^{2-}$)

Complex ion	Temperature, °C	Ionic strength	Method	h	pk	K	pK	Literature main	Literature addit.
BaAspa	25	0,1	pH-potent.	$7,2 \cdot 10^{-2}$	1,14	$7,2 \cdot 10^{-2}$	1,14	[1]	—
CaAspa	25	0,1	„	$2,5 \cdot 10^{-2}$	1,60	$2,5 \cdot 10^{-2}$	1,60	[1]	—
CdAspa	30	0,1	„	$4,3 \cdot 10^{-5}$	4,37	$4,3 \cdot 10^{-5}$	4,37	[2]	—
Cd(Aspa)$_2^{2-}$	30	0,1	„	$7,8 \cdot 10^{-4}$	3,11	$3,3 \cdot 10^{-8}$	7,48	[2]	—
CoAspa	30	0,1	„	$1,26 \cdot 10^{-6}$	5,90	$1,26 \cdot 10^{-6}$	5,90	[2]	—
Co(Aspa)$_2^{2-}$	30	0,1	„	$5,25 \cdot 10^{-5}$	4,28	$6,6 \cdot 10^{-11}$	10,18	[2]	—
CuAspa	30	0,1	„	$2,7 \cdot 10^{-9}$	8,57	$2,7 \cdot 10^{-9}$	8,57	[2]	—
Cu(Aspa)$_2^{2-}$	30	0,1	„	$1,66 \cdot 10^{-7}$	6,78	$4,5 \cdot 10^{-16}$	15,35	[2]	[4]
MgAspa	25	—	„	$3,7 \cdot 10^{-3}$	2,43	$3,7 \cdot 10^{-3}$	2,43	[1]	—
MnAspa	—	—	„	$1,26 \cdot 10^{-4}$	3,90	$1,26 \cdot 10^{-4}$	3,90	[1]	—
NiAspa	30	0,1	„	$7,6 \cdot 10^{-8}$	7,12	$7,6 \cdot 10^{-8}$	7,12	[2]	—
Ni(Aspa)$_2^{2-}$	30	0,1	„	$5,4 \cdot 10^{-6}$	5,27	$4,1 \cdot 10^{-13}$	12,39	[2]	—
RaAspa	25	0,02	„	$1,38 \cdot 10^{-1}$	0,86	$1,38 \cdot 10^{-1}$	0,86	[1]	—
SrAspa	25	0,10	„	$3,3 \cdot 10^{-2}$	1,48	$3,3 \cdot 10^{-2}$	1,48	[3]	—
ZnAspa	30	0,1	„	$1,45 \cdot 10^{-6}$	5,84	$1,45 \cdot 10^{-6}$	5,84	[2]	—
Zn(Aspa)$_2^{2-}$	30	0,1	„	$4,9 \cdot 10^{-5}$	4,31	$7,1 \cdot 10^{-11}$	10,15	[2]	—

LITERATURE CITED

1. A. E. Martell, M. Calvin. Chemistry of the metal chelate compounds. New York, 1953.
2. S. Chabereck, A. E. Martell. J. Am. Chem. Soc., 74, 6021 (1952).
3. J. Schubert, A. Lindenbaum. J. Am. Chem. Soc., 74, 3529 (1952).
4. N. C. Li, E. Doody. J. Am. Chem. Soc., 72, 1891 (1950).

Complexes with β-hydroxyethyliminodiacetic acid $HOCH_2CH_2N \genfrac{}{}{0pt}{}{CH_2COO^-}{CH_2COO^-}$ ($Himda^{2-}$)

Complex ion	Temperature, °C	Ionic strength	Method	k	pk	K	pK
CaHimda	30	0,1	pH-potent.	$1,48 \cdot 10^{-5}$	4,83	$1,48 \cdot 10^{-5}$	4,83
CdHimda	30	0,1	"	$6,6 \cdot 10^{-8}$	7,12	$6,6 \cdot 10^{-8}$	7,12
Cd $(Himda)_2^{2-}$	30	0,1	"	$7,6 \cdot 10^{-6}$	5,12	$5,6 \cdot 10^{-13}$	12,24
CoHimda	30	0,1	"	$5,4 \cdot 10^{-9}$	8,27	$5,4 \cdot 10^{-9}$	8,27
Co $(Himda)_2^{2-}$	30	0,1	"	$3,6 \cdot 10^{-5}$	4,44	$1,95 \cdot 10^{-13}$	12,71
Cu $(Himda)_2^{2-}$	30	0,1	"	$5,9 \cdot 10^{-5}$	4,23	—	—
MgHimda	30	0,1	"	$2,9 \cdot 10^{-4}$	3,54	$2,9 \cdot 10^{-4}$	3,54
MnHimda	30	0,1	"	$2,24 \cdot 10^{-6}$	5,65	$2,24 \cdot 10^{-6}$	5,65
Mn $(Himda)_2^{2-}$	30	0,1	"	$1,18 \cdot 10^{-4}$	3,93	$2,6 \cdot 10^{-10}$	9,58
NiHimda	30	0,1	"	$2,9 \cdot 10^{-10}$	9,54	$2,9 \cdot 10^{-10}$	9,54
Ni $(Himda)_2^{2-}$	30	0,1	"	$7,1 \cdot 10^{-6}$	5,15	$2,04 \cdot 10^{-15}$	14,69
PbHimda	30	0,1	"	$3,16 \cdot 10^{-10}$	9,50	$3,16 \cdot 10^{-10}$	9,50
Pb $(Himda)_2^{2-}$	30	0,1	"	$8,8 \cdot 10^{-5}$	4,17	$2,14 \cdot 10^{-14}$	13,67
ZnHimda	30	0,1	"	$2,7 \cdot 10^{-9}$	8,57	$2,7 \cdot 10^{-9}$	8,57
Zn $(Himda)_2^{2-}$	30	0,1	"	$8,0 \cdot 10^{-5}$	4,10	$2,14 \cdot 10^{-13}$	12,67

LITERATURE CITED

S. Chaberek, R. C. Courney, A. E. Martell J. Am. Chem. Soc., 74, 5057 (1952).

Complexes with glycylglycine $NH_2CH_2CONHCH_2COO^-$ $(Glgl^-)$

Complex ion	Temperature, °C	Ionic strength	Method	k	pk	K	pK	Literature main	addit.
AgGlgl	25	0	pH-potent.	$1,9\cdot10^{-3}$	2,72	$1,9\cdot10^{-3}$	2,72	[1]	—
Ag(Glgl)$_2^-$	25	0	"	$5,5\cdot10^{-3}$	2,26	$1,0\cdot10^{-5}$	5,0	[1]	—
CaGlgl$^+$	25	0	"	$5,7\cdot10^{-2}$	1,25	$5,7\cdot10^{-2}$	1,25	[2]	—
CoGlgl$^+$	25	0	"	$3,24\cdot10^{-1}$	3,49	$3,24\cdot10^{-4}$	3,49	[3]	[5]
Co(Glgl)$_2$	25	0	"	$4,1\cdot10^{-3}$	2,39	$1,32\cdot10^{-6}$	5,88	[3]	[5]
CuGlgl$^+$	25	0	"	$9,2\cdot10^{-7}$	6,04	$9,2\cdot10^{-7}$	6,04	[4]	—
Cu(Glgl)$_2$	25	0	"	$2,4\cdot10^{-6}$	5,64	$2,2\cdot10^{-12}$	11,66	[4]	—
MgGlgl$^+$	25	0	"	$8,7\;10^{-2}$	1,06	$8,7\cdot10^{-2}$	1,06	[3]	—
MnGlgl$^+$	25	0	"	$7,1\cdot10^{-3}$	2,15	$7,1\cdot10^{-3}$	2,15	[3]	—
NiGlgl$^+$	25	0	"	$3,22\cdot10^{-5}$	4,49	$3,22\cdot10^{-5}$	4,49	[3]	—
Ni(Glgl)$_2$	25	0	"	$3,8\cdot10^{-4}$	3,42	$1,22\cdot10^{8-}$	7,91	[3]	—
PbGlgl$^+$	25	0	"	$5,9\cdot10^{-4}$	3,23	$5,9\cdot10^{-4}$	3,23	[3]	—
Pb(Glgl)$_2$	25	0	"	$2,0\cdot10^{-3}$	2,70	$1,18\cdot10^{-6}$	5,93	[3]	—
ZnGlgl$^+$	25	0	"	$1,6\cdot10^{-4}$	3,80	$1,6\cdot10^{-4}$	3,80	[3]	—
Zn(Glgl)$_2$	25	0	"	$1,7\cdot10^{-3}$	2,77	$2,7\cdot10^{-7}$	6,57	[3]	—

LITERATURE CITED

1. C. B. Monk. Trans. Farad. Soc., **47**, 292 (1951).
2. C. W. Davies, G. M. Waind. J. Chem. Soc., 1950, 301.
3. C. B. Monk. Trans. Farad. Soc., **47**, 297 (1951).
4. C. B. Monk. Trans. Farad. Soc., **47**, 285 (1951).
5. J. B. Gilbert, M. C. Otey, J. Z. Hearon. J. Am. Chem. Soc., **77**, 2599 (1955).

Complexes with glycine $NH_2CH_2COO^-$ (Gl^-)

Complex ion	Temperature, °C	Ionic strength	Method	k	pk	K	pK	Literature main	Literature addit.
AgGl	25	0	Sol.	$3,1\cdot10^{-4}$	3,51	$3,1\cdot10^{-4}$	3,51	[1]	—
$Ag(Gl)_2^-$	25	0	"	$4,2\cdot10^{-4}$	3,38	$1,3\cdot10^{-7}$	6,89	[1]	—
$BaGl^+$	25	0	pH-potent.	$1,7\cdot10^{-1}$	0,77	$1,7\cdot10^{-1}$	0,77	[2]	—
$CaGl^+$	25	0	Sol.	$3,7\cdot10^{-2}$	1,43	$3,7\cdot10^{-2}$	1,43	[3]	[8]
$Cd(Gl)_2$	20	0,01	pH-potent.	—	—	$8,0\cdot10^{-9}$	8,1	[4]	—
$CoGl^+$	25	0	"	$5,9\cdot10^{-6}$	5,23	$5,9\cdot10^{-6}$	5,23	[2]	[5]
$Co(Gl)_2$	25	0	"	$9,5\cdot10^{-5}$	4,02	$5,6\cdot10^{-10}$	9,25	[2]	[5]
$Co(Gl)_3^-$	26	—	"	—	—	$1,75\cdot10^{-11}$	10,76	[5]	—
$CuGl^+$	25	0,1	"	$4,15\cdot10^{-9}$	8,38	$4,15\cdot10^{-9}$	8,38	[6]	[9]
$Cu(Gl)_2$	25	0,1	"	$1,35\cdot10^{-7}$	6,87	$5,6\cdot10^{-16}$	15,25	[6]	[7, 9, 10]
$Cu(Gl)_3^-$	25	1,0	Polarog.	—	—	$5,4\cdot10^{-17}$	16,27	[7]	—
$Fe(Gl)_2$	20	0,01	pH-potent.	—	—	$1,6\cdot10^{-8}$	7,8	[4]	—
$MgGl^+$	25	0	"	$3,6\cdot10^{-4}$	3,44	$3,6\cdot10^{-4}$	3,44	[2]	—
$Mg(Gl)_2$	20	0,01	"	—	—	$1\cdot10^{-4}$	4,0	[4]	—
$MnGl^+$	25	0	"	$3,6\cdot10^{-4}$	3,44	$3,6\cdot10^{-4}$	3,44	[2]	—
$Mn(Gl)_2$	25	0,01	"	—	—	$3,2\cdot10^{-6}$	5,5	[4]	—
$NiGl^+$	25	0,1	"	$1,38\cdot10^{-6}$	5,86	$1,38\cdot10^{-6}$	5,86	[6]	[2]
$Ni(Gl)_2$	25	0,1	"	$1,65\cdot10^{-5}$	4,78	$2,3\cdot10^{-11}$	10,64	[6]	[2]
$PbGl^+$	25	0	"	$3,4\cdot10^{-6}$	5,47	$3,4\cdot10^{-6}$	5,47	[2]	—
$Pb(Gl)_2$	25	0	"	$4,1\cdot10^{-4}$	3,39	$1,38\cdot10^{-9}$	8,86	[2]	—
$SrGl^+$	25	0,16	Ion. exch.	$2,5\cdot10^{-1}$	0,6	$2,5\cdot10^{-1}$	0,6	[8]	—
$ZnGl^+$	25	0	pH-potent.	$3,0\cdot10^{-6}$	5,52	$3,0\cdot10^{-6}$	5,52	[2]	—
$Zn(Gl)_2$	25	0	"	$3,6\cdot10^{-5}$	4,44	$1,1\cdot10^{-10}$	9,96	[2]	—

LITERATURE CITED

1. C. B. M o n k. Trans. Farad. Soc., **47**, 292 (1951).
2. C. B. M o n k. Trans. Farad. Soc., **47**, 297 (1951).
3. C. W. D a v i e s, G. M. W a i n d. J. Chem. Soc., 1950, 301.
4. A. E. M a r t e l l, M. C a l v i n. Chemistry of the metal chelate compounds. New York, 1953.
5. J. B. G i l b e r t, M. C. O t e y, J. Z. H e a r o n. J. Am. Chem. Soc., **77**, 2599 (1955).
6. F. B a s o l o, Yun Ti C h e n. J. Am. Chem. Soc., **76**, 953 (1954).
7. R. M. K e e f e r. J. Am. Chem. Soc., **68**, 2329 (1946).
8. J. S c h u b e r t, A. L i n d e n b a u m. J. Am. Chem. Soc., **74**, 3529 (1952).
9. C. B. M o n k. Trans. Farad. Soc., **47**, 285 (1951).
10. N. C. L i, E. D o o d y. J. Am. Chem. Soc., **74**, 4184 (1952).

Complexes with N,N-dihydroxyethylglycine

$$\begin{matrix} HOCH_2CH_2 \\ HOCH_2CH_2 \end{matrix} \Big\rangle N - CH_2COO^- \quad (Dge^-)$$

Complex ion	Temperature °C	Ionic strength	Method	k	pk	K	pK
CdDge$^+$	30	0,1	pH-potent.	$1,65 \cdot 10^{-5}$	4,78	$1,65 \cdot 10^{-5}$	4,78
Cd (Dge)$_2$	30	0,1	"	$4,3 \cdot 10^{-4}$	3,37	$7,1 \cdot 10^{-9}$	8,15
CoDge$^+$	30	0,1	"	$5,25 \cdot 10^{-6}$	5,28	$5,25 \cdot 10^{-6}$	5,28
Co (Dge)$_2$	30	0,1	"	$3,0 \cdot 10^{-4}$	3,52	$1,6 \cdot 10^{-9}$	8,80
CuDge$^+$	30	0,1	"	$7,1 \cdot 10^{-9}$	8,15	$7,1 \cdot 10^{-9}$	8,15
Cu (Dge)$_2$	30	0,1	"	$6,3 \cdot 10^{-6}$	5,20	$4,5 \cdot 10^{-14}$	13,35
FeDge$^+$	30	0,1	"	$5,4 \cdot 10^{-5}$	4,27	$5,4 \cdot 10^{-5}$	4,27
Fe (Dge)$_2$	30	0,1	"	$1,0 \cdot 10^{-3}$	3,00	$5,4 \cdot 10^{-8}$	7,27
MgDge$^+$	30	0,1	"	$7,1 \cdot 10^{-2}$	1,15	$7,1 \cdot 10^{-2}$	1,15
MnDge$^+$	30	0,1	"	$8,3 \cdot 10^{-4}$	3,08	$8,3 \cdot 10^{-4}$	3,08
Mn (Dge)$_2$	30	0,1	"	$4,7 \cdot 10^{-3}$	2,33	$3,9 \cdot 10^{-6}$	5,41
NiDge$^+$	30	0,1	"	$4,2 \cdot 10^{-7}$	6,38	$4,2 \cdot 10^{-7}$	6,38
Ni (Dge)$_2$	30	0,1	"	$4,0 \cdot 10^{-5}$	4,40	$1,65 \cdot 10^{-11}$	10,78
ZnDge$^+$	30	0,1	"	$4,4 \cdot 10^{-6}$	5,36	$4,4 \cdot 10^{-6}$	5,36
Zn (Dge)$_2$	30	0,1	"	$5,5 \cdot 10^{-14}$	3,26	$2,4 \cdot 10^{-9}$	8,62

LITERATURE CITED

S. C h a b e r e c k Jr., R. C. C o u r n e y, A. E. M a r t e l l. J. Am. Chem. Soc., **75**, 2185 (1953).

Complexes with 1,2-diaminocyclohexanetetraacetic acid

$$C - N \underset{\displaystyle CH_2COO^-}{\overset{\displaystyle CH_2COO^-}{}}$$

$$H_2C \quad C - N \underset{\displaystyle CH_2COO^-}{\overset{\displaystyle CH_2COO^-}{}} \quad (Data^{4-})$$

$$H_2C \quad CH_2$$

$$H_2C$$

Complex ion	Temperature, °C	Ionic strength	Method	k	pk	K	pK
AlData⁻	20	0,1	pH-potent.	$2,34 \cdot 10^{-18}$	17,63	$2,34 \cdot 10^{-18}$	17,63
CaData²⁻	20	0,1	"	$8,32 \cdot 10^{-13}$	12,08	$8,32 \cdot 10^{-13}$	12,08
CdData²⁻	20	0,1	"	$5,89 \cdot 10^{-20}$	19,23	$5,89 \cdot 10^{-20}$	19,23
CeData⁻	20	0,1	"	$1,74 \cdot 10^{-17}$	16,76	$1,74 \cdot 10^{-17}$	16,76
CoData²⁻	20	0,1	"	$1,20 \cdot 10^{-19}$	18,92	$1,20 \cdot 10^{-19}$	18,92
CuData²⁻	20	0,1	"	$5,00 \cdot 10^{-22}$	21,30	$5,00 \cdot 10^{-22}$	21,30
DyData⁻	20	0,1	"	$2,04 \cdot 10^{-20}$	19,69	$2,04 \cdot 10^{-20}$	19,69
ErData⁻	20	0,1	"	$2,09 \cdot 10^{-21}$	20,68	$2,09 \cdot 10^{-21}$	20,68
EuData⁻	20	0,1	"	$2,40 \cdot 10^{-19}$	18,62	$2,40 \cdot 10^{-19}$	18,62
GaData⁻	20	0.1	"	$1,23 \cdot 10^{-23}$	22,91	$1.23 \cdot 10^{-23}$	22,91
GdData⁻	20	0,1	"	$1,70 \cdot 10^{-19}$	18,77	$1,70 \cdot 10^{-19}$	18,77
LaData⁻	20	0,1	"	$5,50 \cdot 10^{-17}$	16,26	$5,50 \cdot 10^{-17}$	16,26
LuData⁻	20	0,1	"	$3,09 \cdot 10^{-22}$	21,51	$3,09 \cdot 10^{-22}$	21,51
MnData²⁻	20	0,1	"	$1,66 \cdot 10^{-17}$	16,78	$1,66 \cdot 10^{-17}$	16,78
NdData⁻	20	0,1	"	$2,09 \cdot 10^{-18}$	17,68	$2,09 \cdot 10^{-18}$	17,68
PbData²⁻	20	0,1	"	$2,09 \cdot 10^{-20}$	19,68	$2,09 \cdot 10^{-20}$	19,68
PrData⁻	20	0,1	"	$4,90 \cdot 10^{-18}$	17,31	$4,90 \cdot 10^{-18}$	17,31
SmData⁻	20	0,1	"	$4,17 \cdot 10^{-19}$	18,38	$4,17 \cdot 10^{-19}$	18,38
TbData⁻	20	0,1	"	$3,16 \cdot 10^{-20}$	19,50	$3,16 \cdot 10^{-20}$	19,50
ThData⁻	20	0,1	"	$1,10 \cdot 10^{-21}$	20,96	$1,10 \cdot 10^{-21}$	20,96
VOData⁻	20	0,1	"	$3,98 \cdot 10^{-20}$	19,40	$3,98 \cdot 10^{-20}$	19,40
YData⁻	20	0,1	"	$7,08 \cdot 10^{-20}$	19,15	$7,08 \cdot 10^{-20}$	19,15
YbData⁻	20	0,1	"	$7,59 \cdot 10^{-22}$	21,12	$7,59 \cdot 10^{-22}$	21,12
ZnData²⁻	20	0,1	"	$2,14 \cdot 10^{-19}$	18,67	$2,14 \cdot 10^{-19}$	18,67

LITERATURE CITED

G. Schwarzenbach. Helv. chim. Acta, **37**, 937 (1954).

Complexes with iminodipropionic acid
$NH(C_2H_4COO)_2^{2-}$ ($Imdp^{2-}$)

Complex ion	t, °C	Ionic strength	Method	k	pk	K	pK
CdImdp	30	0,1	pH-potent.	$3,10 \cdot 10^{-4}$	3,51	$3,10 \cdot 10^{-4}$	3,51
CoImdp	30	0,1	"	$1,20 \cdot 10^{-5}$	4,92	$1,20 \cdot 10^{-5}$	4,92
Co $(Imdp)_2^{2-}$	30	0,1	"	$5,50 \cdot 10^{-4}$	3,26	$6,60 \cdot 10^{-9}$	8,18
CuImdp	30	0,1	"	$4,40 \cdot 10^{-10}$	9,36	$4,40 \cdot 10^{-10}$	9,36
Cu $(Imdp)_2^{2-}$	30	0,1	"	$2,10 \cdot 10^{-4}$	3,68	$9,10 \cdot 10^{-14}$	3,04
NiImdp	30	0,1	"	$7,20 \cdot 10^{-7}$	6,14	$7,20 \cdot 10^{-7}$	6,14
Ni $(Imdp)_2^{2-}$	30	0,1	"	$1,70 \cdot 10^{-4}$	3,77	$1,23 \cdot 10^{-10}$	9,91
ZnImdp	30	0,1	"	$1,12 \cdot 10^{-5}$	4,95	$1,12 \cdot 10^{-5}$	4,95

LITERATURE CITED

S. Chabereck Jr., A. E. Martell. J. Am. Chem. Soc., **74**, 5052 (1952).

Complexes with iminodiacetic acid
$NH(CH_2COO)_2^{2-}$ ($Imda^{2-}$)

Complex ion	t, °C	Ionic Strength	Method	k	pk	K	pK
CdImda	30	0,1	pH-potent.	$4,5 \cdot 10^{-6}$	5,35	$4,5 \cdot 10^{-6}$	5,35
Cd $(Imda)_2^{2-}$	30	0,1	"	$6,6 \cdot 10^{-5}$	4,18	$2,95 \cdot 10^{-10}$	9,53
CoImda	30	0,1	"	$1,12 \cdot 10^{-7}$	6,95	$1,12 \cdot 10^{-7}$	6,95
Co $(Imda)_2^{2-}$	30	0,1	"	$4,6 \cdot 10^{-6}$	5,34	$5,1 \cdot 10^{-13}$	12,29
CuImda	30	0,1	"	$2,8 \cdot 10^{-11}$	10,55	$2,8 \cdot 10^{-11}$	10,55
Cu $(Imda)_2^{2-}$	30	0,1	"	$2,24 \cdot 10^{-6}$	5,65	$6,3 \cdot 10^{-17}$	16,20
MgImda	30	0,1	"	$2,5 \cdot 10^{-4}$	3,6	$2,5 \cdot 10^{-4}$	3,6
NiImda	30	0,1	"	$6,2 \cdot 10^{-9}$	8,21	$6,2 \cdot 10^{-9}$	8,21
Ni $(Imda)_2^{2-}$	30	0,1	"	$4,5 \cdot 10^{-7}$	6,35	$2,76 \cdot 10^{-15}$	14,56
ZnImda	30	0,1	"	$9,3 \cdot 10^{-8}$	7,03	$9,3 \cdot 10^{-8}$	7,03
Zn $(Imda)_2^{2-}$	30	0,1	"	$7,2 \cdot 10^{-6}$	5,14	$8,8 \cdot 10^{-13}$	12,17

LITERATURE CITED

S. Chabereck Jr., A. E. Martell. J. Am. Chem. Soc., **74**, 5052 (1952).

Complexes with iminopropionoacetic acid
$$\overset{NH_2}{{}^-OOCCH_2CHCOO^-} \quad (Impa^{2-})$$

Complex ion	$t, °C$	Ionic Strength	Method	k	pk	K	pK
Cd Impa	30	0,1	pH-potent.	$3,0 \cdot 10^{-5}$	4,52	$3,0 \cdot 10^{-5}$	4,52
Cd $(Impa)_2^{2-}$	30	0,1	"	$6,9 \cdot 10^{-4}$	3,16	$2,1 \cdot 10^{-8}$	7,68
Co Impa	30	0,1	"	$6,8 \cdot 10^{-7}$	6,17	$6,8 \cdot 10^{-7}$	6,17
Co $(Impa)_2^{2-}$	30	0,1	"	$5,1,10^{-5}$	4,29	$3,5 \cdot 10^{-11}$	10,46
Cu Impa	30	0,1	"	$3,5 \cdot 10^{-11}$	10,45	$3,5 \cdot 10^{-11}$	10,45
Cu $(Impa)_2^{2-}$	30	0,1	"	$3,5 \cdot 10^{-5}$	4,45	$1,26 \cdot 10^{-15}$	14,90
Ni Jmpa	30	0,1	"	$4,5 \cdot 10^{-8}$	7,35	$4,5 \cdot 10^{-8}$	7,35
Ni $(Impa)_2^{2-}$	30	0,1	"	$5,9 \cdot 0^{-6}$	5,23	$2,6 \cdot 10^{-13}$	12,58
Zn Impa	30	0,1	"	$6,8 \cdot 10^{-7}$	6,17	$6,8 \cdot 10^{-7}$	6,17
Zn $(Impa)_2^{2-}$	30	0,1	"	$4,9 \cdot 10^{-5}$	4,31	$3,3 \cdot 10^{-11}$	10,48

LITERATURE CITED

S. Chaberek, Jr., A. E. Martell. J. Am. Chem. Soc., **74**, 6021 (1952).

Complexes with nitrilodiacetopropionic acid
$$N \overset{\diagup CH_2CH_2COO^-}{\underset{\diagdown CH_2COO^-}{- CH_2COO^-}} \quad (Ndap^{3-})$$

Complex ion	$t, °C$	Ionic strength	Method	k	pk	K	pK
CdNdap$^-$	30	0,1	pH-potent.	$3,2 \cdot 10^{-8}$	7,5	$3,2 \cdot 10^{-8}$	7,5
CoNdap$^-$	30	0,1	"	$8,0 \cdot 10^{-11}$	10,1	$8,0 \cdot 10^{-11}$	10,1
CuNdap$^-$	30	0,1	"	$1,26 \cdot 10^{-12}$	11,9	$1,26 \cdot 10^{-12}$	11,9
MgNdap$^-$	30	0,1	"	$6,3 \cdot 10^{-6}$	5,2	$6,3 \cdot 10^{-6}$	5,2
NiNdap$^-$	30	0,1	"	$4,0 \cdot 10^{-12}$	11,4	$4,0 \cdot 10^{-12}$	11,4
ZnNdap$^-$	30	0,1	"	$8,0 \cdot 10^{-11}$	10,1	$8,0 \cdot 10^{-11}$	10,1

LITERATURE CITED

S. Chabereck, Jr., A. E. Martell. J. Am. Chem. Soc., **75**, 2888 (1953).

Complexes with nitrilodipropionoacetic acid

$$\begin{array}{c} \diagup CH_2CH_2COO^- \\ N-CH_2COO^- \qquad (Ndpa^{3-}) \\ \diagdown CH_2CH_2COO^- \end{array}$$

Complex ion	Temperature, °C	Ionic strength	Method	k	pk	K	pK
CdNdpa⁻	30	0,1	pH-potent.	$2,5\cdot10^{-6}$	5,6	$2,5\cdot10^{-6}$	5,6
CoNdpa⁻	30	0,1	„	$1,26\cdot10^{-8}$	7,9	$1,26\cdot10^{-8}$	7,9
CuNdpa⁻	30	0,1	„	$1,26\cdot10^{-12}$	11,9	$1,26\cdot10^{-12}$	11,9
MgNdpa⁻	30	0,1	„	$2,5\cdot10^{-4}$	3,6	$2,5\cdot10^{-4}$	3,6
NiNdpa⁻	30	0,1	„	$8,0\cdot10^{-10}$	9,1	$8,0\cdot10^{-10}$	9,1
ZnNdpa⁻	30	0,1	„	$1,0\cdot10^{-8}$	8,0	$1,0\cdot10^{-8}$	8,0

LITERATURE CITED

S. Chabereck, Jr., A. E. Martell. J. Am. Chem. Soc., **75**, 2888 (1953).

Complexes with nitrilotripropionic acid

$$\begin{array}{c} \diagup CH_2CH_2COO^- \\ N-CH_2CH_2COO^- \qquad (Ntp^{3-}) \\ \diagdown CH_2CH_2COO^- \end{array}$$

Complex ion	t, °C	Ionic strength	Method	k	pk	K	pK
CdNtp⁻	30	0,1	pH-potent.	$4,0\cdot10^{-4}$	3,4	$4,0\cdot10^{-4}$	3,4
CoNtp⁻	30	0,1	„	$1,6\cdot10^{-5}$	4,8	$1,6\cdot10^{-5}$	4,8
CuNtp⁻	30	0,1	„	$8,0\cdot10^{-10}$	9,1	$8,0\cdot10^{-10}$	9,1
NiNtp⁻	30	0,1	„	$1,6\cdot10^{-6}$	5,8	$1,6\cdot10^{-6}$	5,8
ZnNtp⁻	30	0,1		$5,0\cdot10^{-6}$	5,3	$5,0\cdot10^{-6}$	5,3

LITERATURE CITED

S. Chabereck, Jr., A. E. Martell. J. Am. Chem. Soc., **75**, 2888 (1953).

Complexes with nitrilotriacetic acid

$$N \diagup\hspace{-0.5em}\begin{matrix} CH_2COO^- \\ CH_2COO^- \\ CH_2COO^- \end{matrix} \quad (Nta^{3-})$$

Complex ion	Temperature, °C	Ionic strength	Method	k	pk	K	pK	Literature main	Literature addit.
$BaNta^-$	20	0	pH-potent.	$3;9\cdot10^{-7}$	6,41	$3,9\cdot10^{-7}$	6,41	[1]	[5]
$CaNta^-$	20	0	"	$6,6\cdot10^{-9}$	8,18	$6,6\cdot10^{-9}$	8,18	[1]	[3,5]
$Ca(Nta)_2^{4-}$	20	0	"	$3,7\cdot10^{-4}$	3,43	$2,44\cdot10^{-12}$	11,61	[1]	[3]
$CdNta^-$	20	0,1	"	$2,9\cdot10^{-10}$	9,54	$2,9\cdot10^{-10}$	9,54	[2]	[2]
$Cd(Nta)_2^{4-}$	–	0,001	"	$2,0\cdot10^{-6}$	5,7	–	–	[3]	–
$CeNta$	–	0,001	"	$8,0\cdot10^{-9}$	8,1	$8,0\cdot10^{-9}$	8,1	[3]	–
$CoNta^-$	20	0,1	"	$2,46\cdot10^{-11}$	10,61	$2,46\cdot10^{-11}$	10,61	[2]	–
$Co(Nta)_2^{4-}$	–	0,001	"	$1,26\cdot10^{-4}$	3,9	–	–	[3]	–
$CuNta^-$	20	0,1	"	$2,1\cdot10^{-13}$	12,68	$2,1\cdot10^{-13}$	12,68	[2]	–
$FeNta^-$	20	0,1	"	$1,45\cdot10^{-9}$	8,84	$1,45\cdot10^{-9}$	8,84	[2]	–
$Fe(Nta)_2^{3-}$	20	0,1	"	$6,3\cdot10^{-9}$	8,2	–	–	[4]	–
$LaNta$	20	0,1	"	$4,25\cdot10^{-11}$	10,37	$4,25\cdot10^{-11}$	10,37	[2]	–
$La(Nta)_2^{3-}$	–	0,001	"	$4,0\cdot10^{-8}$	7,4	–	–	[3]	–
$LiNta^{2-}$	20	0	"	$5,25\cdot10^{-4}$	3,28	$5,25\cdot10^{-4}$	3,28	[1]	–
$MgNta^-$	20	0,1	"	$1\cdot10^{-7}$	7,0	$1\cdot10^{-7}$	7,0	[3]	[5]
$Mg(Nta)_2^{4-}$	20	0,1	"	$6,3\cdot10^{-11}$	3,2	$6,3\cdot10^{-11}$	10,2	[3]	–

Complex ion	Temperature, °C	Ionic strength	Method	h	p^h	K	pK	Literature main	Literature addit.
MnNta⁻	20	0,1	pH-potent.	$5,64 \cdot 10^{-8}$	7,44	$5,64 \cdot 10^{-8}$	7,44	[2]	—
Mn(Nta)$_2^{4-}$	—	0,001	"	$2,0 \cdot 10^{-4}$	3,7	—	—	[3]	—
NaNta²⁻	20	0	"	$7,1 \cdot 10^{-3}$	2,15	$7,1 \cdot 10^{-3}$	2,15	[1]	—
NiNta⁻	20	0,1	"	$5,5 \cdot 10^{-12}$	11,26	$5,5 \cdot 10^{-12}$	11,26	[2]	—
Ni(Nta)$_2^{4-}$	—	0,001	"	$2,0 \cdot 10^{-5}$	4,7	—	—	[3]	—
PbNta⁻	20	0,1	"	$1,6 \cdot 10^{-12}$	11,8	$1,6 \cdot 10^{-12}$	11,8	[3]	—
SrNta⁻	20	0	"	$1,86 \cdot 10^{-7}$	6,73	$1,86 \cdot 10^{-7}$	6,73	[1]	[5]
ZnNta⁻	20	0,1	"	$3,55 \cdot 10^{-11}$	10,45	$3,55 \cdot 10^{-11}$	10,45	[2]	[2]
Zn(Nta)$_2^{4-}$	—	0,001	"	$1 \cdot 10^{-3}$	3,0	—	—	[3]	—

LITERATURE CITED

1. G. Schwarzenbach, E. Kampitsch, R. Steiner. Helv. chim. Acta, 28, 828 (1945).
2. G. Schwarzenbach, E. Freitag. Helv. chim. Acta, 34, 1492 (1951).
3. G. Schwarzenbach, W. Beiderman. Helv. chim. Acta, 31, 331 (1948).
4. J. Heller, G. Schwarzenbach. Helv. chim. Acta, 34, 1876 (1951).
5. G. Schwarzenbach, H. Ackermann, P. Ruckstuhl. Helv. chim. Acta, 32, 1175 (1949).

Complexes with 2-sulfonoanilinediacetic acid

$$SO_3^-$$

$$\langle\rangle\!\!-\!\!N\!\!\left\langle\begin{array}{l}CH_2COO^-\\CH_2COO^-\end{array}\right. \quad (Saa^{3-})$$

Complex ion	t, °C	Ionic Strength	Method	k	pk	K	pK
BaSaa⁻	20	0,1	pH-potent.	$5,5\cdot10^{-3}$	2,26	$5,5\cdot10^{-3}$	2,26
CaSaa⁻	20	0,1	„	$2,7\cdot10^{-5}$	4,57	$2,7\cdot10^{-5}$	4,57
LiSaa²⁻	20	0,1	„	$5,5\cdot10^{-3}$	2,26	$5,5\cdot10^{-3}$	2,26
MgSaa⁻	20	0,1	„	$2,2\cdot10^{-3}$	2,68	$2,2\cdot10^{-3}$	2,68
NaSaa²⁻	20	0,1	„	$1,1\cdot10^{-1}$	0,98	$1,1\cdot10^{-1}$	0,98
SrSaa⁻	20	0,1	„	$3,2\cdot10^{-4}$	3,50	$3,2\cdot10^{-4}$	3,50

LITERATURE CITED

G. Schwarzenbach, A. Willi, R. O. Bach. Helv. chim. Acta, **30**, 1303 (1947).

Complexes with trimethylenediaminetetraacetic acid

$$\begin{array}{l}OOCH_2C\\OOCH_2C\end{array}\!\!\!\rangle N(CH_2)_3\!-\!N\!\!\left\langle\begin{array}{l}CH_2COO^-\\CH_2COO^-\end{array}\right. \quad (Tmta^{4-})$$

Complex ion	t, °C	Ionic strength	Method	k	pk	K	pK
BaTmta²⁻	20	0,1	pH-potent.	$5,75\cdot10^{-5}$	4,24	$5,75\cdot10^{-5}$	4,24
CaTmta²⁻	20	0,1	„	$7,60\cdot10^{-8}$	7,12	$7,60\cdot10^{-8}$	7,12
MgTmta²⁻	20	0,1	„	$9,50\cdot10^{-7}$	6,02	$9,50\cdot10^{-7}$	6,02
SrTmta²⁻	20	0,1	„	$6,60\cdot10^{-6}$	5,18	$6,60\cdot10^{-6}$	5,18

LITERATURE CITED

G. Schwarzenbach, H. Ackermann. Helv. chim. Acta, 31, 1029 (1948).

Complexes with ethylenediaminetetraacetic acid

$$H_2C - N \begin{array}{l} CH_2COO^- \\ CH_2COO^- \end{array} (Edta^{4-})$$
$$H_2C - N \begin{array}{l} CH_2COO^- \\ CH_2COO^- \end{array}$$

Complex ion	Temperature, °C	Ionic strength	Method	k	pk	K	pK	Literature main	Literature addit.
BaEdta²⁻	20	0,1	pH-potent.	$1,74 \cdot 10^{-8}$	7,76	$1,74 \cdot 10^{-3}$	7,76	[1]	—
CaEdta²⁻	20	0,1	"	$2,58 \cdot 10^{-11}$	10,59	$2,58 \cdot 10^{-11}$	10,59	[1]	—
CdEdta²⁻	20	0,1	"	$3,3 \cdot 10^{-17}$	16,48	$3,3 \cdot 10^{-17}$	16,48	[2]	—
CeEdta⁻	20	0,1	"	$4,1 \cdot 10^{-16}$	15,39	$4,1 \cdot 10^{-16}$	15,39	[3]	—
CoEdta²⁻	20	0,1	"	$7,9 \cdot 10^{-17}$	16,10	$7,9 \cdot 10^{-17}$	16,10	[2]	—
CuEdta²⁻	20	0,1	"	$1,38 \cdot 10^{-19}$	18,86	$1,38 \cdot 10^{-19}$	18,86	[4]	[2]
DyEdta⁻	20	0,1	"	$2,7 \cdot 10^{-18}$	17,57	$2,7 \cdot 10^{-18}$	17,57	[3]	—
ErEdta⁻	20	0,1	"	$1,05 \cdot 10^{-18}$	17,98	$1,05 \cdot 10^{-18}$	17,98	[3]	—
EuEdta⁻	20	0,1	"	$2,04 \cdot 10^{-17}$	16,69	$2,04 \cdot 10^{-17}$	16,69	[3]	—
FeEdta²⁻	20	0,1	"	$3,54 \cdot 10^{-15}$	14,45	$3,54 \cdot 10^{-15}$	14,45	[4]	[2]
FeEdta⁻	20	0,1	"	$8,0 \cdot 10^{-26}$	25,1	$8,0 \cdot 10^{-26}$	25,1	[5]	—
GdEdta⁻	20	0,1	"	$2,0 \cdot 10^{-17}$	16,70	$2,0 \cdot 10^{-17}$	16,70	[3]	—
HgEdta²⁻	20	0,1	"	$7,1 \cdot 10^{-23}$	22,15	$7,1 \cdot 10^{-23}$	22,15	[6]	—
HoEdta⁻	20	0,1	"	$2,14 \cdot 10^{-18}$	17,67	$2,14 \cdot 10^{-18}$	17,67	[3]	—
LaEdta⁻	20	0,1	"	$1,9 \cdot 10^{-15}$	14,72	$1,9 \cdot 10^{-15}$	14,72	[3]	—
LiEdta³⁻	20	0,1	"	$1,62 \cdot 10^{-3}$	2,79	$1,62 \cdot 10^{-3}$	2,79	[1]	—
LuEdta⁻	20	0,1	"	$8,7 \cdot 10^{-20}$	19,06	$8,7 \cdot 10^{-20}$	19,06	[3]	—

Complex ion	Temperature, °C	Ionic strength	Method	k	pk	K	pK	Literature main	addit.
MgEdta²⁻	20	0,1	pH-potent.	$2,04\cdot10^{-9}$	8,69	$2,04\cdot10^{-9}$	8,69	[1]	—
MnEdta²⁻	20	0,1	"	$3,4\cdot10^{-14}$	13,47	$3,4\cdot10^{-14}$	13,47	[2]	—
NaEdta³⁻	20	0,1	"	$2,2\cdot10^{-2}$	1,66	$2,2\cdot10^{-2}$	1,66	[1]	—
NdEdta⁻	20	0,1	"	$8,7\cdot10^{-17}$	16,06	$8,7\cdot10^{-17}$	16,06	[3]	—
NiEdta²⁻	20	0,1	"	$3,54\cdot10^{-19}$	18,45	$3,54\cdot10^{-19}$	18,45	[2]	[7]
PbEdta²⁻	20	0,1	"	$6,3\cdot10^{-19}$	18,2	$6,3\cdot10^{-19}$	18,2	[2]	—
PrEdta⁻	20	0,1	"	$1,78\cdot10^{-16}$	15,75	$1,78\cdot10^{-16}$	15,75	[3]	—
SmEdta⁻	20	0,1	"	$2,8\cdot10^{-17}$	16,55	$2,8\cdot10^{-17}$	16,55	[3]	—
SrEdta²⁻	20	0,1	"	$2,34\cdot10^{-9}$	8,63	$2,34\cdot10^{-9}$	8,63	[1]	—
TbEdta⁻	20	0,1	"	$5,6\cdot10^{-18}$	17,25	$5,6\cdot10^{-18}$	17,25	[3]	—
TuEdta⁻	20	0,1	"	$2,56\cdot10^{-19}$	18,59	$2,56\cdot10^{-19}$	18,59	[3]	—
YEdta⁻	20	0,1	"	$4,17\cdot10^{-18}$	17,38	$4,17\cdot10^{-18}$	17,38	[3]	—
YbEdta⁻	20	0,1	"	$2,1\cdot10^{-19}$	18,68	$2,1\cdot10^{-19}$	18,68	[3]	—
ZnEdta²⁻	20	0,1	"	$2,63\cdot10^{-17}$	16,58	$2,63\cdot10^{-17}$	16,58	[4]	[2]

LITERATURE CITED

1. G. Schwarzenbach, H. Ackermann. Helv. chim. Acta, **30**, 1798 (1947).
2. G. Schwarzenbach, E. Freitag. Helv. chim. Acta, **34**, 1503 (1951).
3. E. J. Wheelwright, F. H. Spedding, G. Schwarzenbach. J. Am. Chem. Soc., **75**, 4196 (1953).
4. H. Ackermann, G. Schwarzenbach. Helv. chim. Acta, **32**, 1543 (1949).
5. G. Schwarzenbach, J. Heller. Helv. chim. Acta, **31**, 1029 (1948).
6. T. Goffart, G. Michel, G. Dnychaerts. Anal. Chim. Acta, **9**, 184 (1953).
7. C. M. Cook, F. A. Long. J. Am. Chem. Soc., **73**, 4119 (1951).

4. COMPLEXES WITH DIKETONES AND ALDEHYDES

Complexes with acetylacetone $CH_3CO^- = CHCOCH_2$ $(Acac^-)$

Complex ion	Temperature, °C	Ionic strength	Method	k	pk	K	pK	Literature	
								main	addit.
AlAcac²⁺	30	0	pH-potent.	$2,5\cdot10^{-9}$	8,6	$2,5\cdot10^{-9}$	8,6	[1]	[1]
Al (Acac)₂⁺	30	0	»	$1,26\cdot10^{-8}$	7,9	$3,14\cdot10^{-17}$	16,5	[1]	[1]
Al (Acac)₃	30	0	»	$1,6\cdot10^{-6}$	5,8	$5,0\cdot10^{-23}$	22,3	[1]	[1]
BeAcac⁺	20	0	»	$1,32\cdot10^{-8}$	7,88	$1,32\cdot10^{-8}$	7,88	[2]	[2]
Be (Acac)₂	20	0	»	$1,78\cdot10^{-7}$	6,75	$2,35\cdot10^{-15}$	14,63	[2]	[2]
CdAcac⁺	20	0	»	$1,44\cdot10^{-4}$	3,84	$1,44\cdot10^{-4}$	3,84	[2]	[2]
Cd (Acac)₂	20	0	»	$1,32\cdot10^{-3}$	-2,83	$1,9\cdot10^{-7}$	6,72	[2]	[2]
CeAcac²⁺	20	0	»	$5,0\cdot10^{-6}$	5,30	$5,0\cdot10^{-6}$	5,30	[2]	[2]
Ce (Acac)₂⁺	20	0	»	$1,07\cdot10^{-4}$	3,97	$5,35\cdot10^{-10}$	9,27	[2]	[2]
Ce (Acac)₃	20	0	»	$4,16\cdot10^{-4}$	3,38	$2,23\cdot10^{-13}$	12,65	[2]	[2]
CoAcac⁺	20	0	»	$4,0\cdot10^{-6}$	**5,40**	$4,0\cdot10^{-6}$	5,40	[2]	[2]
Co (Acac)₂	20	0	»	$6,75\cdot10^{-5}$	4,17	$2,7\cdot10^{-10}$	9,57	[2]	[2]
CuAcac⁺	20	0	»	$4,9\cdot10^{-9}$	8,31	$4,9\cdot10^{-9}$	8,31	[2]	[2]
Cu (Acac)₂	20	0	»	$1,41\cdot10^{-7}$	6,85	$6,9\cdot10^{-16}$	15,16	[2]	[2]
EuAcac²⁺	30	0	»	$1\cdot10^{-6}$	6,0	$1\cdot10^{-6}$	6,0	[1]	[1]
Eu (Acac)₂⁺	30	0	»	$3,16\cdot10^{-5}$	4,5	$3,16\cdot10^{-11}$	10,5	[1]	[1]
Eu (Acac)₃	30	0	»	$3,16\cdot10^{-4}$	3,5	$1\cdot10^{-14}$	14,0	[1]	[1]
FeAcac²⁺	30	0	»	$1,6\cdot10^{-10}$	9,8	$1,6\cdot10^{-10}$	9,8	[1]	[1,3]
Fe (Acac)₂⁺	30	0	»	$1\cdot10^{-9}$	9,0	$1,6\cdot10^{-19}$	18,8	[1]	[1,3]
Fe (Acac)₃	30	0	»	$4,0\cdot10^{-8}$	7,4	$6,4\cdot10^{-27}$	26,2	[1]	[1,3]

Complex ion	Temperature, °C	Ionic strength	Method	k	pk	K	pK	Literature main	addit.
GaAcac²⁺	30	0	pH-potent.	$4,0\cdot10^{-10}$	9,4	$4,0\cdot10^{-10}$	9,4	[1]	[1]
Ga(Acac)₂⁺	30	0	"	$5,0\cdot10^{-9}$	8,3	$2,0\cdot10^{-18}$	17,7	[1]	[1]
Ga(Acac)₃	30	0	"	$1,26\cdot10^{-6}$	5,9	$2,5\cdot10^{-24}$	23,6	[1]	[1]
InAcac²⁺	30	0	"	$1\cdot10^{-8}$	8,0	$1\cdot10^{-8}$	8,0	[1]	[1]
In(Acac)₂⁺	30	0	"	$8\cdot10^{-8}$	7,1	$8\cdot10^{-16}$	15,1	[1]	[1]
LaAcac²⁺	30	0	"	$7,95\cdot10^{-6}$	5,1	$7,95\cdot10^{-6}$	5,1	[1]	[1]
La(Acac)₂⁺	30	0	"	$1,58\cdot10^{-4}$	3,8	$1,25\cdot10^{-9}$	8,9	[1]	[1]
La(Acac)₃	30	0	"	$1,26\cdot10^{-3}$	2,9	$1,6\cdot10^{-12}$	11,8	[1]	[1]
MgAcac⁺	20	0	"	$2,14\cdot10^{-4}$	3,67	$2,14\cdot10^{-4}$	3,67	[2]	[2]
Mg(Acac)₂	20	0	"	$1,95\cdot10^{-3}$	2,71	$2,16\cdot10^{-7}$	6,38	[2]	[2]
MnAcac⁺	20	0	"	$5,75\cdot10^{-5}$	4,24	$5,75\cdot10^{-5}$	4,24	[2]	[2]
Mn(Acac)₂	20	0	"	$7,76\cdot10^{-4}$	3,11	$4,45\cdot10^{-8}$	7,35	[2]	[2]
NdAcac²⁺	30	0	"	$2,51\cdot10^{-6}$	5,6	$2,51\cdot10^{-6}$	5,6	[1]	[1]
Nd(Acac)₂⁺	30	0	"	$5,0\cdot10^{-5}$	4,3	$1,25\cdot10^{-10}$	9,9	[1]	[1]
Nd(Acac)₃	30	0	"	$6,3\cdot10^{-4}$	3,2	$7,9\cdot10^{-14}$	13,1	[1]	[1]
NiAcac⁺	20	0	"	$8,7\cdot10^{-7}$	6,06	$8,7\cdot10^{-7}$	6,06	[2]	[2]
Ni(Acac)₂	20	0	"	$1,95\cdot10^{-5}$	4,71	$1,7\cdot10^{-11}$	10,77	[2]	[2]
Ni(Acac)₃⁻	20	0	"	$4,8\cdot10^{-3}$	2,32	$8,15\cdot10^{-14}$	13,09	[2]	[2]
ScAcac²⁺	30	0	"	$1\cdot10^{-8}$	8,0	$1\cdot10^{-8}$	8,0	[1]	[1]
Sc(Acac)₂⁺	30	0	"	$6,3\cdot10^{-8}$	7,2	$6,3\cdot10^{-16}$	15,2	[1]	[1]
SmAcac²⁺	30	0	"	$1,26\cdot10^{-6}$	5,9	$1,26\cdot10^{-6}$	5,9	[1]	[1]
Sm(Acac)₂⁺	30	0	"	$3,16\cdot10^{-5}$	4,5	$4,0\cdot10^{-11}$	10,4	[1]	[1]
Sm(Acac)₃	30	0	"	$6,3\cdot10^{-4}$	3,2	$2,5\cdot10^{-14}$	13,6	[1]	[1]
ThAcac³⁺	30	0	"	$1,6\cdot10^{-9}$	8,8	$1,6\cdot10^{-9}$	8,8	[1]	[1]

Complex ion	Temperature, °C	Ionic strength	Method	k	pk	K	pK	Literature	
								main	addit.
Th(Acac)$_2^{2+}$	30	0	pH-potent.	$4,0\cdot10^{-8}$	7,4	$6,4\cdot10^{-17}$	16,2	[1]	[1]
Th(Acac)$_3^+$	30	0	"	$5,0\cdot10^{-7}$	6,3	$3,2\cdot10^{-23}$	22,5	[1]	[1]
Th(Acac)$_4$	30	0	"	$6,3\cdot10^{-5}$	4,2	$2,0\cdot10^{-27}$	26,7	[1]	[1]
UO$_2$Acac$^+$	20	0	"	$2,19\cdot10^{-8}$	7,66	$2,19\cdot10^{-8}$	7,66	[2]	[2]
UO$_2$(Acac)$_2$	20	0	"	$3,24\cdot10^{-7}$	6,49	$7,1\cdot10^{-15}$	14,15	[2]	[2]
YAcac^{2+}	30	0	"	$4,0\cdot10^{-7}$	6,4	$4,0\cdot10^{-7}$	6,4	[1]	[1]
Y(Acac)$_2^+$	30	0	"	$2,0\cdot10^{-5}$	4,7	$8\cdot10^{-12}$	11,1	[1]	[1]
Y(Acac)$_3$	30	0	"	$1,6\cdot10^{-3}$	2,8	$1,26\cdot10^{-14}$	13,9	[1]	[1]
ZnAcac$^+$	20	0	"	$8,5\cdot10^{-6}$	5,07	$8,5\cdot10^{-6}$	5,07	[2]	[2]
Zn(Acac)$_2$	20	0	"	$1,12\cdot10^{-4}$	3,95	$9,5\cdot10^{-10}$	9,02	[2]	[2]

LITERATURE CITED

1. R. M. Izatt, W. C. Fernelius, C. G. Haas, Jr., B. P. Block. J. Phys. Chem., 59, 170 (1955).
2. R. M. Izatt, W. C. Fernelius, B. P. Block. J. Phys. Chem., 59, 235 (1955).
3. J. Badoz-Lambling. Ann. chimie, 8, No 12, 586 (1953); cit. in Chem. Abst. J., 13790 (1955).

189

Complexes with β-methyltropolone.*

Complex ion	Temperature, °C	Ionic strength	Method	k	pk	K	pK
Be βMet⁺	30	—	pH-potent.	$4,0 \cdot 10^{-10}$	9,4	$4,0 \cdot 10^{-10}$	9,4
Be (βMet)₂	30	—	"	$2,0 \cdot 10^{-8}$	7,7	$8,0 \cdot 10^{-8}$	17,1
Ca βMet⁺	30	—	"	$5,0 \cdot 10^{-6}$	5,3	$5,0 \cdot 10^{-6}$	5,3
Ca (βMet)₂	30	—	"	$2,5 \cdot 0^{-4}$	3,6	$1,3 \cdot 10^{-9}$	8,9
Co βMet⁺	30	—	"	$1,3 \cdot 10^{-8}$	7,9	$1,3 \cdot 10^{-8}$	7,9
Co (βMet)₂	30	—	"	$6,3 \cdot 10^{-7}$	6,2	$8,0 \cdot 10^{-15}$	14,1
Mg βMet⁺	30	—	"	$1,0 \cdot 10^{-6}$	6,0	$1,0 \cdot 10^{-6}$	6,0
Mg (βMet)₂	30	—	"	$2,5 \cdot 10^{-5}$	4,6	$2,5 \cdot 10^{-11}$	10,6
Mg (βMet)₃⁻	30	—	"	$8,0 \cdot 10^{-7}$	3,1	$2,0 \cdot 10^{-14}$	13,7
Ni βMet⁺	30	—	"	$4,0 \cdot 10^{-9}$	8,4	$4,0 \cdot 10^{-9}$	8,4
Ni (βMet)₂	30	—	"	$2,5 \cdot 10^{-7}$	6,6	$1,0 \cdot 10^{-15}$	15,0
Ni (βMet)₃⁻	30	—	"	$8,0 \cdot 10^{-5}$	4,1	$8,0 \cdot 10^{-20}$	19,1
Pb βMet⁺	30	—	"	$2,5 \cdot 10^{-10}$	9,6	$2,5 \cdot 10^{-10}$	9,6
Pb (βMet)₂	30	—	"	$2,5 \cdot 10^{-7}$	6,6	$6,3 \cdot 10^{-17}$	16,2
Zn βMet⁺	30	—	"	$4,0 \cdot 10^{-9}$	8,4	$4,0 \cdot 10^{-9}$	8,4
Zn (βMet)₂	30	—	"	$1,6 \cdot 10^{-7}$	6,8	$6,3 \cdot 10^{-16}$	15,2
Zn (βMet)₃⁻	30	—	"	$2,5 \cdot 10^{-4}$	3,6	$1,6 \cdot 10^{-19}$	18,8

*In a 50% dioxane—water mixture

LITERATURE CITED

B. E. Bryant, W. C. Fernelius. J. Am. Chem. Soc., 76, 1696 (1954).

Complexes with sulfosalicylaldehyde

$$^-O_3S-\langle\underline{\quad}\rangle-O^- \quad (SSald^{2-})$$
$$\quad\quad\quad\quad COH$$

Complex ion	Temperature, °C	Ionic strength	Method	k	pk	K	pK
CoSSald	25	—	pH-potent.	$3,8 \cdot 10^{-4}$	3,42	$3,8 \cdot 10^{-4}$	3,42
CuSSald	25	—	"	$4,5 \cdot 10^{-6}$	5.35	$4,5 \cdot 10^{-6}$	5,35
Cu (SSald)$_2^{2-}$	25	—	"	$1,2 \cdot 10^{-4}$	3,92	$5.4 \cdot 10^{-10}$	9,27
NiSSald	25	—	"	$1,62 \cdot 10^{-4}$	3,79	$1,62 \cdot 10^{-4}$	3,79
Ni (SSald)$_2^{2-}$	25	—	"	$1,7 \cdot 10^{-3}$	2,77	$2,76 \cdot 10^{-7}$	6,56
ZnSSald	25	—	"	$1,0 \cdot 10^{-3}$	3,0	$1,0 \cdot 10^{-3}$	3,0

LITERATURE CITED

M. Calvin, N. C. Melchior. J. Am. Chem. Soc., **70**, 3270 (1948).

Complexes with thenoyltrifluoroacetone

$$\langle\underline{\quad}\rangle_S COCHC\bar{O}CF_3 (Tf^-)$$

Complex ion	$t, °C$	Ionic strength	Method	k	pk	K	pK
CuTf$^+$	20	0,1	pH-potent.	$2,8 \cdot 10^{-7}$	6,55	$2,8 \cdot 10^{-7}$	6,55
Cu (Tf)$_2$	—	—	"	—	—	$1,0 \cdot 10^{-13}$	13,0
FeTf^{2+}	25	0,1	Spectr.	$1,26 \cdot 10^{-7}$	6,9	$1,26 \cdot 10^{-7}$	6,9
Ni(Tf)$_2$	—	—	pH-potent.	—	—	$1,0 \cdot 10^{-10}$	10,00
PuTf^{3+}	25	0,2	Spectr.	$1,0 \cdot 10^{-8}$	8,0	$1,0 \cdot 10^{-8}$	8,0
ThTf^{3+}	25	0,11	"	$4,0 \cdot 10^{-8}$	7,4	$4,0 \cdot 10^{-8}$	7,4
UTf^{3+}	25	0,1	"	$6,3 \cdot 10^{-8}$	7,2	$6,3 \cdot 10^{-8}$	7,2

LITERATURE CITED

A. E. Martell, M. Calvin. Chemistry of the metal chelate compounds. New York, 1953.

Complexes with tropolone [*]

Complex ion	Temperature, °C	Ionic strength	Method	k	pk	K	pK
BeTrop⁺	30	—	pH- potent.	$4{,}0 \cdot 10^{-9}$	8,4	$4{,}0 \cdot 10^{-9}$	8,4
Be (Trop)$_2$	30	—	„	$1{,}0 \cdot 10^{-7}$	7,0	$4{,}0 \cdot 10^{-16}$	15,4
CaTrop⁺	30	—	„	$1{,}6 \cdot 10^{-5}$	4,8	$1{,}6 \cdot 10^{-5}$	4,8
Ca (Trop)$_2$	30	—	„	$6{,}3 \cdot 10^{-4}$	3,2	$1{,}0 \cdot 10^{-8}$	8,0
CoTrop⁺	30	—	„	$1{,}0 \cdot 10^{-7}$	7,0	$1{,}0 \cdot 10^{-7}$	7,0
Co (Trop)$_2$	30	—	„	$1{,}26 \cdot 10^{-6}$	5,9	$1{,}26 \cdot 10^{-13}$	12,9
Co (Trop)$_3$⁻	30	—	„	$1{,}6 \cdot 10^{-4}$	3,8	$2{,}0 \ \ 10^{-17}$	16,7
Cu (Trop)$_2$	30	—	„	$1{,}26 \cdot 10^{-8}$	7,9	—	—
Mg Trop⁺	30	—	„	$3{,}2 \cdot 10^{-6}$	5,5	$3{,}2 \cdot 10^{-6}$	5,5
Mg (Trop)$_2$	30	—	„	$4{,}0 \cdot 10^{-5}$	4,4	$1{,}3 \cdot 10^{-10}$	9,9
NiTrop⁺	30	—	„	$2{,}0 \cdot 10^{-8}$	7,7	$2{,}0 \cdot 10^{-8}$	7,7
Ni (Trop)$_2$	30	—	„	$8{,}0 \cdot 10^{-7}$	6,1	$1{,}6 \cdot 10^{-14}$	13,8
Ni (Trop)$_3$⁻	30	—	„	$1{,}0 \cdot 10^{-4}$	4,0	$1{,}6 \cdot 10^{-18}$	17,8
PbTrop⁺	30	—	„	$1{,}0 \cdot 10^{-8}$	8,0	$1{,}0 \cdot 10^{-8}$	8,0
Pb (Trop)$_2$	30	—	„	$1{,}0 \cdot 10^{-6}$	6,0	$1{,}0 \cdot 10^{-14}$	14,0
ZnTrop⁺	30	—	„	$3{,}2 \cdot 10^{-8}$	7,5	$3{,}2 \cdot 10^{-8}$	7,5
Zn (Trop)$_2$	30	—	„	$3{,}2 \cdot 10^{-7}$	6,5	$1{,}0 \cdot 10^{-14}$	14,0
Zn (Trop)$_3$⁻	30	—	„	$3{,}2 \cdot 10^{-4}$	3,5	$3{,}2 \cdot 10^{-18}$	17,5

[*] In a 50% dioxane—water mixture

LITERATURE CITED

B. E. Bryant, W. C. Fernelius, B. E. Douglas. J. Am. Chem. Soc., 75, 3784 (1953).

Complexes with salicylaldehyde

$$O^- \!\!-\!\!CHO \quad (Sald^-)$$

Complex ion	Temperature, °C	Ionic strength	Method	k	pk	K	pK	Literature main	Literature addit.
Cd (Sald)₂	20	0,1	pH-potent.	—	—	$1,6 \cdot 10^{-8}$	7,8	[1]	—
CoSald⁺	20	0,1	"	$2,14 \cdot 10^{-5}$	4,67	$2,14 \cdot 10^{-5}$	4,67	[1]	—
Co (Sald)₂	20	0,1	"	$2,34 \cdot 10^{-4}$	3,63	$5,0 \cdot 10^{-9}$	8,3	[1]	—
CuSald⁺	20	0,1	"	$4,0 \cdot 10^{-8}$	7,40	$4,0 \cdot 10^{-8}$	7,40	[1]	[2]
Cu (Sald)₂	20	0,1	"	$1,26 \cdot 10^{-6}$	5,90	$5,0 \cdot 10^{-14}$	13,3	[1]	—
FeSald⁺	20	0,1	"	$6,0 \cdot 10^{-5}$	4,22	$6,0 \cdot 10^{-5}$	4,22	[1]	—
Fe (Sald)₂	20	0,1	"	$4,17 \cdot 10^{-4}$	3,38	$2,5 \cdot 10^{-8}$	7,6	[1]	—
MnSald⁺	20	0,1	"	$1,86 \cdot 10^{-4}$	3,73	$1,86 \cdot 10^{-4}$	3,73	[1]	—
Mn (Sald)₂	20	0,1	"	$8,5 \cdot 10^{-4}$	3,07	$1,6 \cdot 10^{-7}$	6,8	[1]	—
NiSald⁺	20	0,1	"	$6,0 \cdot 10^{-6}$	5,22	$6,0 \cdot 10^{-6}$	5,22	[1]	—
Ni (Sald)₂	20	0,1	"	$1,05 \cdot 10^{-4}$	3,98	$6,3 \cdot 10^{-10}$	9,2	[1]	—
Pb (Sald)₂	20	0,1	"	—	—	$8,0 \cdot 10^{-10}$	9,1	[1]	—
ZnSald⁺	20	0,1	"	$3,16 \cdot 10^{-5}$	4,50	$3,16 \cdot 10^{-5}$	4,50	[1]	—
Zn (Sald)₂	20	0,1	"	$2,5 \cdot 10^{-4}$	3,60	$7,9 \cdot 10^{-9}$	8,1	[1]	—

LITERATURE CITED

1. D. C. Mellor, L. Maley. Nature, 159, 370 (1947).
2. M. Calvin, K. W. Wilson. J. Am. Chem. Soc., 67, 2003 (1945).

Complexes with α-isopropyltropolone *

(αIst⁻)

Complex ion	Temperature, °C	Ionic strength	Method	k	pk	K	pK
BeαIst⁺	30	—	pH-potent.	$2,0 \cdot 10^{-11}$	10,7	$2,0 \cdot 10^{-11}$	10,7
Be (αIst)₂	30	—	»	$8,0 \cdot 10^{-10}$	9,1	$1,6 \cdot 10^{-20}$	9,8
CaαIst⁺	30	—	»	$6,3 \cdot 10^{-6}$	5,2	$6,3 \cdot 10^{-6}$	5,2
Ca (αIst)₂	30	—	»	$2,5 \cdot 10^{-4}$	3,6	$1,6 \cdot 10^{-9}$	8,8
CoαIst⁺	30	—	»	$8,0 \cdot 10^{-9}$	8,1	$8,0 \cdot 10^{-9}$	8,1
Co (αIst)₂	30	—	»	$2,0 \cdot 10^{-7}$	6,7	$4,0 \cdot 10^{-14}$	13,4
MgαIst⁺	30	—	»	$6,3 \cdot 10^{-7}$	6,2	$6,3 \cdot 10^{-7}$	6,2
Mg (αIst)₂	30	—	»	$6,3 \cdot 10^{-6}$	5,2	$4,0 \cdot 10^{-12}$	11,4
NiαIst⁺	30	—	»	$2,5 \cdot 10^{-9}$	8,6	$2,5 \cdot 10^{-9}$	8,6
Ni (αIst)₂	30	—	»	$1,3 \cdot 10^{-7}$	6,9	$3,2 \cdot 10^{-16}$	15,5
Ni (αIst)₃⁻	30	—	»	$2,0 \cdot 10^{-4}$	3,7	$6,3 \cdot 10^{-20}$	19,2
PbαIst⁺	30	—	»	$3,2 \cdot 10^{-10}$	9,5	$3,2 \cdot 10^{-10}$	9,5
Pb (αIst)₂	30	—	»	$3,2 \cdot 10^{-8}$	7,5	$1,0 \cdot 10^{-17}$	17,0
ZnαIst⁺	30	—	»	$2,0 \cdot 10^{-9}$	8,7	$2,0 \cdot 10^{-9}$	8,7
Zn (αIst)₂	30	—	»	$3,2 \cdot 10^{-8}$	7,5	$6,3 \cdot 10^{-17}$	16,2

*In a 50% dioxane—water mixture

LITERATURE CITED

B. E. Bryant, W. C. Fernelius. J. Am. Chem. Soc., 76, 1696 (1954).

Complexes with β-isopropyltropolone*

(βIst^-) —CH(CH₃)₂ → $-CH(CH_3)_2$

Complex ion	Temperature, °C	Ionic strength	Method	k	pk	K	pK
Beβlst+	30	—	pH-potent.	$8,0 \cdot 10^{-10}$	9,1	$8,0 \cdot 10^{-10}$	9,1
Be (βlst)₂	30	—	"	$3,2 \cdot 10^{-8}$	7,5	$2,5 \cdot 10^{-17}$	16,6
Caβlst+	30	—	"	$4,0 \cdot 10^{-6}$	5,4	$4,0 \cdot 10^{-6}$	5,4
Ca (βlst)₂	30	—	"	$2,5 \cdot 10^{-4}$	3,6	$1,0 \cdot 10^{-9}$	9,0
Coβlst+	30	—	"	$1,3 \cdot 10^{-8}$	7,9	$1,3 \cdot 10^{-8}$	7,9
Co (βlst)₂	30	—	"	$5,0 \cdot 10^{-7}$	6,3	$6,3 \cdot 10^{-15}$	14,2
Co (βlst)₃⁻	30	—	"	$1,6 \cdot 10^{-4}$	3,8	$1,0 \cdot 10^{-18}$	18,0
Mgβlst+	30	—	"	$6,3 \cdot 10^{-7}$	6,2	$6,3 \cdot 10^{-7}$	6,2
Mg (βlst)₂	30	—	"	$1,6 \cdot 10^{-5}$	4,8	$1,0 \cdot 10^{-11}$	11,0
Mg (βlst)₃⁻	30	—	"	$1,0 \cdot 10^{-8}$	3,0	$1,0 \cdot 10^{-14}$	14,0
Niβlst+	30	—	"	$3,2 \cdot 10^{-9}$	8,5	$3,2 \cdot 10^{-9}$	8,5
Ni (βlst)₂	30	—	"	$3,2 \cdot 10^{-7}$	6,5	$1,0 \cdot 10^{-16}$	15,0
Ni (βlst)₃⁻	30	—	"	$1,0 \cdot 10^{-4}$	4,0	$1,0 \cdot 10^{-19}$	19,0
Pbβlst+	30	—	"	$1,0 \cdot 10^{-9}$	9,0	$1,0 \cdot 10^{-9}$	9,0
Pb (βlst)₂	30	—	"	$2,0 \cdot 10^{-6}$	6,7	$2,0 \cdot 10^{-16}$	15,7
Znβlst+	30	—	"	$2,0 \cdot 10^{-9}$	8,7	$2,0 \cdot 10^{-9}$	8,7
Zn (βlst)₂	30	—	"	$1,0 \cdot 10^{-7}$	7,0	$2,0 \cdot 10^{-16}$	15,7
Zn (βlst)₃⁻	30	—	"	$2,5 \cdot 10^{-4}$	3,6	$5,0 \cdot 10^{-20}$	19,3

*In a 50% dioxane—water mixture

LITERATURE CITED

B. E. Bryant, W. C. Fernelius. J. Am. Chem. Soc., 76, 1696 (1954).

Complexes with α-methyltropolone*

(αMet⁻)

Complex ion	Temperature, °C	Ionic strength	Method	k	pk	K	pK
Beα Met⁺	30	—	pH-potent.	$5,0·10^{-11}$	10,3	$5,0·10^{-11}$	10,3
Be(αMet)₂	30	—	"	$1,0·10^{-9}$	9,0	$5,0·10^{-20}$	19,3
Caα Met⁺	30	—	"	$8,0·10^{-6}$	5,1	$8,0·10^{-6}$	5,1
Ca(αMet)₂	30	—	"	$4,0·10^{-4}$	3,4	$3,2·10^{-9}$	8,5
Coα Met⁺	30	—	"	$1,0·10^{-8}$	8,0	$1,0·10^{-8}$	8,0
Co(αMet)₂	30	—	"	$5,0·10^{-7}$	6,3	$5,0·10^{-15}$	14,3
Mgα Met⁺	30	—	"	$1·10^{-6}$	6,0	$1,0·10^{-6}$	6,0
Mg(αMet)₂	30	—	"	$2,5·10^{-5}$	4,6	$2,5·10^{-11}$	10,6
Mg(αMet)₃⁻	30	—	"	$2,5·10^{-3}$	2,6	$1,6·10^{-13}$	12,8
Niα Met⁺	30	—	"	$4,0·10^{-9}$	8,4	$4,0·10^{-9}$	8,4
Ni(αMet)₂	30	—	"	$2,0·10^{-7}$	6,7	$8,0·10^{-16}$	15,1
Ni(αMet)₃⁻	30	—	"	$2,0·10^{-4}$	3,7	$1,6·10^{-19}$	18,8
Pbα Met⁺	30	—	"	$4,0·10^{-10}$	9,4	$4,0·10^{-10}$	9,4
Pb(αMet)₂	30	—	"	$2,0·10^{-7}$	6,7	$8,0·10^{-17}$	16,1
Znα Met⁺	30	—	"	$2,5·10^{-9}$	8,6	$2,5·10^{-9}$	8,6
Zn(αMet)₂	30	—	"	$8,0·10^{-8}$	7,1	$2,0·10^{-16}$	15,7

*In a 50% dioxane—water mixture

LITERATURE CITED

B. E. Bryant, W. C. Fernelius. J. Am. Chem. Soc., 76, 1696 (1954).

5. COMPLEXES WITH OTHER ORGANIC ADDENDS

Complexes with o-aminophenol *

(Aph)

Complex ion	t, °C	Ionic strength	Method	k	pk	K	pK
CoAph$^+$	25	0,01	pH-potent.	$1,38 \cdot 10^{-6}$	5,86	$1,38 \cdot 10^{-6}$	5,86
Co(Aph)$_2$	25	0,01	"	$2,7 \cdot 10^{-5}$	4,57	$3,70 \cdot 10^{-11}$	10,43
CuAph$^+$	25	0,01	"	$5,6 \cdot 10^{-10}$	9,25	$5,6 \cdot 10^{-10}$	9,25
Cu(Aph)$_2$	25	0,01	"	$3,4 \cdot 10^{-9}$	8,47	$1,90 \cdot 10^{-18}$	17,72
Ni Aph$^+$	25	0,01	"	$2,4 \cdot 10^{-7}$	6,62	$2,4 \cdot 10^{-7}$	6,62
Ni(Aph)$_2$	25	0,01	"	$1,62 \cdot 10^{-5}$	4,79	$3,9 \cdot 10^{-12}$	11,41
PbAph$^+$	25	0,01	"	$6,6 \cdot 10^{-8}$	7,18	$6,6 \cdot 10^{-8}$	7,18
Pb(Aph)$_2$	25	0,01	"	$4,16 \cdot 10^{-6}$	5,38	$2,75 \cdot 10^{-13}$	12,56
ZnAph$^+$	25	0,01	"	$4,07 \cdot 10^{-7}$	6,39	$4,07 \cdot 10^{-7}$	6,39
Zn(Aph)$_2$	25	0,01	"	$1,7 \cdot 10^{-6}$	5,77	$6,9 \cdot 10^{-13}$	12,16

LITERATURE CITED

R. G. Charles, H. Freiser. J. Am. Chem. Soc., 74, 1385 (1952).

Complexes with 8-hydroxy-2,4-dimethylquinazoline *

(DmHas$^-$)

Complex ion	t, °C	Ionic strength	Method	$\varkappa$	p$\varkappa$	K	pK
CuDmHas$^+$	20	0,3	pH-potent.	$5,5 \cdot 10^{-11}$	10,26	$5,5 \cdot 10^{-11}$	10,26
Cu(DmHas)$_2$	20	0,3	"	$1,8 \cdot 10^{-10}$	9,74	$1,0 \cdot 10^{-20}$	20,00
MgDmHas$^+$	20	0,3	"	$1,55 \cdot 10^{-4}$	3,81	$1,55 \cdot 10^{-4}$	3,81
Mg(DmHas)$_2$	20	0,3	"	$8,1 \cdot 10^{-4}$	3,09	$1,25 \cdot 10^{-7}$	6,90
NiDmHas$^+$	20	0,3	"	$1,32 \cdot 10^{-8}$	7,88	$1,32 \cdot 10^{-8}$	7,88
Ni(DmHas)$_2$	20	0,3	"	$1,0 \cdot 10^{-7}$	7,00	$1,32 \cdot 10^{-15}$	14,88
UO$_2$DmHas$^+$	20	0,3	"	$1,7 \cdot 10^{-9}$	8,77	$1,7 \cdot 10^{-9}$	8,77
UO$_2$(DmHas)$_2$	20	0,3	"	$4,7 \cdot 10^{-8}$	7,33	$8,0 \cdot 10^{-17}$	16,10
ZnDmHas$^+$	20	0,3	"	$1,7 \cdot 10^{-8}$	7,77	$1,7 \cdot 10^{-8}$	7,77
Zn(DmHas)$_2$	20	0,3	"	$9,8 \cdot 10^{-8}$	7,81	$1,65 \cdot 10^{-15}$	14,78

*In a 50% dioxane—water mixture

LITERATURE CITED

H. Irving, H. S. Rossotti. J. Chem. Soc., 1954, 2910.

Complexes with 8-hydroxy-4-methyl-2-phenylquinazoline*

CH$_3$

(MpHas$^-$)

C$_6$H$_5$

O$^-$

Complex ion	t, °C	Ionic strength	Method	k	pk	K	pK
CuMpHas$^+$	20	0,3	pH- potent.	$1,48\cdot10^{-9}$	8,83	$1,48\cdot10^{-9}$	8,83
Cu (MpHas)$_2$	20	0,3	"	$4,9\cdot10^{-9}$	8,31	$7,25\cdot10^{-18}$	17,14
UO$_2$MpHas$^+$	20	0,3	"	$2,95\cdot10^{-9}$	8,53	$2,95\cdot10^{-9}$	8,53
UO$_2$(MpHas)$_2$	20	0,3	"	$1,41\cdot10^{-8}$	7,85	$4,16\cdot10^{-17}$	16,38
ZnMpHas$^+$	20	0,3	"	$9,3\cdot10^{-8}$	7,03	$9,3\cdot10^{-8}$	7,03
Zn (MpHas)$_2$	20	0,3	,"	$1,35\cdot10^{-6}$	5,87	$1,26\cdot10^{-13}$	12,90

LITERATURE CITED

H. Irving, H. S. Rossotti. J. Chem. Soc., 1954, 2910.

Complexes with 8-hydroxy-5-methylquinoline *

CH$_3$

(mOxin$^-$)

N

$^-$O

Complex ion	t, °C	Ionic strength	Method	k	pk	K	pK
Cu mOxin$^+$	20	0,3	pH- potent.	$3\cdot10^{-14}$	13,55	$2,8\cdot10^{-14}$	13,55
Cu(mOxin)$_2$	20	0,3	"	$4,5\cdot10^{-13}$	12,35	$1,26\cdot10^{-26}$	25,90
Mg mOxin$^+$	20	0,3	"	$6,16\cdot10^{-6}$	5,21	$6,16\cdot10^{-6}$	5,21
Mg (mOxin)$_2$	20	0,3	"	$3,4\cdot10^{-5}$	4,47	$2,1\cdot10^{-10}$	9,68
UO$_2$ mOxin$^+$	20	0,3	"	$5,6\cdot10^{-12}$	11,25	$5,6\cdot10^{-12}$	11,25
UO$_2$ (mOxin)$_2$	20	0,3	"	$3,0\cdot10^{-10}$	9,52	$1,7\cdot10^{-21}$	20,77
Zn mOxin$^+$	20	0,3	"	$6,2\cdot10^{-6}$	5,21	$6,2\cdot10^{-6}$	5,21
Zn (mOxin)$_2$	20	0,3	"	$3,4\cdot10^{-5}$	4,47	$2,1\cdot10^{-10}$	9,68

*In a 50% dioxane—water mixture

LITERATURE CITED

H. Irving, H. S. Rossotti. J. Chem. Soc., 1954, 2910.

Complexes with 8-hydroxy-2-methylquinoline*

N — CH_3 , $-O$, (Oxd^-)

Complex ion	Temperature, °C	Ionic strength	Method	k	pk	K	pK	Literature main	Literature addit.
CeOxd^{2+}	25	—	pH-potent.	$1,95 \cdot 10^{-8}$	7,71	$1,95 \cdot 10^{-8}$	7,71	[1]	—
CoOxd$^+$	25	—	»	$2,10 \cdot 10^{-10}$	9,68	$2,10 \cdot 10^{-10}$	9,68	[1]	—
Co(Oxd)$_2$	25	—	»	$1,2 \cdot 10^{-9}$	8,92	$2,5 \cdot 10^{-19}$	18,60	[1]	—
CuOxd$^+$	20	0,3	»	$6,0 \cdot 10^{-11}$	10,22	$6,0 \cdot 10^{-11}$	10,22	[2]	[1]
Gu(Oxd)$_2$	20	0,3	»	$4,8 \cdot 10^{-10}$	9,32	$2,9 \cdot 10^{-20}$	19,54	[2]	[1]
MgOxd$^+$	20	0,3	»	$1,86 \cdot 10^{-4}$	3,73	$1,86 \cdot 10^{-4}$	3,73	[2]	—
Mg(Oxd)$_2$	20	0,3	»	$7,4 \cdot 10^{-4}$	3,13	$1,38 \cdot 10^{-7}$	6,86	[2]	—
MnOxd$^+$	25	—	»	$1,9 \cdot 10^{-8}$	7,72	$1,9 \cdot 10^{-8}$	7,72	[1]	—
Mn(Oxd)$_2$	25	—	»	$1,45 \cdot 10^{-7}$	6,84	$2,76 \cdot 10^{-15}$	14,56	[1]	—
NiOxd$^+$	20	0,3	»	$3,0 \cdot 10^{-9}$	8,52	$3,0 \cdot 10^{-9}$	8,52	[2]	[1]
Ni(Oxd)$_2$	20	0,3	»	$1,1 \cdot 10^{-8}$	7,96	$3,3 \cdot 10^{-17}$	16,48	[2]	[1]
PbOxd$^+$	25	—	»	$4,5 \cdot 10^{-11}$	10,35	$4,5 \cdot 10^{-11}$	10,35	[1]	—
Pb(Oxd)$_2$	25	—	»	$5,6 \cdot 10^{-9}$	8,25	$2,5 \cdot 10^{-19}$	18,60	[1]	—
UO$_2$Oxd$^+$	20	0,3	»	$4,0 \cdot 10^{-10}$	9,4	$4,0 \cdot 10^{-10}$	9,4	[2]	—
UO$_2$(Oxd)$_2$	20	0,3	»	$1,0 \cdot 10^{-8}$	8,0	$4,0 \cdot 10^{-18}$	17,4	[2]	—
ZnOxd$^+$	20	0,3	»	$2,2 \cdot 10^{-9}$	8,66	$2,2 \cdot 10^{-9}$	8,66	[2]	[1]
Zn(Oxd)$_2$	20	0,3	»	$8,0 \cdot 10^{-9}$	8,10	$1,74 \cdot 10^{-17}$	16,76	[2]	[1]

*In a 50% dioxane—water mixture

LITERATURE CITED

1. W. D. Johnston, H. Freiser. J. Am. Chem. Soc., 74, 5239 (1952).
2. H. Irving, H. S. Rossotti, J. Chem. Soc., 1954, 2910.

Complexes with 8-hydroxy-6-methylquinoline[*]

(MeOxin⁻) → (MeOxin^-)

Complex ion	t, °C	Ionic strength	Method	k	pk	K	pK
MgMeOxin⁺	20	0,3	pH-potent.	$8,14\cdot10^{-6}$	5,09	$8,14\cdot10^{-6}$	5,09
Mg(MeOxin)₂	20	0,3	"	$4,90\cdot10^{-5}$	4,31	$4,0\cdot10^{-10}$	9,40
UO₂MeOxin⁺	20	0,3	"	$1,29\cdot10^{-11}$	10,89	$1,29\cdot10^{-11}$	10,89
UO₂(MeOxin)₂	20	0,3	"	$5,5\cdot10^{-10}$	9,26	$7,1\cdot10^{-21}$	20,15

LITERATURE CITED

H. Irving, H. S. Rossotti. J. Chem. Soc., 1954, 2910.

Complexes with 8-hydroxy-7-methylquinoline[*]

(meOxin⁻) → (meOxin^-)

Complex ion	t, °C	Ionic strength	Method	k	pk	K	pK
MgmeOxin⁺	20	0,3	pH-potent.	$2,3\cdot10^{-5}$	4,64	$2,3\cdot10^{-5}$	4,64
Mg(meOxin)₂	20	0,3	"	$7,6\cdot10^{-5}$	4,12	$1,74\cdot10^{-9}$	8,76
UO₂meOxin⁺	20	0,3	"	$5,25\cdot10^{-12}$	11,28	$5,25\cdot10^{-12}$	11,28
UO₂(meOxin)₂	20	0,3	"	$1,66\cdot10^{-10}$	9,78	$8,7\cdot10^{-22}$	21,06
ZnmeOxin⁺	20	0,3	"	$4,9\cdot10^{-10}$	9,31	$4,9\cdot10^{-10}$	9,31
Zn(meOxin)₂	20	0,3	"	$7,8\cdot10^{-9}$	8,11	$3,8\cdot10^{-18}$	17,42

[*]In a 50% dioxane—water mixture

LITERATURE CITED

H. Irving, H. S. Rossotti. J. Chem. Soc., 1954, 2910.

Complexes with 8-hydroxy-4-methylcinnoline*

$(Mcin^-)$

Complex ion	t, °C	Ionic strength	Method	k	pk	K	pK
MgMcin$^+$	20	0,3	pH- potent.	$2,2 \cdot 10^{-4}$	3,66	$2,2 \cdot 10^{-4}$	3,66
Mg(Mcin)$_2$	20	0,3	"	$2,62 \cdot 10^{-3}$	2,58	$5,75 \cdot 10^{-7}$	6,24
NiMcin$^+$	20	0,3	"	$3,2 \cdot 10^{-9}$	8,5	$3,2 \cdot 10^{-9}$	8,5
Ni(Mcin)$_2$	20	0,3	"	$6,3 \cdot 10^{-9}$	8,2	$2,0 \cdot 10^{-17}$	16,7
UO$_2$Mcin$^+$	20	0,3	"	$1,0 \cdot 10^{-9}$	9,00	$1,0 \cdot 10^{-9}$	9,00
UO$_2$(Mcin)$_2$	20	0,3	"	$5,0 \cdot 10^{-8}$	7,30	$5,0 \cdot 10^{-17}$	16,30
ZnMcin$^+$	20	0,3	"	$6,0 \cdot 10^{-8}$	7,22	$6,0 \cdot 10^{-8}$	7,22
Zn(Mcin)$_2$	20	0,3	"	$3,4 \cdot 10^{-7}$	6,47	$2,04 \cdot 10^{-14}$	13,69

LITERATURE CITED

H. Irving, H. S. Rossotti. J. Chem. Soc., 1954, 2910.

Complexes with 8-hydroxyquinazoline *

(Has^-)

Complex ion	t, °C	Ionic strength	Method	k	pk	K	pK
CuHas$^+$	20	0,3	pH- potent.	$2,76 \cdot 10^{-11}$	10,56	$2,76 \cdot 10^{-11}$	10,56
Cu(Has)$_2$	20	0,3	"	$2,9 \cdot 10^{-10}$	9,54	$8,0 \cdot 10^{-21}$	20,10
MgHas$^+$	20	0,3	"	$1,3 \cdot 10^{-4}$	3,89	$1,3 \cdot 10^{-4}$	3,89
Mg(Has)$_2$	20	0,3	"	$1,23 \cdot 10^{-3}$	2,91	$1,6 \cdot 10^{-7}$	6,80
UO$_2$Has$^+$	20	0,3	"	$1,02 \cdot 10^{-9}$	8,99	$1,02 \cdot 10^{-9}$	8,99
UO$_2$(Has)$_2$	20	0,3	"	$2,0 \cdot 10^{-8}$	7,70	$2,04 \cdot 10^{-17}$	16,69
ZnHas$^+$	20	0,3	"	$3,3 \cdot 10^{-8}$	7,48	$3,3 \cdot 10^{-8}$	7,48
Zn(Has)$_2$	20	0,3	"	$1,1 \cdot 10^{-7}$	6,96	$3,6 \cdot 10^{-15}$	14,44

*In a 50% dioxane—water mixture

LITERATURE CITED

H. Irving, H. S. Rossotti. J. Chem. Soc., 1954, 2910.

Complexes with 5-hydroxyquinoxaline *

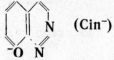

(Hox⁻) → (Hox^-)

Complex ion	t, °C	Ionic strength	Method	k	pk	K	pK
CuHox⁺	20	0,3	pH-potent.	$2,18 \cdot 10^{-10}$	9,66	$2,18 \cdot 10^{-10}$	9,66
Cu(Hox)₂	20	0,3	„	$1,45 \cdot 10^{-9}$	8,84	$3,16 \cdot 10^{-19}$	18,50
MgHox⁺	20	0,3	„	$3,63 \cdot 10^{-4}$	3,44	$3,63 \cdot 10^{-4}$	3,44
Mg(Hox)₂	20	0,3	„	$1,12 \cdot 10^{-3}$	2,95	$4,07 \cdot 10^{-7}$	6,39
NiHox⁺	20	0,3	„	$1,62 \cdot 10^{-8}$	7,79	$1,62 \cdot 10^{-8}$	7,79
Ni(Hox)₂	20	0,3	„	$9,5 \cdot 10^{-8}$	7,02	$1,55 \cdot 10^{-15}$	14,81
UO₂Hox⁺	20	0,3	„	$4,0 \cdot 10^{-9}$	8,40	$4,0 \cdot 10^{-9}$	8,40
UO₂(Hox)₂	20	0,3	„	$3,1 \cdot 10^{-8}$	7,51	$1,23 \cdot 10^{-16}$	15,91
ZnHox⁺	20	0,3	„	$8,5 \cdot 10^{-8}$	7,07	$8,5 \cdot 10^{-8}$	7,07
Zn(Hox)₂	20	0,3	„	$1,95 \cdot 10^{-6}$	5,71	$1,65 \cdot 10^{-13}$	12,78

LITERATURE CITED

H. Irving, H. S. Rossotti. J. Chem. Soc., 1954, 2910.

Complexes with 8-hydroxycinnoline *

(Cin⁻) → (Cin^-)

Complex ion	t, °C	Ionic strength	Method	k	pk	K	pK
CuCin⁺	20	0,3	pH- potent.	$3,3 \cdot 10^{-10}$	9,48	$3,3 \cdot 10^{-10}$	9,48
Cu(Cin)₂	20	0,3	„	$2,56 \cdot 10^{-9}$	8,59	$8,5 \cdot 10^{-19}$	18,07
MgCin⁺	20	0,3	„	$9,5 \cdot 10^{-4}$	3,02	$9,5 \cdot 10^{-4}$	3,02
Mg(Cin)₂	20	0,3	„	$6,6 \cdot 10^{-3}$	2,18	$6,3 \cdot 10^{-6}$	5,20
NiCin⁺	20	0,3	„	$5,6 \cdot 10^{-9}$	8,25	$5,6 \cdot 10^{-9}$	8,25
Ni(Cin)₂	20	0,3	„	$5,9 \cdot 10^{-8}$	7,23	$3,3 \cdot 10^{-16}$	15,48
UO₂Cin⁺	20	0,3	„	$2,1 \cdot 10^{-9}$	8,68	$2,1 \cdot 10^{-9}$	8,68
UO₂(Cin)₂	20	0,3	„	$6,9 \cdot 10^{-8}$	7,16	$1,45 \cdot 10^{-16}$	15,84
ZnCin⁺	20	0,3	„	$1,17 \cdot 10^{-7}$	6,93	$1,17 \cdot 10^{-7}$	6,93
Zn(Cin)₂	20	0,3	„	$1,6 \cdot 10^{-6}$	5,80	$1,86 \cdot 10^{-13}$	12,73

*In a 50% dioxane—water mixture

LITERATURE CITED

H. Irving, H. S. Rossotti. J. Chem. Soc., 1954, 2910.

Complexes with 8-hydroxyquinoline* (Oxin⁻)

$$O^- \quad N$$

Complex ion	Temperature, °C	Ionic strength	Method	k	pk	K	pK	Literature main	Literature addit.
Cd Oxin⁺	25	—	pH-potent.	$3,7 \cdot 10^{-10}$	9,43	$3,7 \cdot 10^{-10}$	9,43	[1]	—
Cd (Oxin)₂	25	—	"	$2,09 \cdot 10^{-8}$	7,68	$7,75 \cdot 10^{-18}$	17,11	[1]	—
Ce Oxin²⁺	25	—	"	$7,1 \cdot 10^{-10}$	9,15	$7,1 \cdot 10^{-10}$	9,15	[1]	—
Ce (Oxin)₂⁺	25	—	"	$1,05 \cdot 10^{-8}$	7,98	$7,45 \cdot 10^{-18}$	17,13	[1]	—
Co Oxin⁺	25	—	"	$2,82 \cdot 10^{-11}$	10,55	$2,82 \cdot 10^{-11}$	10,55	[1]	—
Co (Oxin)₂	25	—	"	$7,8 \cdot 10^{-10}$	9,11	$2,2 \cdot 10^{-20}$	19,66	[1]	—
Cu Oxin⁺	25	—	"	$3,24 \cdot 10^{-14}$	13,49	$3,24 \cdot 10^{-14}$	13,49	[1]	[2]
Cu (Oxin)₂	25	—	"	$1,86 \cdot 10^{-13}$	12,73	$6,0 \cdot 10^{-27}$	26,22	[1]	[2]
La Oxin²⁺	25	—	"	$2,19 \cdot 10^{-9}$	8,66	$2,19 \cdot 10^{-9}$	8,66	[1]	—
La (Oxin)₂⁺	25	—	"	$1,82 \cdot 10^{-8}$	7,74	$4,0 \cdot 10^{-17}$	16,40	[1]	—
Mg (Oxin)⁺	25	—	"	$4,17 \cdot 10^{-7}$	6,38	$4,17 \cdot 10^{-17}$	6,38	[1]	[2]
Mg (Oxin)₂	25	—	"	$3,72 \cdot 10^{-6}$	5,43	$1,55 \cdot 10^{-12}$	11,81	[1]	[2]
Mn Oxin⁺	25	—	"	$5,25 \cdot 10^{-9}$	8,28	$5,25 \cdot 10^{-9}$	8,28	[1]	—
Mn (Oxin)₂	25	—	"	$6,8 \cdot 10^{-8}$	7,17	$3,57 \cdot 10^{-16}$	15,45	[1]	—
Ni Oxin⁺	25	—	"	$3,6 \cdot 10^{-12}$	11,44	$3,6 \cdot 10^{-12}$	11,44	[1]	[2]

203

Complex ion	Temperature, °C	Ionic strength	Method	k	pk	K	pK	Literature main	Literature addit.
Ni (Oxin)$_2$	25	—	pH-potent.	$1,15 \cdot 10^{-10}$	9,94	$4,16 \cdot 10^{-22}$	21,38	[1]	[2]
Pb Oxin$^+$	25	—	"	$2,46 \cdot 10^{-11}$	10,61	$2,46 \cdot 10^{-11}$	10,61	[1]	—
Pb (Oxin)$_2$	25	—	"	$8,1 \cdot 10^{-9}$	8,09	$2,0 \cdot 10^{-19}$	18,70	[1]	[2]
Zn Oxin$^+$	25	—	"	$1,1 \cdot 10^{-10}$	9,96	$1,1 \cdot 10^{-10}$	9,96	[1]	[2]
Zn (Oxin)$_2$	25	—	"	$1,26 \cdot 10^{-9}$	8,90	$1,38 \cdot 10^{-19}$	18,86	[1]	[2]
UO$_2$ Oxin$^+$	20	0,3	"	$5,62 \cdot 10^{-12}$	11,25	$5,52 \cdot 10^{-12}$	11,25	[2]	—
UO$_2$ (Oxin)$_2$	20	0,3	"	$2,29 \cdot 10^{-10}$	9,64	$1,29 \cdot 10^{-21}$	20,89	[2]	—

*In a 50% dioxane—water mixture

LITERATURE CITED

1. W. D. Johnston, H. Freiser. J. Am. Chem. Soc., 74, 5239 (1952).
2. H. Irving, H. Rossotti. J. Chem. Soc., 1954, 2910.

Complexes with eriochrome blue-black B

$$^-O_3S \underset{}{\diagdown} N = N - \quad (Esb^{3-})$$

Complex ion	t, °C	Ionic strength	Method	k	pk	K	pK
CaEsb$^-$	Room	0,02	Spectr.	$2,0\cdot10^{-6}$	5,7	$2,0\cdot10^{-6}$	5,7
MgEsb$^-$	„	0,08	„	$4,0\cdot10^{-8}$	7,4	$4,0\cdot10^{-8}$	7,4

LITERATURE CITED

G. Schwarzenbach, W. Biederman. Helv. chim. Acta, 31, 678 (1948).

Complexes with eriochrome blue-black R

$$^-O_3S - \underset{}{\diagdown} N = N - \quad (Ers^{3-})$$

Complex ion	t, °C	Ionic strength	Method	k	pk	K	pK
Ca Ers$^-$	Room	0,02	Spectr.	$5,6\cdot10^{-6}$	5,25	$5,6\cdot10^{-6}$	5,25
Mg Ers$^-$	„	0,08	„	$2,75\cdot10^{-8}$	7,56	$2,75\cdot10^{-8}$	7,56

LITERATURE CITED

G. Schwarzenbach, W. Biederman. Helv. chim. Acta, 31, 678 (1948).

Complexes with eriochrome black A

$$^-O_3S \underset{^-O_2N}{\diagdown} \diamond \diagup N=N- \diamond \quad (Esa^{3-})$$

Complex ion	t, °C	Ionic strength	Method	k	pk	K	pK
CaEsa⁻	Room	0,02	Spectr.	$5,6\cdot10^{-6}$	5,25	$5,6\cdot10^{-6}$	5,25
MgEsa⁻	"	0,08	"	$6,3\cdot10^{-8}$	7,2	$6,3\cdot10^{-8}$	7,2

LITERATURE CITED

G. Schwarzenbach, W. Biederman. Helv. chim. Acta, 31, 678 (1948).

Complexes with eriochrome black T

$$^-O_3S \underset{^-O_2N-}{\diagdown} \diamond -N=N- \diamond \quad (Est^{3-})$$

Complex ion	t, °C	Ionic strength	Method	k	pk	K	pK
CaEst⁻	Room	0,02	Spectr.	$4,0\cdot10^{-6}$	5,4	$4,0\cdot10^{-6}$	5,4
MgEst⁻	"	0,08	"	$1,0\cdot10^{-7}$	7,0	$1,0\cdot10^{-7}$	7,0

LITERATURE CITED

G. Schwarzenbach, W. Biederman. Helv. chim. Acta, 31, 678 (1948).

TABLES OF
COMPLETE THERMODYNAMIC CHARACTERISTICS
OF COMPLEX FORMATION REACTIONS
IN SOLUTION

EXPLANATION OF TABLES

All data in the tables refer to reactions of the type

$$M_{aq} + nA_{aq} = MA_{naq},$$

where M is a metal ion, A an addend, and n the coordination number.

Data for processes of stepwise complex formation may be obtained from the figures presented by very simple arithmetical operations and therefore are not given in the tables.

All figures refer to 25° or room temperature.

If the experimental conditions differed from those indicated, then this is noted in brackets.

The tables give data on the enthalpy change only when the determination was made calorimetrically. We omitted from the tables those complex compounds for which there are no data on the change in free energy and entropy.

The data in the tables are arranged in groups for complexes with the same addends, which are in the following order:

Complexes

1. Ammonia
2. Bromide
3. Iodide
4. Oxalate
5. Pyrophosphate
6. Thiourea
7. Thiosulfate
8. Trimethylenediamine
9. Fluoride
10. Chloride

11. Cyanide
12. Ethylenediamine
13. Ethylenediaminetetraacetate

Within each group, the metal-complex formers are arranged in alphabetical order of their chemical symbols.

The first column gives the formula of the complex compound. When the formulas of the addends are large, we use conventional abbreviations, given at the beginning of each group.

The second column gives the change in enthalpy (ΔH) of the reaction indicated above (in calories).

The third column gives the change in free energy (ΔZ) in calories, calculated from the formula

$$\Delta Z = RT \ln K_{inst.}$$

where $K_{inst.}$ is the over-all instability constant of the given complex compound.

The fourth column gives the value of the change in entropy during the same reaction (ΔS) in cal/deg.

The last column gives the reference to the literature, presented at the end of the table.

COMPLETE THERMODYNAMIC CHARACTERISTICS OF COMPLEX FORMATION REACTIONS IN SOLUTION

Complex ion	ΔH, cal.	ΔZ, cal	ΔS, cal/deg.	Literature
Ammonia complexes*				
$CdNH_3^{2+}$	— 3500	— 3640	0,5	[1]
$Cd\ (NH_3)_2^{2+}$	— 7000	— 6520	— 1,6	[1]
$Cd\ (NH_3)_3^{2+}$	—10500	— 8500	— 6,7	[1]
$Cd\ (NH_3)_4^{2+}$	—14000	— 9780	—14,1	[1]
$Cd\ (NH_3)_5^{2+}$	—17500	— 9340	—27,1	[1]
$Cd\ (NH_3)_6^{2+}$	—21000	— 7060	—46,5	[1]
$CuNH_3^{2+}$	— 5600	— 5700	0,3	[2]
$Cu\ (NH_3)_2^{2+}$	—11100	—10500	— 2,0	[2]
$Cu\ (NH_3)_3^{2+}$	—16700	— 14480	— 7,4	[2]
$Cu\ (NH_3)_4^{2+}$	—22000	—17400	—15,3	[2]
$Cu\ (NH_3)_5^{2+}$	—27100	—16700	—34,7	[2]
$Hg\ (NH_3)_2^{2+}$	—24700	—24000	— 2,3	[1]
$Hg\ (NH_3)_3^{2+}$	--28000	—25400	— 8,7	[1]
$Hg\ (NH_3)_4^{2+}$	—31600	—26500	—17,0	[1]
$Ni\ NH_3^{2+}$	— 4000	— 3840	— 0,5	[2]
$Ni\ (NH_3)_2^{2+}$	— 8000	— 6920	— 3,6	[2]
$Ni\ (NH_3)_3^{2+}$	—12000	— 9300	— 9,0	[2]
$Ni\ (NH_3)_4^{2+}$	—16000	—10930	—16,9	[2]
$Ni\ (NH_3)_5^{2+}$	—20300	—11960	—27,8	[2]
$Ni\ (NH_3)_6^{2+}$	—24600	—12000	—42,0	[2]
$Zn\ NH_3^{2+}$	— 2600	— 3260	2,1	[1]
$Zn\ (NH_3)_2^{2+}$	— 5700	— 6610	3,0	[1]
$Zn\ (NH_3)_3^{2+}$	— 9600	—10040	1,5	1]
$Zn\ (NH_3)_4^{2+}$	—14800	—13000	— 6,0	[1]

Temperature 26.8°C.
Ionic strength $\mu = 2.0$

Bromide complexes				
$HgBr_2$	—22500	—23600	4	[3]
$HgBr_3^-$	—26500	—26800	2	[3]
$HgBr_4^{2-}$	—28700	—28600	0	[3]
Iodide complexes				
CdI^+	— 1350	— 4200	9	[4]
CdI_4^{2-}	—10800	— 8400	— 8	[5]

Complex ion	ΔH, cal	ΔZ, cal	ΔS, cal/deg.	Literature
HgI^+	—16600	—18400	6	[4]
HgI_4^{2-}	—43500	—41300	— 7	[3]
PbI^+	— 1000	— 3130	7	[4]
PbI_4^{2-}	—15600	—· 8500	—23	[5]

Oxalate complexes ($C_2O_4^{2-} = Ox^{2-}$)

Complex ion	ΔH, cal	ΔZ, cal	ΔS, cal/deg.	Literature
$CoOx_2^{2-}$	— 800	— 9700	30	[6]
$CoOx_3^{4-}$	— 3100	—10800	26	6]
$CuOx_2^{2-}$	— 1470	—10900	32	[6]
$MgOx_2^{2-}$	170	— 6000	21	6]
$MnOx_2^{2-}$	—· 190	— 7900	25	[6]
$NiOx_2^{2-}$	— 1100	—1(400	31	[6]
$ZnOx_2^{2-}$	— 1300	—10300	30	[6]

Pyrophosphate complexes

Complex ion	ΔH, cal	ΔZ, cal	ΔS, cal/deg.	Literature
$Cu\,(P_2O_7)_2^{6-}$	— 690	—12300	39,0	[7]
$Mg\,P_2O_7^{2-}$	2920	— 6280	31,1	[8]
$Ni\,P_2O_7^{2-}$	4220	— 7950	40,8	[7]
$Ni\,(P_2O_7)_2^{6-}$	2000	— 9800	39,6	[7]
$Pb\,(P_2O_7)_2^{6-}$	— 1030	— 7250	20,9	[7]
$Zn\,(P_2O_7)_2^{6-}$	2640	— 8860	38,6	[7]

Thiourea complexes

Complex ion	ΔH, cal	ΔZ, cal	ΔS, cal/deg.	Literature
$Ag\,(CSN_2H_4)_3^+$	—30700	—17900	—43	[9]
$Bi\,(CSN_2H_4)_6^{3+}$	—22000	—16200	—19,5	[9]
$Cd\,(CSN_2H_4)_3^{2+}$	—13000	— 4000	—30	[9]
$Cu\,(CSN_2H_4)_3^+$	—32300	—17500	—50	[9]
$Hg\,(CSN_2H_4)_4^{2+}$	—50000	—38000	—40	[9, 4]
$Pb\,(CSN_2H_4)_3^{2+}$	—13300	— 2400	—36	[9]

Thiosulfate complexes

Complex ion	ΔH, cal	ΔZ, cal	ΔS, cal/deg.	Literature
CdS_2O_3	000	— 3700	12	[10]
$Cd\,(S_2O_3)_2^{2-}$	— 1500	— 7090	18	[10]
$Cd\,(S_2O_3)_3^{4-}$	— 3400	— 8560	17	[10]
ZnS_2O_3	— 3500	— 1690	17	[10]

Complex ion	ΔH, cal	ΔZ, cal	ΔS, cal/deg.	Literature

Trimethylenediamine complexes
($H_2NCH_2CH_2CH_2NH_2$ = Tmen)

Complex ion	ΔH, cal	ΔZ, cal	ΔS, cal/deg.	Literature
$CuTmen_2^{2+}$	-22760	-23400	2	[11]
$NiTmen^{2+}$	-7770	-8700	3	[11]
$Ni(Tmen)_2^{2+}$	-15000	-14700	-1	[11]
$Ni(Tmen)_3^{2+}$	-21340	-16400	-17	[11]

Fluoride complexes

Complex ion	ΔH, cal	ΔZ, cal	ΔS, cal/deg.	Literature
AlF^{2+}	1150	-8370	32	[12]
AlF_2^{+}	1930	-15220	58	[12]
AlF_3	2120	-20470	76	[12]
AlF_4^{-}	2400	-24210	89	[12]
AlF_5^{2-}	1650	-26430	94	[12]
AlF_6^{3-}	100	-27070	91	[12]

Chloride complexes

Complex ion	ΔH, cal	ΔZ, cal	ΔS, cal/deg.	Literature
$HgCl_2$	-12300	-17400	17	[3]
$HgCl_3^{-}$	-13000	-19000	20	[3]
$HgCl_4^{2-}$	-13500	-20300	23	[3]

Cyanide complexes

Complex ion	ΔH, cal	ΔZ, cal	ΔS, cal/deg.	Literature
$Hg(CN)_4^{2-}$	-59500	-56300	-10	[3]
$Zn(CN)_4^{2-}$	-24700	-22700	-7	[3]

Ethylenediamine complexes ($H_2NCH_2CH_2NH_2$ = En)

Complex ion	ΔH, cal	ΔZ, cal	ΔS, cal/deg.	Literature
$CuEn^{2+}$	-13030	-14350	4	[11]
$CuEn_2^{2+}$	-25420	-26660	-4	[11]
$NiEn^{2+}$	-9010	-10200	4	[11]
$NiEn_2^{2+}$	-18190	-18800	2	[11]
$NiEn_3^{2+}$	-27190	-24800	-8	[11]

213

Complex ion	ΔH, cal	ΔZ, cal	ΔS, cal/deg.	Literature

Ethylenediaminetetraacetate complexes

Complex ion	ΔH, cal	ΔZ, cal	ΔS, cal/deg.	Literature
BaEdta^{2-}	— 5100	—10540	18	[13]
CaEdta^{2-}	— 5800	—14970	31	[13]
CdEdta^{2-}	— 9100	—20500	38	[13]
CoEdta^{2-}	— 4100	—21400	58	[13]
CuEdta^{2-}	— 8200	—24400	55	[13]
LiEdta^{3-}	100	— 3800	13	[13]
MgEdta^{2-}	3100	—12400	52	[13]
MnEdta^{2-}	— 5200	—17200	41	[13]
NaEdta^{3-}	— 1400	— 2300	3	[13]
NiEdta^{2-}	— 7600	—24000	55	[13]
PbEdta^{2-}	—13100	—23600	35	[13]
SrEdta^{2-}	— 4200	—11900	26	[13]
ZnEdta^{2-}	— 4500	—20900	55	[13]

LITERATURE CITED

1. K.B. Yatsimirskii, P.M. Milyukov. J. Inorg. Chem., 2, 1046 (1957).
2. K.B. Yatsimirskii, P.M. Milyukov. J. Phys. Chem., 31, 842 (1957).
3. M. Berthelot. Thermochimie, Paris, 1897.
4. K.B. Yatsimirskii, A.A. Shutov. J. Phys. Chem., 28, 30(1954).
5. K.B. Yatsimirskii, A.A. Astasheva. J. Phys. Chem., 26, 239 (1952).
6. E.K. Zolotarev. Investigation of Oxalate Complexes in Solution. Dissertation, Chemicotechnological Institute, Ivanovo, 1955.
7. K.B. Yatsimirskii, V.P. Vasil'ev. J. Phys. Chem., 30, 901 (1956).
8. V.P. Vasil'ev. J. Phys. Chem., 31, 692 (1957).
9. K.B. Yatsimirskii, A.A. Astasheva. J. Phys. Chem., 27, 1533 (1953).
10. K.B. Yatsimirskii, L.V. Gus'kova. J. Inorg. Chem., 2, 2039 (1957).
11. J. Poulsen, J. Bjerrum. Acta. Chem. Scand., 9, 1407 (1955).
12. W.M. Latimer, W.L. Jolly. J. Am. Chem. Soc., 75, 1548 (1954).
13. R.G. Charles. J. Am. Chem. Soc., 76, 5854 (1954).